BIOINFORMATICS: NEW RESEARCH

BIOINFORMATICS: NEW RESEARCH

PETER V. YAN
(EDITOR)

Nova Biomedical Books
New York

For permission to use material from this book please contact us:
Telephone 631-231-7269; Fax 631-231-8175
Web Site: http://www.novapublishers.com

NOTICE TO THE READER

LIBRARY OF CONGRESS CATALOGING-IN-PUBLICATION DATA:
Available Upon Request

ISBN: 1-59454-242-2

Published by Nova Science Publishers, Inc. ✢ New York

Contents

Preface

The genomic revolution that has spawned microarrays and high throughput technologies has produced vast amounts of complex biological data that require integration and multidimensional analysis. Bioinformatics incorporates sub-disciplines ranging from databases and ontologies to the modeling of complex biological systems by way of molecular evolution and protein structure prediction. This new book provides state-of-the-art research from around the world.

With the rapid advances in microarray technology, it has now become possible to simultaneously study the expression levels of thousands of genes. Elucidating biologically significant information from the generated high dimensional gene expression data is a challenging task. To address this challenge, advanced computational methods that can extract useful information and help organize large gene expression data are needed. One of the key computational methods to address this problem is clustering. Clustering gene expression data helps identify groups of genes that manifest similar expression patterns, thereby offering useful insight into biological processes and enabling investigations into the molecular basis of diseases. Common challenges in clustering include identifying the number of clusters and validating the accuracy of the clusters formed by an algorithm. Computational intelligence-based techniques such as artificial neural networks, fuzzy systems, and genetic algorithms are promising candidates to address these challenges. Chapter I provides a detailed description of computational intelligence-based algorithms such as fuzzy c-means, adaptive resonance theory, and self-organizing maps. Some applications of these algorithms in clustering gene expression data are presented. Furthermore, recent methods developed to detect optimal number of clusters as well as to validate the resulting clustering results obtained by these algorithms are discussed.

The rapid accumulation of complete genome sequences and the advance of high-throughput expression profiling technology have made the computational approach to the study of transcription regulation networks attractive and feasible. In Chapter II, computational approaches to deciphering the transcriptional regulatory network, including promoter prediction, transcription factor binding site identification, combinatorial regulatory element predictions, transcription factor target gene identification and the attempt to reconstruct the global regulatory network are discussed. The role of comparative genomics in transcription regulatory region analysis is also reviewed.

Boinformatics can play a special role in studying emerging infectious diseases, where a fast characterization of the diseases is often urgently needed before they are widespread. In

Chapter III, we described a computational framework for fast modeling of emerging infectious diseases, including five components: (1) gene survey of the biological sequences related to the emerging diseases; (2) biological problem definition; (3) computational analyses of each gene sequence, which may include molecular characterization, structure prediction, phylogenetic analysis, and regulatory motif prediction; (4) literature review; (5) inference of the biological mechanism and hypothesis for experimental testing. We selected Severe Acute Respiratory Syndrome coronavirus (SARS-CoV) as an example to illustrate the computational framework. SARS-CoV is a most recently emerging coronavirus causing the worldwide SARS pandemic. It is a novel coronavirus, which is similar in genome organization but distantly related to previously characterized coronaviruses in gene sequences. Among the identified Open Reading Frames (ORFs), replicase ORF1ab, spike [S], envelope [E], membrane [M] and nucleocapsid [N] are found in other known coronaviruses with a conserved genome organization. In addition to this common genome organization, this novel virus also has a number of nonstructural proteins with unknown functions. We first computationally surveyed all the ORFs within SARS-CoV, and then predicted the cleavage sites between S1 and S2. According to the literature, M and S proteins play an important role in the processing of assembly, attachment, and fusion for coronavirus-host interaction. However, there has not been a systematically description about the mechanism of the M and S proteins. Although the cellular roles of the S and M proteins are known, it requires structural information to understand the molecular mechanisms of how these two proteins perform their functions. The protein structure of either the M protein or the S protein has not been solved. Questions remains include: (1) How S1 protein interacts with the associated human receptor? (2) How the S protein interacts with M protein? (3) What is the role of the S-M complex in virus fusion? (4) What are the other possible roles of the M protein in the virus infection besides its role in cell assembly? In this chapter, we only focused on question 2. We first performed the molecular characterization of S and M proteins. Then we predicted the three-dimensional structures for the S and M proteins and the potential human receptor N-aminopeptidase. We further illustrated how the S-M complex assembles based on correlated mutation analysis. In the end, hypotheses about the S-M complex were proposed based on our computational results and previous experimental results.

Chapter IV focuses on, to understand the cellular mechanisms of malignant transformation induced by constitutive activation of the ras oncogene (Ha-ras) as well as by estrogens and anti-estrogens treatments, we used a subtractive hybridization method (VGID^{TM}) together with an integrative analytical procedure based upon literature databases in the form of extensive interaction graphs. We found 731 over- and under-expressed genes which, in the human MCF7-ras and MCF7 breast epithelial cell lines, are involved in the different aspects of tumoral transformation such as defined signaling pathways, cellular growth, protection against apoptosis, extracellular matrix and cytoskeleton remodeling. Integrative analysis led to the construction of physiological models defining cross talk and signaling pathway alterations which explicitly suggested mechanisms directly involved in tumor progression. The models further suggested points and means of intervention which could induce cell death in Ha-ras-transformed cells specifically. These hypotheses were directly tested in vitro and found to be largely correct, hence indicating that these new analytical and technological approaches allow the discovery of pathology-associated cellular mechanisms and physiologically defined targets leading to phenotype-specific pharmacological interventions.

As reported in Chapter V, unified models for analysis of structure-function relationship are essential for post-genomic biology, biochemistry and biophysics. Very often, in biological macromolecules only some region of the native molecule is functionally important. Molecular mechanics study presented here shows that many of the important functional residues in proteins and ribozymes are characterized by unusual energy values. The results show that functional regions in macromolecules can be accurately predicted using spatial structure as the only input and with no additional biochemical or sequence information. These predictions appear to be in good agreement with the available biochemical data.

In Chapter VI, the advent of complete genome sequencing has enabled a systematic analysis of the functions required in a genome. Sets of orthologous genes have been determined that describe the basic protein functions found in all multicellular genome sequences to date. Gene duplication and gene loss have obscured the one to one relationship of genes between organisms in some gene families. Furthermore, the rapid sequence evolution of both orthologs and paralogs has enabled the evolution of new functions and the analogous replacement of lost functions. Lateral transfer, including the transfer of organellar genes to the nucleus, has also shaped the protein content of chordates and embryophytes. Taken together, these processes allow a new understanding of protein content and feed into our general understanding of biological systems.

In: Bioinformatics: New Research
Editor: Peter V. Yan, pp. 1-25
ISBN 1-59454-242-2

Chapter I

Gene Expression Clustering Using Computational Intelligence

Habtom W. Ressom
Lombardi Comprehensive Cancer Center
Department of Oncology
Georgetown University Medical Center
Washington, DC 20057 USA

Padma Natarajan
Intelligent Systems Laboratory
Department of Electrical and Computer Engineering
University of Maine
Orono, ME 04468 USA

Abstract

With the rapid advances in microarray technology, it has now become possible to simultaneously study the expression levels of thousands of genes. Elucidating biologically significant information from the generated high dimensional gene expression data is a challenging task. To address this challenge, advanced computational methods that can extract useful information and help organize large gene expression data are needed. One of the key computational methods to address this problem is clustering. Clustering gene expression data helps identify groups of genes that manifest similar expression patterns, thereby offering useful insight into biological processes and enabling investigations into the molecular basis of diseases. Common challenges in clustering include identifying the number of clusters and validating the accuracy of the clusters formed by an algorithm. Computational intelligence-based techniques such as artificial neural networks, fuzzy systems, and genetic algorithms are promising candidates to address these challenges. This chapter provides a detailed description of computational intelligence-based algorithms such as fuzzy c-means, adaptive resonance theory, and self-organizing maps. Some applications of these algorithms in clustering gene expression data are presented. Furthermore, recent methods developed to detect optimal number of clusters as well as to validate the resulting clustering results obtained by these algorithms are discussed.

1. Introduction

DNA microarray technology provides a powerful tool for studying the expression of thousands of genes simultaneously. It allows a global view on the transcription levels of many genes when the cell undergoes specific conditions or processes. Gene expression data generated by this technology can be organized as matrices where the rows represent genes (or clones) and columns represent various experimental conditions or samples. As shown in Figure 1, each entry in the matrix corresponds to the expression level of a gene for a given condition or sample. A set of entries in a row or a column forms an expression profile. For example, a temporal expression profile of a gene, where the conditions are developmental stages is shown in Figure 1. A typical gene expression data matrix consists of 10,000s of rows (genes) and 10s to 100s of columns (conditions). Though the technology provides researchers with such large amount of gene expression data, analysis of the massive data has been one of the major bottlenecks in the utilization of the technology. Computational tools that can mine and discover biologically meaningful knowledge in such large gene expression data are needed.

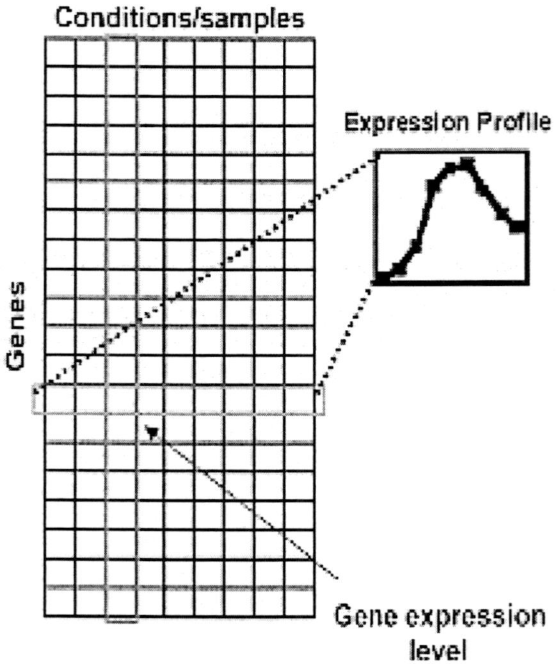

Figure 1. Gene expression data matrix.

Clustering is a useful exploratory technique for analysis of large volume and high-dimensional data when there is no *a priori* information about existing common properties. Clustering algorithms help discover common properties contained within the data and create groups of objects according to their properties. For gene expression data, these groups could be objects clustered by conditions or by gene. The former will help researchers identify which of the experimental conditions resulted in similar profiles or responses across all genes. The latter identifies genes with similar expression profiles across various experimental conditions.

Genes with similar expression profiles might be transcriptionally regulated through a same transduction pathway or share some common function or regulatory elements.

Depending on how they cluster data, we can classify clustering algorithms into hierarchical and non-hierarchical clustering methods. Hierarchical clustering organizes the input patterns into a hierarchical tree structure, which allows the detection of higher order relationships between clusters of patterns. Non-hierarchical clustering begins from a pre-defined number of clusters and iteratively reallocates cluster members to minimize the overall within-cluster dispersion. We can also divide clustering algorithms into two categories, hard and fuzzy. While a hard clustering algorithm assigns each data point to only one of the clusters, a fuzzy clustering assigns a certain degree of closeness or similarity to each object in a cluster.

A wide variety of clustering algorithms (hierarchical/non-hierarchical as well as hard/fuzzy) have been applied to group similar gene expression profiles together. In particular, hierarchical clustering (Eisen *et al*., 1998), self-organizing maps (SOM; Tamayo *et al*., 1999), and k-means (Somogyi, 1999) are widely used by the bioinformatics research community for clustering gene expression data. While these and other clustering methods such as fuzzy c-means (Gasch and Eisen, 2002), and adaptive resonance theory (Tomida *et al*., 2002) have provided useful results, the research community has yet to address the issue of determining the "correct" number of clusters or selecting a "good" clustering algorithm.

To address the challenges of detecting the number of clusters and choosing a good clustering algorithm, several statistical methods have been proposed in the literature. For example, Yeung *et al.* (2001a) suggested a metric known as figure of merit (FOM) that they calculated by clustering the data set while leaving out one experiment at a time. They used FOM to evaluate the performance of different clustering results as they vary the number of clusters. Tibshirani *et al.* (2000) proposed estimating the number of clusters in a dataset via the gap statistic. The gap statistic estimates the number of clusters by comparing within-cluster dispersion to that of a reference null distribution. Kerr and Churchill (2001) introduced a technique based on the application of a randomization technique, bootstrapping, for making statistical inference from clustering tools. They applied this technique to assess the stability of results from a cluster analysis of gene expression microarray data. Dudoit and Fridlyand (2002) developed a new prediction-based resampling method to estimate the number of clusters in data set. Fraley and Raftery (2002) provided functionality for visualizing cluster results in their model-based clustering technique. They characterize and compare the various probability models in their clustering algorithm through a Bayesian information criterion (BIC) introduced by Yeung *et al.* (2001b). They calculate BIC scores for each model over a given range of number of clusters. A model with large BIC scores is selected, and the number of clusters with the highest BIC value for the chosen model is considered to be the best number of clusters. The model-based approach assumes that a finite mixture of underlying probability distributions such as multivariate normal distributions generates the data. With the underlying probability model, the problems of determining the number of clusters and of choosing an appropriate clustering method become statistical model choice problems. These and many other heuristic methods have provided useful results in gene expression clustering.

Computational intelligence techniques such as neural networks, fuzzy systems, and genetic algorithms offer alternative solutions to the current challenges of identifying the number of clusters in gene expression data and validating the corresponding results. Thus, many researchers have begun an endeavor to use computational intelligence for developing advanced clustering techniques for analyzing gene expression data. This chapter provides a review summarizing the work that has been done in this area and illustrates in detail the use of computational intelligence-based clustering algorithms for gene expression data analysis.

The chapter is organized as follows: Section 2 provides a brief overview of computational intelligence such as artificial neural networks, fuzzy logic systems, and genetic algorithms. Section 3 discusses computational intelligence-based clustering techniques and their applications in gene expression data analysis. Section 4 presents a comparative study conducted by the authors for clustering gene expression data. Section 5 provides a brief summary on currently available software tools for gene expression data analysis. Section 6 summarizes the chapter and discusses future trends in clustering gene expression data.

2. Computational Intelligence: An Overview

Computational intelligence (CI) is the study of adaptive mechanisms to enable or facilitate intelligent behavior in complex and changing environments. These mechanisms include mathematical models that exhibit an ability to learn or adapt to new situations, to generalize, abstract, discover, and associate. CI encompasses a variety of fields including neural networks (NN), fuzzy systems (FS), and genetic algorithms (GA). Each of these CI paradigms has its origins in biological systems. For example, NN model biological neural systems, fuzzy systems originated from studies on how organisms interact with their environment, and GA model natural evolution. Hybrid systems use a combination of these biologically and linguistically inspired computational models to take advantage of their collective features. In the following, we briefly describe NN, FS, and GA. It must be noted that CI is an expansive discipline that embodies a vast array of terminology and techniques. We provide here only a concise description of the salient features of CI. The reader is directed to Haykin (1999), Mitchell (1998), Yen and Langari (1999), and Engelbrecht (2002) for a more thorough treatise on the subject.

2.1.Neural Networks

Neural networks generally consist of a number of interconnected processing elements known as neurons. The way neurons are interconnected or how the inter-neuron connections are arranged determine the architecture of a neural network. The way the strengths of the connections (known as weights or synaptic weights) are adjusted or trained to achieve a desired overall behavior of the network is governed by the learning algorithm used. NN are classified according to their architecture and learning algorithms.

The most popular architecture is a *feedforward* neural network, where the neurons are grouped into layers. All connections are feedforward; that is, they allow information transfer only from an earlier layer to the next consecutive layers. Neurons within a layer are not connected, and neurons in non adjacent layers are not connected. Input signals are presented to the network via an "input layer." The nodes in the input layers do not process input signals but pass them to one or more "hidden layers" where the actual processing is done via a system of weighted "connections". The hidden layers then link to an "output layer" which provides the outputs of the network. Figure 2 depicts a feedforward neural network that has four layers: an input layer, two hidden layers, and an output layer. As shown in the figure, the inputs to the network are x_1, x_2,…,x_n, and the network output is y. Figure 3 illustrates the details of a single neuron, where net_1, known as activation level, is the sum of the weighted inputs to the neuron; and $f(.)$ represents an activation function, which transforms the activation level of a neuron into an output signal. Typically, an activation function could be a threshold function, a sigmoid function (an S-shaped, symmetric function that is continuous and differentiable), a Gaussian function, or a linear function. For example, the output of the neuron in Figure 3 (i.e., the output of the first neuron in the first hidden layer of the network in Figure 2) can be written as:

$$o_1 = f(net_1) = f\left(\sum_{j=1}^{n} w_{1j}x_j\right) \tag{1}$$

where the synaptic weights w_{11}, w_{12},…, w_{1n} define the strength of connection between the neuron and its inputs. Such synaptic weights exist between all pairs of neurons in each successive layer of the network. They are adapted during learning to yield the desired output at the output layer of the network.

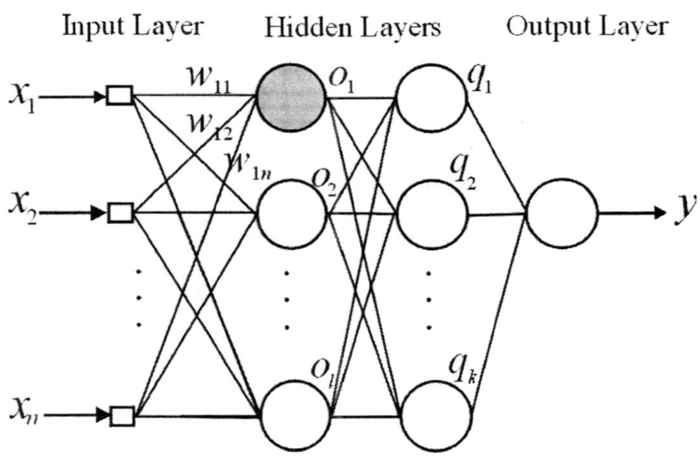

Figure 2. Multilayer feedforward network.

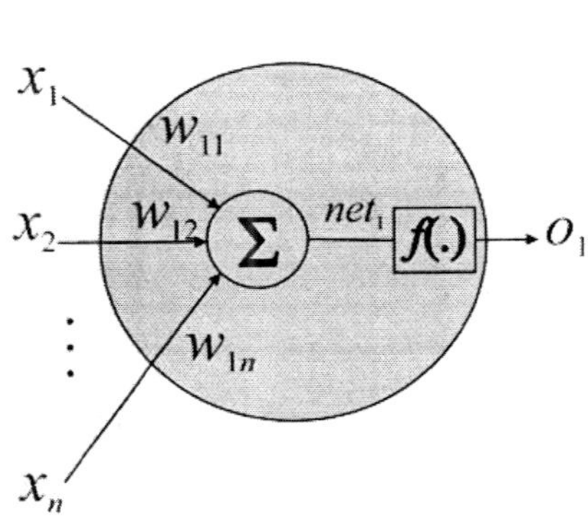

Figure 3. Details of a neuron.

A *recurrent* neural network is one in which the outputs of some neurons are fed back to the same neurons or to other neurons in the same or preceding layers. Thus, signals can flow in both forward and backward directions. Recurrent neural networks have a dynamic memory - their outputs at a given instant reflect the current model input as well as previous inputs and outputs.

In a *supervised* learning paradigm, a neural network uses training examples (specifically, the desired outputs for a given set of inputs) to determine how well it has learned, and to guide adjustments of the synaptic weights in order to reduce its overall error. A typical example is a classification problem, where a neural network is trained to group input patterns into pre-specified categories. For example, in cancer classification, one may train a neural network using gene expression profiles with known phenotypic information and use the resulting network to classify gene expression profiles without phenotypic information into pre-defined categories.

In contrast to supervised learning, *unsupervised* learning discovers patterns or features in the input patterns with no help from a teacher, essentially performing a clustering of the input patterns. Typical unsupervised learning rules include Hebbian learning, principal component learning, and Kohonen learning rules. These rules have been applied in training self-organizing neural network architectures such as adaptive resonance theory (ART) and self-organizing maps (SOM). These network architectures, their corresponding learning rules, and their application in gene expression data analysis are discussed in Section 3.

2.2. Fuzzy Logic

Fuzzy logic is a superset of conventional two-valued (Boolean) logic that has been extended to handle the concept of partial truth. Thus, in fuzzy logic, the truth-value of a statement is defined in the continuous interval between 0 (completely false) and 1 (completely true). It enables designers to simulate human thinking by quantifying concepts such as far, near, soon, low, and high.

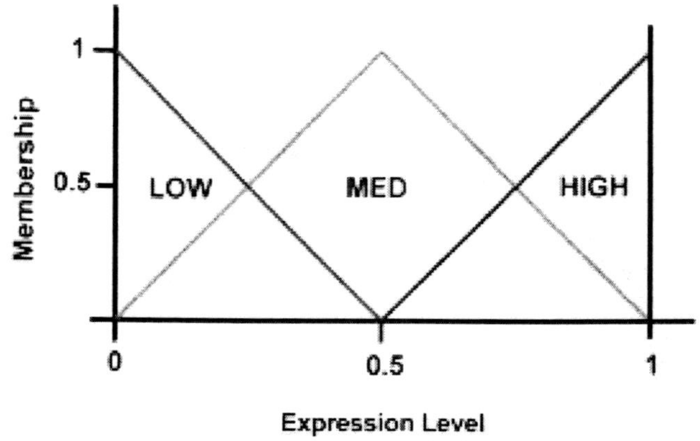

Figure 4. Membership functions for “low”, “medium”, and “high” expression levels.

Thus, in contrast to a traditional set theory that requires elements to be either part of a set or not, fuzzy logic allows an element to belong to a set to a certain degree of certainty. A membership function is used to associate a degree of membership of each of the elements of the domain to a fuzzy set. The degree of membership to a fuzzy set indicates the certainty that the element belongs to that set. For example, a gene expression level can be defined by the membership functions in Figure 4 as low, medium, and high. Here, we assume that expression levels are scaled between 0 and 1.

Besides membership functions, a fuzzy system consists of a set of fuzzy rules. A fuzzy rule has two components, an *if* part (also referred to as premise) and a *then* part (also referred to as conclusion). Such rules can be used to represent knowledge and association, which are inexact and imprecise in nature, expressed in qualitative values that a human can easily understand. For example, one might say, "If temperature is high and humidity low, then the weather is medium hot."

Figure 5 depicts a fuzzy system that has four principal units: fuzzification, knowledge base, decision-making (inference), and defuzzification. The fuzzy system accepts a set of inputs (x_1, x_2, ... x_n) as its information about the outside world (also referred to as crisp data). The fuzzification unit converts these inputs into fuzzy sets based up on fuzzy values, such as "high", "medium", and "low." In this unit, the membership functions defined on the input variables are applied to their actual values, to determine the degree of truth for each rule premise. The knowledge base contains member functions defining fuzzy values and a set of fuzzy rules. The inference unit executes these fuzzy rules. The truth-value for the premise of each rule is computed, and applied to the conclusion part of each rule. When all the rules are executed, a fuzzy region will be created for the output variable y. With the process of defuzzification, a discrete value of the output will be generated as a solution.

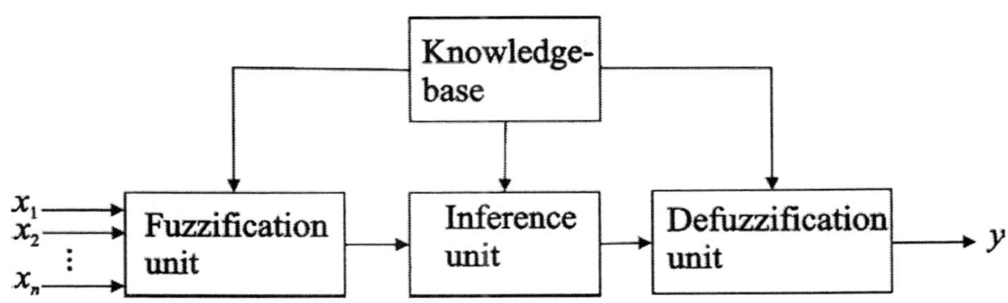

Figure 5. A fuzzy-based model of a system.

Fuzzy logic has been successfully applied for clustering. While most clustering algorithms such as SOM, ART, and k-means assign each data point to only one of the clusters, a fuzzy clustering assigns a certain degree of closeness or similarity to each object in a cluster. Fuzzy clustering methods such as fuzzy c-means (FCM) and fuzzy adaptive resonance theory (Fuzzy ART) and their application in gene expression data analysis are discussed in Section 3.

2.3. Genetic Algorithms

Genetic algorithms (GA) are global optimization algorithms that originated from mechanics of natural genetics and selection (Holland, 1975; Goldberg, 1989). They provide a method of problem solving that is based on genetic evolution. Based on probabilistic decisions, they exploit historic information to guide the search for better solutions in the problem space. Using a direct analogy of natural evolution, they work with a population of chromosomes, where each chromosome encodes a possible solution to the problem as a string of bits (0100101010), list of real values (0.2, 6.5, 4.1, 1.3), string of characters (B2, A3, C1, A1), or some other representation.

The algorithm starts by randomly creating a population of chromosomes. The chromosomes in the population are evaluated by a fitness function indicating how good encoded solutions appear with respect to the problem under consideration. The algorithm takes the chromosomes with higher relative fitness (chosen as parents) and then creates a new generation of chromosomes using genetic operators such as crossover or mutation. In crossover, new offspring are created from two parents by swapping a portion of their strings. In mutation, offspring are identical to their parents, but have random changes in portions of their strings. The algorithm repeats the above steps until a predefined number of generations or fitness value is reached.

Therefore, GA begin with a random process and arrive at an optimized solution. They are thus well suited for those tasks that seek global optimization. They are highly effective in situations where many inputs interact to produce a large number of possible outputs or solutions. They are a robust search method requiring little information to search effectively in a large or poorly understood search space.

Although GA have been widely used in solving various optimization problems, there has been little research on using GA for clustering. Recent application of GA for clustering gene expression data is presented in Section 3.5.

3. Clustering Gene Expression Data Using Computational Intelligence

In this section, we introduce some of the most commonly used computational intelligence-based clustering methods along with a few examples from literature in which they were applied for gene expression data analysis. First, aspects of data preprocessing are briefly mentioned. Then, we describe fuzzy c-means (FCM), adaptive resonance theory (ART), self-organizing maps (SOM), and variants of these methods as applied to clustering gene expression data.

3.1. Data Preprocessing

Many times the "raw" gene expression data are not the best data to use for clustering. Hence, it is a common practice to pre-process the raw data prior to using a CI paradigm for clustering. Preprocessing of the raw microarray data is needed to identify and remove the effects of systematic variation in the measured fluorescence intensities or to ensure that differences in intensities are indeed due to differential expression, and not some printing, hybridization, or scanning artifact (Quackenbush, 2002). Algorithms for data preprocessing vary depending on the microarray platform used to generate the data. For example, high density oligonucleotide array (e.g. Affymetrix GeneChip) data preprocessing involves three probe-level analyses following image quantification: i) background adjustment to minimize the effect of non-specific binding and optical noise, ii) normalization to ensure that the measurements from different arrays are comparable; and iii) summarization to obtain an expression value for a probe set by combining multiple probe intensities. cDNA microarray data preprocessing involves image quantification, background correction, and normalization.

Other data preprocessing procedures that make the clustering task easier include data transformation, handling missing or input patterns, removing outliers, removing inconsistent replicates, standardizing the data into acceptable range, flat pattern filtering, and dimensionality reduction.

Since ratios treat up- and down-regulated genes differently, log-transformation is performed to achieve symmetry between negative and positive fold changes. Missing values are handled by removing the entire pattern or replacing each missing value with an average value, a median, or through KNN imputation (Herrero *et al.*, 2003). An outlier is a data pattern that deviates substantially from the data distribution. Outliers can have severe effects on the performance of a clustering algorithm. The problem can be addressed by removing outliers through statistical techniques or by using a robust clustering algorithm that is not influenced by outliers. Flat patterns are filtered based on minimum number peaks, or minimum standard deviation, or patterns that shown a reasonable fold changes of expression level across all conditions.

Data standardization allows the input patterns to be clustered based on the shape of their profile rather than their absolute values. Min-max scaling preserves the relationships among the original data. Mean centering is more appropriate when the data contain no biases. Variance scaling is appropriate when training data are measured with different units. Z-score normalization is a combination of mean centering and variance scaling, and can be very useful when there are outliers present in the data. Normalization methods such as quantile and cyclic loess use information from across all arrays to produce the normalization. For example, quantile normalization uses this approach to give the same distribution to each array.

Dimensionality reduction is essential in exploratory data analysis, where the purpose is to map data onto a low-dimensional space for improved visualization. It also reduces the complexity of a problem and makes it *easier* to cluster. Dimensionality reduction can be accomplished through feature selection, where an optimum subset of features derived from the input variables is selected. Feature selection methods keep only useful features and discard others. For example, principal component analysis (PCA) reduces input dimensionality by transforming the input variables to a new set of variables (features), which captures most of the information in the original data. The new variables are computed as a linear combination of the original variables.

3.2. Fuzzy C-Means

Bezdek (1981) developed a fuzzy clustering algorithm known as fuzzy c-means (FCM). FCM is a fuzzy extension of the classic k-means clustering method. In fuzzy c-means clustering, each data point belongs to a cluster to a degree that is specified by a membership function. The algorithm iteratively updates the cluster centroids and the membership function's values for each input pattern. This iteration is based on minimizing an objective function that represents the distance from any given input pattern to a cluster centroid weighted by the pattern's membership function value. Thus, the objective function for FCM algorithm is given by

$$J(c,m)=\sum_{k=1}^{c}\sum_{i=1}^{N}(u_{ki})^{m}d^{2}(\boldsymbol{x}_{i},\boldsymbol{v}_{k}) \tag{2}$$

where c is the number of clusters; N is the number of input patterns; $\boldsymbol{x}_i$ is the ith input pattern (e.g. gene expression profile); and $\boldsymbol{v}_k$ is the kth cluster centroid; u_{ki} is the degree of membership of $\boldsymbol{x}_i$ to cluster k; and $d^2(x_i,v_k)$ is the distance from $\boldsymbol{x}_i$ to $\boldsymbol{v}_k$.

FCM clustering thus facilitates the identification of overlapping groups of objects by allowing the objects to belong to more than one group. The essential difference between FCM and k-means is the partitioning of genes into each group. Instead of hard partitioning, where profiles belong to only a single cluster, FCM clustering considers each profile to be a member of every cluster, with a variable degree of membership. Each profile has a total membership of one that is apportioned to clusters on the basis of the similarity between the profile and that of each cluster centroid. Expression profiles that are very similar to a given centroid will be assigned a high membership in that cluster, whereas profiles that bear little similarity to the centroid will have a low membership.

As in many clustering algorithms, one of the challenges that need to be addressed in applying FCM for gene expression analysis is the identification of the optimal number of clusters. Several indices were proposed to help the detection of number of clusters. One of these is the partition coefficient introduced by Bezdek (1981), which ranges from 0 to 1. A partition coefficient of one indicates no membership sharing between clusters, while low value indicates overlap between clusters. Thus, a high partition coefficient is desired. Although this is a good indicator, its calculation is solely based on membership values without involving the structure of the data. Other indices that are based on both membership values as well as the data structure include the Xie and Beni's index (Xie and Beni, 1991), the Fukuyama and Sugeno's index (Pal and Bezdek, 1995), the Gath and Geva's index (Gath and Geva, 1989), and the Rezaee, Lelieveldt and Reiber's index (Rezaee, 1998). In the following, we briefly present some applications of FCM and cluster validation indices from the literature where they were applied for clustering gene expression data.

Futschik and Kasabov (2002) used FCM to cluster gene expression data derived from a time-series experiment of the yeast cell cycle and gene expression data simulated by statistical models. They showed the robustness of fuzzy clustering against background noise and outliers by comparing it to hard k-means clustering. They also evaluated the performance of cluster validity methods such as the normalized partition coefficient and Xie-Beni index in detecting an optimal number of clusters (c) and an optimal fuzzification parameter (m), see Equation 2.

Gasch and Eisen (2002) implemented a modified version of FCM that incorporated PCA and hierarchical clustering to analyze yeast gene expression data that followed the response of yeast cells to environmental changes. They used this variant of FCM to identify overlapping clusters and validated the clustering results by identifying groups of functionally related and co-regulated genes.

Dembélé and Kastner (2003) proposed a new method for computing an upper bound for the fuzziness parameter (m) and choosing it independent of the number of clusters in the data set. They show that FCM clustering of microarray data, combined with threshold-based gene selection, offers a convenient way of defining subsets of genes which are more tightly associated to a given cluster. They demonstrate their method in clustering microarray data from three studies: yeast cell cycles, serum concentration in human fibroblasts, and 60 human cancer cell lines.

Arima *et al.* (2003) selected 45 genes, whose functions were biologically characterized, out of about 6100 genes of expression profiles from yeast gene expression data from a study of Chu *et al.* (1998). They clustered the selected genes using FCM and compared the clustering accuracy to four other clustering techniques, hierarchical, k-means, Fuzzy ART and SOM. Their results indicate that fuzzy k-means and Fuzzy ART provided better performance than the other three.

Möller-Levet *et al.* (2003) introduced an extension of FCM known as fuzzy c-varieties (FCV) clustering algorithm. FCV defines the cluster centroids as linear subspaces of the data space. Hence, the centroids could be lines, planes, or hyperplanes rather than just points. They applied the FCV along with transitional state discrimination (TSD) preclustering method for clustering short time-series gene expression data. They validated the method using mitotic cell cycle of *Saccaromyces cervisiae* data collected at 17 time points taken at 10 minute intervals. They utilized the first four time points that contain temperature-induced effects to produce a short time-series data set. Using this data set, they demonstrated that their algorithm showed better performance over the k-means clustering algorithm in terms of internal cluster correlation and the geometrical properties of the clusters.

3.3. Adaptive Resonance Theory

Adaptive resonance theory (ART), introduced by Carpenter and Grossberg (1987), is an unsupervised *incremental* clustering neural network. ART is known for its stability-plasticity property. It can be used not only to cluster data but also to determine the optimal number of clusters available in the data by dynamically adding nodes as needed by the data. This is accomplished by a parameter known as "vigilance" (ρ), which dictates whether a new input pattern should go to an existing recognition category (cluster) or a new node should be created for it. Higher vigilances lead to more nodes and lower vigilances lead to fewer nodes. In other words, the number of clusters is controlled by the vigilance parameter.

Each cluster (node) of an ART is represented by a weight vector. For example, Figure 6 illustrates the weight vector of cluster j (W_j) in an ART network. The cluster with the highest output value of a similarity function is chosen as the winner cluster. The similarity function gives a measure of the similarity between the input vector and the weight vector. Once the winning cluster is identified, it will be judged to follow either the "resonance" or "mismatch reset" procedure. This is determined based on the output of a mismatch function that tests the similarity of the weight vector of the winning cluster and the input vector. The resonance procedure is carried out if the output of the mismatch function is bigger than the vigilance parameter. In which case, weight vector will be updated in order to look similar to the input vector. The mismatch reset procedure is carried out if the output of the matching function is lower than the vigilance. In this case, a new cluster that has the next similarity will be chosen again. If any cluster cannot result in a value larger than the vigilant parameter, a new cluster is generated according to the input vector. The above steps are repeated until every vector belongs to any cluster.

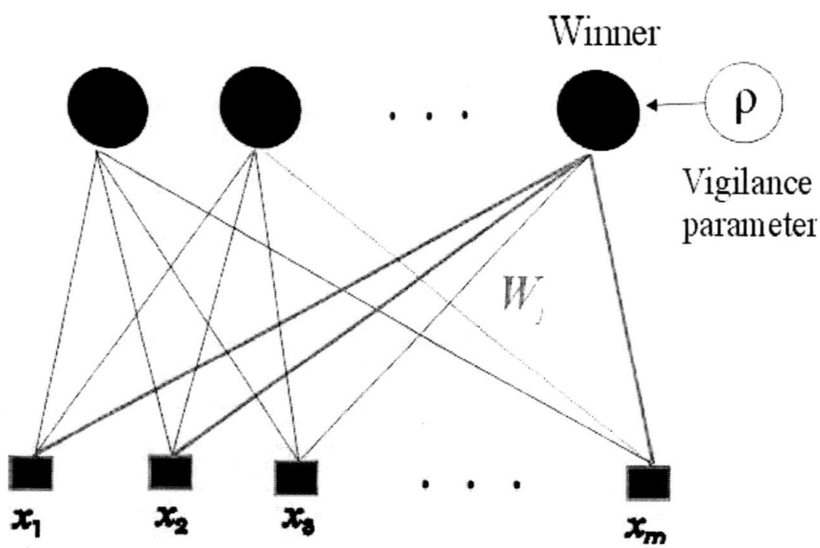

Figure 6. Architecture of adaptive resonance map.

Musavi *et al.* (2002) applied ART to cluster yeast gene expression data. In order to find accurate number of clusters, they examined internode distance as a function of the number of nodes as well as a function of vigilance. Internode distance is the distance between two nodes measured as city block distance. Note that as vigilance increases, the number of clusters increases, while the internode distance decreases. By plotting the internode distance as a function of number of clusters, they identified the saturation point where adding further nodes does not increase internode distance significantly. They presented the number of clusters at the saturation point as the optimal number of clusters.

He *et al.* (2003) implemented a variant of ART known as adaptive resonant theory under constraint (ART-C). ART-C allows the incorporation of user-defined constraint when learning its category representation. It has the capability of self-adjusting its vigilance parameter to generate desired number of output clusters. He *et al.* applied ART-C to cluster gene expression data from rat central nervous system and evaluated the clustering results with functional categories previously identified through human inspection. Based on a set of quantitative measures, namely, cluster compactness and cluster separation, they compared the performance of ART-C with that of k-means, SOM, and conventional ART in clustering two gene expression data sets from yeast cell cycle and human hematopoietic differentiation. They concluded that ART-C produces reasonably good quantitative performance and provides a significantly higher learning efficiency.

Tomida *et al.* (2002) applied fuzzy adaptive resonance theory (Fuzzy ART) as a clustering method for analyzing the time series expression data during sporulation of *Saccharomyces cerevisiae*. Fuzzy ART, introduced by Carpenter *et al.* (1991) is a member of ART network involving fuzzy operators in defining the similarity and mismatch functions. Using 45 sporulation-specific genes that they extracted from the yeast time series gene expression data, Tomida *et al.* compared the clustering results obtained by Fuzzy ART with those of hierarchical clustering, k-means algorithm, and self-organizing maps. They reported that Fuzzy ART achieved the most reasonable clustering among the four algorithms. They validated their results via biological knowledge that was available for the 45 genes they selected. They also verified the robustness of Fuzzy ART in clustering data that involved noise.

Kato *et al.* (2002) applied Fuzzy ART to assess genetic response following heat shock. They used human microarray data containing 12,814 clones. Through preprocessing, they identified 752 genes that were up or down-regulated after heat shock. The temporal pattern of these genes was clustered into eight groups using Fuzzy ART. They reported that the clustering result discovered a gene that plays an important role when cells are exposed to heat shock.

3.4. Self-Organizing Maps

Self-organizing maps (SOM) can be visualized as a neural network array, the nodes of which become specifically tuned to various input patterns in an orderly manner (Kohonen, 2001). The design of SOM for clustering gene expression data starts with defining a geometric configuration for the partitions in a one- or two-dimensional grid. Then, random weight vectors are assigned to each node (cluster). For example, Figure 7 depicts the layout of SOM with 9 nodes in a two dimensional grid (3x3) and it illustrates the weight vector of cluster j (W_j) which is the representative pattern for cluster j. In the self-organization process, a gene expression profile is selected randomly. The weight vector closest (usually in terms of Euclidean distance or correlation) to the expression profile is identified. The identified weight vector (e.g. W_j in Figure 7) and its neighbors (defined by a neighborhood function) are adjusted to look similar to the expression profile. This process is repeated while updating the neighborhood function and learning parameters until the weight vectors converge.

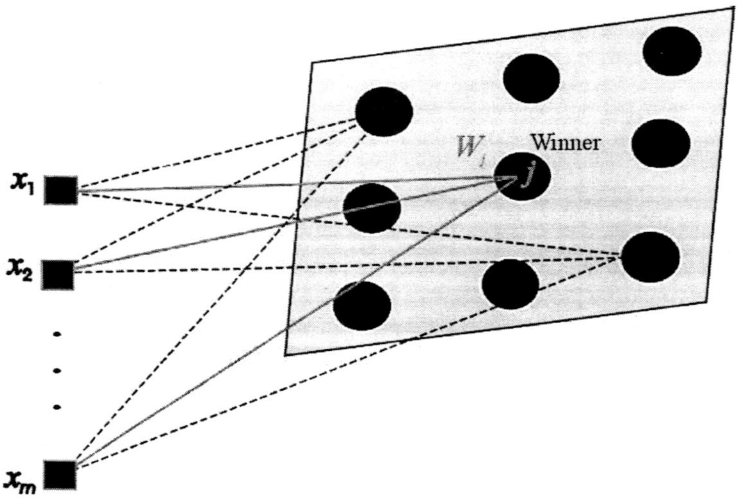

Figure 7. A two dimensional-grid (3x3) self-organizing map. Note that each node is connected to each input.

During operation, SOM maps gene expression profiles to the relevant partitions based on the weight vectors to which they are most similar. Figure 8 shows nine clusters formed by *GeneCluster* (Reich *et al.*, 2004) after training SOM with 1891 gene expression profiles. The 1891 expression profiles are extracted from *Saccharomyces cerevisiae* cDNA microarrays generated in a sporulation experiment. Each cluster in the figure shows the cluster centroid (mean) and its error bars (standard deviation) computed from the profiles that belong to the cluster.

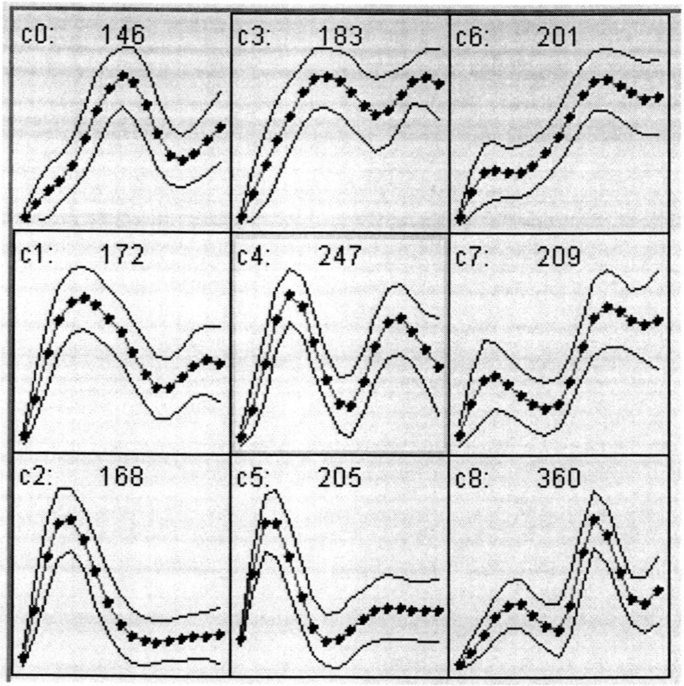

Figure 8. 1891 gene expression profiles from *Saccharomyces cerevisiae* cDNA microarrays generated in a sporulation experiment clustered by GeneCluster in to 9 groups.

Thus, SOM construct a mapping from the high-dimensional space onto map units in such a way that relative distances between data points are preserved. Because of their typical two-dimensional shape, they are easy to visualize. They have a number of features that make them suitable for clustering gene expression data. They are easy to implement, reasonably fast, and scalable to large data sets. They have the capability to generalize. In other words, they can interpolate between previously encountered inputs.

Tamayo *et al.* (1999) used SOM implemented in *GeneCluster* for gene expression data analysis. They tested *GeneCluster* on yeast data that involved 828 genes after data preprocessing. *GeneCluster* grouped the yeast data into 30 clusters via SOM of a 6 x 5 grid. Also, they applied SOM for recognizing and classifying features in complex, multidimensional human gene expression data comprising of an array of some 6000 genes to study hematopoietic differentiation in four well-studied models (HL-60, U937, Jurkat, and NB4 cells). After data preprocessing, *GeneCluster* organized 567 genes into 12 (SOM, 3 x 4) biologically relevant clusters that highlighted certain genes and pathways involved in "differentiation therapy" used in the treatment of acute promyelocytic leukemia.

Törönen *et al.* (1999) used a variation of the SOM, called tree-structured SOM (Koikkalainen, 1994), for clustering and visualization of gene expression data. The tree-structured SOM consists of several SOM that are organized hierarchically in a pyramid-like fashion in several layers. The number of nodes at higher level is four times the number of nodes at the previous level. The algorithm organizes the data into a two-dimensional matrix by an iterative process based on the relative similarity of the expression pattern of genes. Törönen *et al.* applied the tree-structured SOM algorithm implemented in software called *GenePoint* to cluster gene expression data consisting of 6400 yeast genes at seven different time points during a diauxic shift. They reported that a 16 x 16 grid SOM produced good separation of different patterns. Furthermore, they applied Sammon's mapping algorithm to transform the data into a format where the relationship between individual neurons is more clearly visualized.

Golub *et al.* (1999) applied a two-cluster SOM to automatically group 38 initial leukemia samples into two classes on the basis of the expression pattern of 6817 genes. They evaluated the two clusters by comparing them to the known two classes, acute lymphoblastic leukemia (ALL) and acute myeloid leukemia (AML). They demonstrated that SOM was effective at automatically discovering the two types of leukemia.

Kaski (2001) applied methods for detecting, visualizing, and interpreting clusters generated by SOM in gene expression data analysis. One of the methods was the so-called *U*-matrix (Ultsch, 1993). *U*-matrix can be used to determine the natural cluster boundaries in SOM. It allows visual inspection of clusters in the SOM by calculating distance between the adjacent neurons and presenting them with different colors between the adjacent nodes. It shows low values inside a cluster and high values between the clusters. The data set for this experiment was gene expression level of 1551 yeast genes containing 79 time points from 8 treatments. Cluster structures created by SOM in clustering the data set were visualized using the proposed methods in an intuitive manner with colors. The clusters are interpreted by visualizing changes of the data variables (expression in different treatments) at the cluster borders.

Nikkilä *et al.* (2002) analyzed and visualized the cluster structure of gene expression data with the SOM algorithm. They demonstrated their methods by computing a SOM (30 x 50) of yeast genes. The data set for their experiments included 2460 yeast genes containing 79 time points. These were genes whose functional classification was known. The relationships of known functional classes of genes were investigated by analyzing their distribution on the SOM. With the help of the *U*-matrix, Nikklä *et al.* showed that SOM visualizes the similarity of genes in a way better than multidimensional scaling and hierarchical clustering.

Sugiyama and Kotani (2002) introduced a method of combining SOM and k-means clustering for analyzing and categorizing the gene expression data. They applied k-means clustering to the results of SOM to find clustering boundaries. The input vectors of the SOM are the gene expression profiles and the input vectors of the k-means clustering are the centroids of the SOM. Sugiyama and Kotani applied this method to cluster time series gene expression data of 656 cell cycle-regulated yeast genes at 16 time points.

Herrero and Dopazo (2002) proposed a combination of SOM and hierarchical method for clustering gene expression data. They applied SOM to reduce the dimensionality of the data set to relatively small clusters and used the centroids of the clustered data as input values for hierarchical clustering. They used this approach to cluster gene expression profiles of 6102 yeast genes, during a diauxic shift, as an example to demonstrate their method. First, they applied SOM (5 x 8) to obtain 40 centroids, in which each centroid was a vector of size 7. Then, the 40 centroids were clustered using hierarchical clustering method. They applied SOTA to cluster expression profiles of the 6102 yeast genes. SOTA (Herrero *et al.*, 2001) combines hierarchical clustering with a neural network. It splits a data set in a hierarchy of clusters and sub-clusters by means of a self-organizing process (like in SOM) but using a binary tree topology with a splitting scheme based on inter-cluster distances.

Su and Chang (2001) proposed double self-organizing maps (DSOM) that extend the features of SOM. Unlike SOM, the nodes of DSOM are represented not only by their weight vectors but also by two-dimensional *position vectors*. The weight vectors serve the same purpose as in SOM. The position vectors are projection of the weight vectors into a two-dimensional space and serve as a visualization tool for deciding how many clusters are needed, thus combining clustering and cluster visualization in one computational procedure. In other words, with the help of position vectors, DSOM adjusts its network structure during the learning phase so that neurons that respond to similar stimuli will not only have similar weight vectors but also move spatially nearer to each other.

The selection of DSOM's free parameters is vital for proper projection of the position vectors in a two dimensional space. Some combinations of these parameters make all the position vectors converge too quickly into a small dense area. Some other combinations lead the updating process to "get stuck" after several epochs and result in wrong number of clusters. Thus, the regulation of these parameters is very important. To achieve this, Ressom *et al.* (2003) developed an adaptive double self-organizing map (ADSOM), which updates not only the weight vectors and position vectors but also all the free parameters involved in DSOM during the training process. After training, the final location of the positions vectors is used to detect the number of clusters by visually counting the clusters they form. ADSOM gives fairly consistent number of clusters provided that the initial number of nodes is greater than the expected number of clusters. Once ADSOM obtains the final locations of the position vectors, one can visually determine the number of clusters. To minimize possible human error resulting from counting the number of clusters visually, Ressom *et al.* (2003) developed a novel technique that provides a hierarchical tree-based index for each cluster. The index is calculated based on the outcome of clustering the position vectors themselves using hierarchical method. The technique starts with a matrix that consists of the final locations of all two-dimensional position vectors. Then, it calculates the Euclidean distances between each pair of position vectors in the matrix. Based on these distances and subsequent distances between centers of merged clusters, it creates a hierarchical cluster tree that grows vertically upwards. During clustering, it stores the single linkage distance between two clusters that are merged together through a branch. Hence, the height of each branch corresponds to the distance assigned to it. Consider a horizontal line that cuts c branches of the hierarchical cluster tree perpendicularly, the horizontal line picks c clusters that are embraced by the branches it cuts. An index corresponding to this horizontal line is designated as $\gamma(c)$ and is defined as the sum of the heights of each branch it cuts:

$$\gamma(c) = \sum_{i=1}^{c} z_c(i) \qquad c = 2,..N \tag{3}$$

where $z_c(i)$ is the height contributed by the ith branch for the case when a horizontal branch cuts c branches of the tree. The index is calculated for c = 2,..,N. Note that $\gamma(1)=0$, since there will be no horizontal line that would cut the tree only once. The number of clusters at which the index reaches its highest peak is considered as an indicator of the maximum separation between clusters in a two-dimensional space. Hence, it represents as the optimal number of clusters. Figure 9 illustrates the way the hierarchical tree-based index is calculated. The top figure shows 18 position vectors and the bottom figure depicts the corresponding hierarchical tree.

Ressom *et al.* (2003) applied ADSOM to cluster gene expression data. They demonstrated the reliance of ADSOM in identifying the number of clusters by applying it to publicly available gene expression data from multiple biological systems such as yeast, human, and mouse.

3.5. Genetic Algorithms

Although genetic algorithms (GA) have been widely used in solving various optimization problems, there has been little research on using GA for clustering. In clustering, GA can be used to minimize the square error of the cluster dispersion given by the following equation:

$$E(c) = \sum_{k=1}^{c} \sum_{i=1}^{N} d^2(\boldsymbol{x}_i, \boldsymbol{v}_k) \tag{4}$$

where c is the number of clusters; N is the number of input patterns; $\boldsymbol{x}_i$ is the ith input pattern (e.g. gene expression profile); and $\boldsymbol{v}_k$ is the kth cluster centroid; and $d^2(\boldsymbol{x}_i,\boldsymbol{v}_k)$ is the distance from $\boldsymbol{x}_i$ to $\boldsymbol{v}_k$.

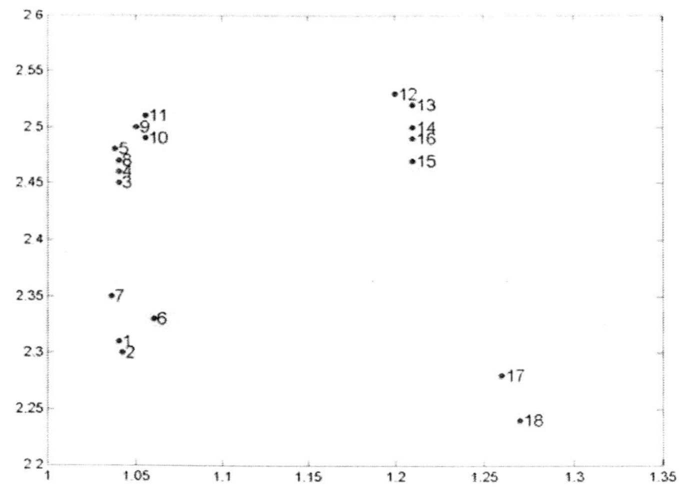

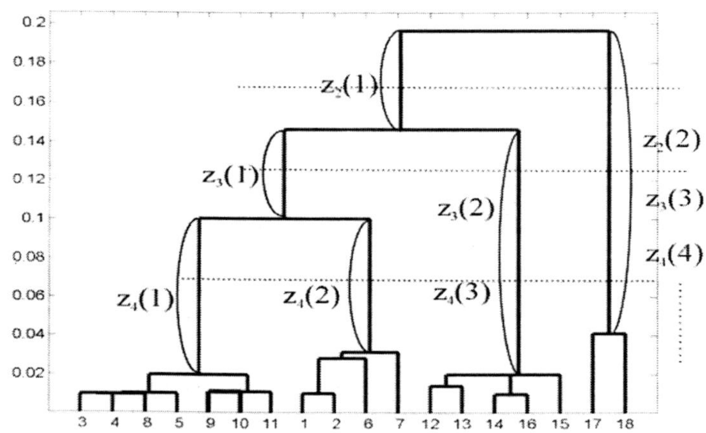

Figure 9. 18 position vectors (top figure) and corresponding hierarchical tree (bottom figure).

The advantage of GA is that large search space can be effectively explored by utilizing the evolutionary algorithm techniques. They are able to discover underlying patterns in noisy gene expression data for meaningful data groupings, and also statistically significant patterns hidden in each cluster can be extracted at the same time.

Ma and Chan (2003) presented a generic clustering algorithm that uses a hybrid GA approach to discover clusters in gene expression data. They tested the effectiveness of the algorithm on real expression data. The experimental results revealed meaningful groupings and uncovered many known transcription factor-binding sites.

4. Comparative Study

In this section, we investigate the relative merits of three computational intelligence based algorithms in detecting number of clusters using gene expression data from *Saccharomyces cerevisiae* studied during sporulation. The clustering methods chosen for this study are the self-organizing maps (SOM), adaptive double self-organizing maps (ADSOM), and fuzzy c-means (FCM). The clusters obtained using SOM were validated using figure of merit (FOM), which is calculated based on the method described by Yueng *et al.* (2001a). We obtained FOM for various numbers of clusters. We used a plot of FOM vs. number of clusters to detect the saturation point. To detect the optimal number of clusters for the outcomes of FCM, we employed the Xie-Beni index, which quantifies the ratio of the total variation within clusters and the separation of clusters. The clusters formed by ADSOM were validated using the hierarchical tree-based index described in Section 3.4.

From the yeast sporulation data, we extracted 218x11 gene expression data that belonged to four classes. The data were normalized to have a mean of zero and standard deviation of one. The four classes were ribosomal proteins, respiration, mitochodrial organization, and tricarboxylic-acid pathway. This functional classification was made using information from Munich Information Center for Protein Sequences (MIPS) (Mewes *et al.*, 1997).

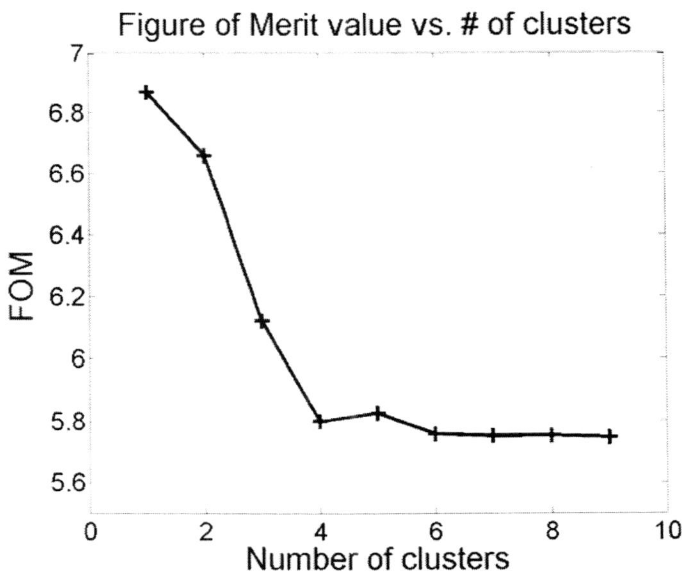

Figure 10. FOM obtained in clustering yeast data using SOM.

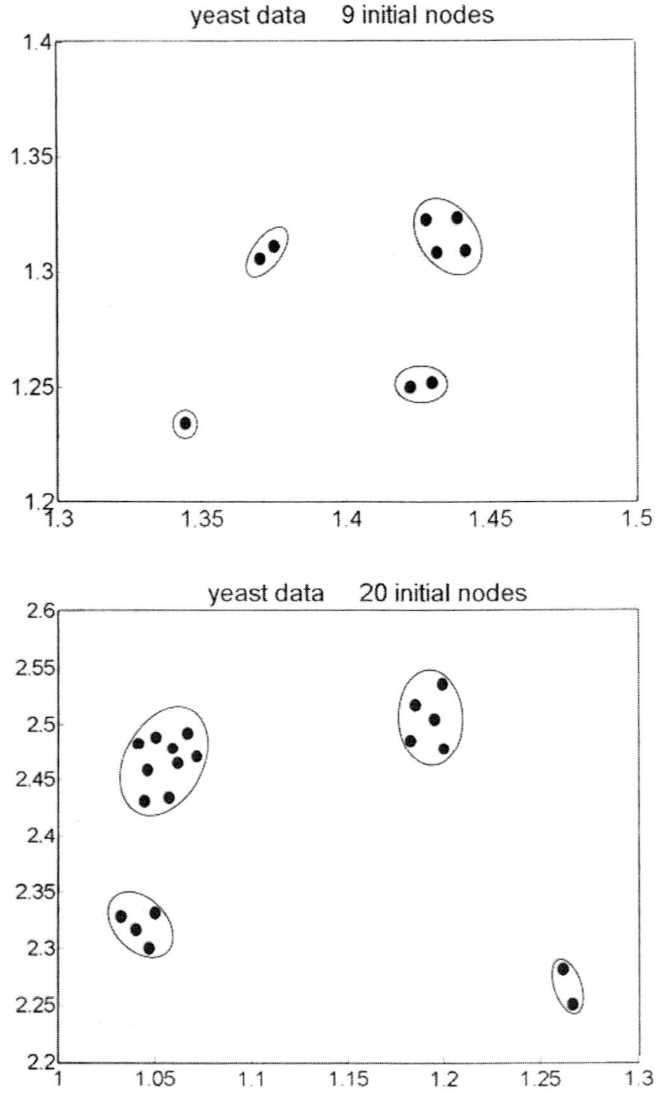

Figure 11. Final position vectors with initial nodes 9 (top figure) or 20 (bottom figure) using ADSOM for yeast sporulation data with 4 classes.

SOM was applied to group the yeast data into different number of clusters. The resulting clusters were evaluated using FOM. Figure 10 reveals that the optimal number of clusters is six. On the other hand, ADSOM clustered the data into its four distinct classes without having the knowledge of the actual number of clusters. The beauty of ADSOM algorithm is that it would converge to the actual number of clusters without having to go through tedious cluster validation techniques. To demonstrate this, two experiments were conducted with this dataset; once ADSOM was assigned (3 x 3) initial nodes and once (5 x 4) nodes. ADSOM's position vectors that were assigned to these initial nodes converged to four final clusters regardless of the initial number of nodes chosen. Figure 11 shows the position vectors for 9 (top figure) or 20 initial nodes (bottom figure). The four clusters, which represent the actual number of clusters in the data, are shown by enclosed boundaries. Figure 12 shows the results obtained after applying the hierarchical tree-based validation index. As can be seen from the figure, the optimal number of clusters is 4 regardless of different number of initial nodes (9 and 20). Figure 13 depicts the Xie-Beni index calculated for various numbers of clusters after clustering the yeast data using FCM. As shown in the figure, the index has its first minimum at four, confirming the existence of four clusters in the yeast data.

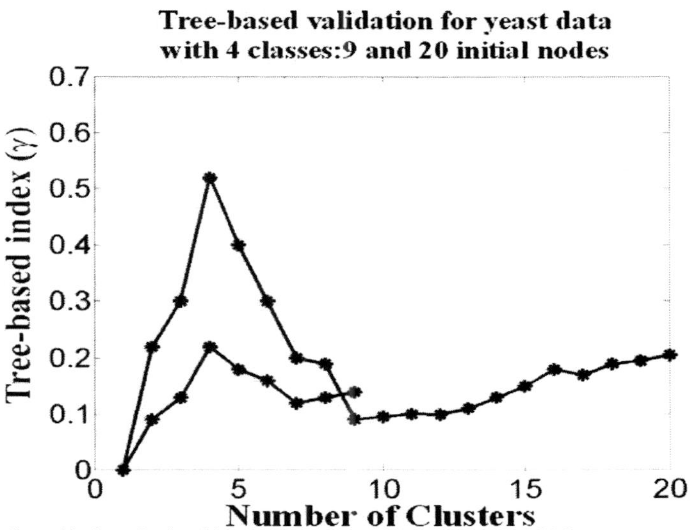

Figure 12. Tree-based index obtained in clustering yeast data using ADSOM.

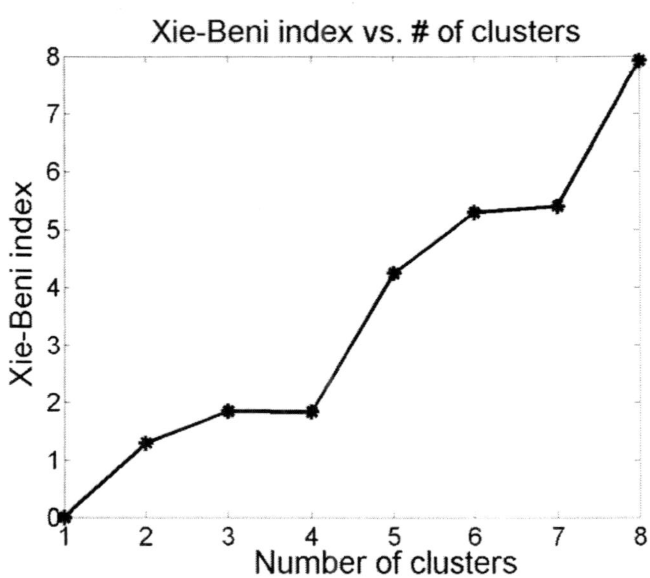

Figure 13. Xie-Beni indices obtained in clustering yeast data using FCM

5. Software Tools for Clustering Gene Expression Data

A wide variety of software tools are available for gene expression data analysis. Some of these tools provide methods for background correction, normalization, filtering, and other data pre-processing tasks. Most of them provide statistical methods for identification of differentially expressed genes, clustering and classification. Several tools incorporate computational intelligence-based clustering and classification algorithms including *GeneCluster* (Broad Institute), *GeneSpring* (Slicon Graphics), *GeneSight* (BioDiscovery), *Data Mining Tool* (Affymetrix), *Partek Discover* (Partek), *GeneLinker Gold* (Predictive Patterns), *Cluster* and *TreeView* (Stanford Univeristy/Eisen's Lab), *Resolver* (Rosetta Biosoftware), *BioMine* (Gene Network Sciences), GeneSifter.net (VizXLabs), and *Gene Expression Pattern Analysis Suite* (Spanish National Cancer Centre).

While the above software packages have provided useful tools for gene expression data analysis, MATLAB (The MathWorks Inc.) offers an integrated programming environment for design and implementation of various computational intelligence paradigms, and has been commonly used in computational intelligence research and development. It offers powerful numeric computation and visualization tools. It consists of application-specific functions grouped into toolboxes, each extending the core MATLAB language. The toolbox functions can be easily viewed and modified. The MATLAB Neural Network Toolbox offers comprehensive support for the design, training, and simulation of many proven neural network paradigms (e.g. MLP, SOM, etc.) and is completely customizable. The MATLAB Fuzzy Logic Toolbox features graphical interfaces for guiding the user through the steps of fuzzy inference system design and visualization. It can also be used to implement FCM clustering and neuro-fuzzy systems. The MATLAB Genetic Algorithm and Direct Search Toolbox features graphical user interfaces and command-line functions for solving problems using genetic algorithms. It provides numerous options for creation, fitness scaling, selection, crossover, and mutation. In addition, MATLAB's Statistical Toolbox and Bioinformatics Toolbox offer researchers several mathematical methods that can be used for gene expression data analysis.

6. Summary

This chapter presents an overview of computational intelligence and its application in clustering and cluster visualization. A survey of some popular computational intelligence-based methods for clustering gene expression data as well as some existing methods for detecting number of clusters is provided. The examples presented in this chapter represent only a small fraction of the vast literature available on implementing fuzzy c-means, adaptive resonance theory, and self-organizing maps as well as their variants for clustering gene expression data. Relative performance of three computational intelligence-based clustering techniques (SOM, FCM and ADSOM) in detecting number of clusters is illustrated through a comparative study using gene expression data extracted from known groups.

The issues of detecting the number of clusters and validating clustering results still remain a challenging task. However, recent use of computational intelligence-based clustering methods has demonstrated a great potential for addressing these issues. In view of this, many researches have investigated the use of computational intelligence-based algorithms in gene expression data analysis where detection of cluster numbers and cluster validity plays a critical role. To this end, numerous software tools have integrated computational intelligence-based algorithms in the past few years. Some of these software packages are mentioned in this chapter. We believe that the trend of incorporating computational intelligence methods in gene expression analysis tools will continue to rise.

We also believe that future work will include integration of computational intelligence with statistical approaches to take advantage of their beneficial features and application of evolutionary computing techniques such as genetic algorithms for clustering gene expression data.

References

Arima, C., T. Hanai, and M. Okamoto (2003). Gene expression analysis using fuzzy k-means clustering. *Genome Informatics* 14: 334:335.

Bezdek, J.C. (1981). *Pattern Recognition with Fuzzy Objective Function Algorithms*. Plenum Press, New York.

Carpenter, G.A. and S. Grossberg (1987). A massively parallel architecture for a self-organizing neural pattern recognition machine. *Computer Vision, Graphics, and Image Processing* 34:54-115.

Carpenter, G.A., S. Grossberg, and D.B. Rosen (1991). Fuzzy ART: fast stable learning and categorization of analog patterns by an adaptive resonance system. *Neural Networks* 4(6), 759-771.

Chu, S., J. Derisi, M. Eisen, J. Mulholland, D. Botstein, P.O. Brown, and I. Herskowitz (1998). The transcriptional program of sporulation in budding yeast. *Science* 282:699-705.

Dembélé, D. and P. Kastner (2003). Fuzzy c-means method for clustering microarray data. *Bioinformatics* 19: 973-980.

Dudoit, S. and J. Fridlyand (2002). A prediction-based resampling method to estimate the number of clusters in a dataset. *Genome Biology* 3(7): 0036.1-0036.21.

Eisen, M.B., P.T. Spellman, P.O. Brown, and D. Botstein (1998). Cluster analysis and display of genome-wide expression patterns. *Proc. Natl. Acad. Sci. USA* 95: 14863-14868.

Engelbrecht, A.P. (2002). *Computational Intelligence: An Introduction*. John Wiley and Sons, Inc., England.

Fraley C., and A.E. Raftery (2002). Model-based clustering, discriminant analysis, and density estimation. *Journal of the American Statistical Association* 97: 611-631.

Futschik, M.E. and N.K. Kasabov (2002). Fuzzy clustering of gene expression data. Proceedings of World Congress of Computational Intelligence, WCCI 2002, Hawaii, IEEE Press.

Goldberg, D.E. (1989). *Genetic Algorithms in Search, Optimization, and Machine Learning*. Addison-Wesley, Reading, Mass.

Gasch, A.P. and M.B. Eisen (2002). Exploring the conditional coregulation through fuzzy k-means clustering. *Genome Biology* 3(11), research 0059.1–0059.22.

Gath, I. and A.B. Geva (1989). Unsupervised optimal fuzzy clustering. *IEEE Transactions on Pattern Analysis and Machine Intelligence* 11(7): 773-781.

Golub T.R., D.K. Slonim, P. Tamayo, C. Huard, M. Gaasenbeek , J.P. Mesirov, H. Coller, M.L. Loh, J.R. Downing, M.A. Caligiuri, C.D. Bloomfield, E.S. Lander (1999). Molecular classification of cancer: class discovery and class prediction by gene expression monitoring. *Science* 286: 531-537.

Haykin, S. (1999). *Neural Networks: A Comprehensive Foundation.* (2nd Edition), Prentice Hall, Upper Saddle River, NJ.

He, J., A.-H. Tan and C.-L.Tan (2003). Self-organizing neural networks for efficient clustering of gene expression data. *Proceedings of International Joint Conference on Neural Networks* (IJCNN), Portland, OR, USA, pp. 1684-1689.

Herrero, J., A. Valencia and J. Dopazo (2001). A hierarchical unsupervised growing neural network for clustering gene expression patterns. *Bioinformatics* 17: 126-136.

Herrero, J., and J. Dopazo (2002). Combining hierarchical clustering and self-organizing maps for exploratory analysis of gene expression patterns. *Journal of Proteome Research* 1(5): 467-470.

Herrero, J., R. Díaz-Uriarte, and J. Dopazo, J. (2003). Gene expression data preprocessing. *Bioinformatics* 19: 655-656.

Holland, J.H. (1975). *Adaptation in Natural and Artificial Systems.* University of Michigan Press, Ann Arbor.

Kaski, S. (2001). SOM-based exploratory analysis of gene expression data. In N. Allinson, H. Yin, L. Allinson, and J. Slack, (Eds). *Advances in Self-Organizing Maps*, London: Springer-Verlag, pp. 124-131.

Kato, N., T. Kobayashi, and H. Honda (2002). Gene expression analysis of heat shock response using Fuzzy ART. *Genome Informatics* 13: 272-273.

Kerr, M.K. and G.A. Churchill (2001). Bootstrapping cluster analysis: assessing the reliability of conclusions from microarray experiments. *Proc Natl Acad Sci U.S.A.*, 98(16): 8961-8965.

Kohonen, T. (2001). *Self-Organizing Maps.* 3rd Edition. Springer-Verlag, Berlin, Heidelberg, New York.

Koikkalainen, P. (1994). Progress with the tree-structured self-organizing map. *Proceedings of the 11th European Conference on Artificial Intelligence* (Cohn, A., Ed.), Wiley and Sons, New York, pp. 211–215.

Ma, P.C.H. and K.C.C. Chan (2003). Discovering clusters in gene expression data using evolutionary approach. *Proceedings of the 15th IEEE International Conference on Tools with Artificial Intelligence* (ICTAI'03), Sacramento, CA.

Mewes, H.W., K. Albermann, K. Heumann, S. Liebl, F. Pfeiffer (1997). MIPS: A database for protein sequences, homology data and yeast genome information. *Nucleic Acid Research* 25: 28-30.

Mitchell, M. (1998). *An Introduction to Genetic Algorithms* (*Complex Adaptive Systems*). MIT Press, Cambridge, MA.

Möller-Levet, C.S., K.-H. Cho, and O. Wolkenhauer. (2003). DNA microarray data clustering based on temporal variation: FCV with TSD preclustering. *Applied Bioinformatics*, Vol. 2 (1), pp. 35-45.

Musavi, M., D. Wang, and S. Chelian (2002). Gene expression data clustering using adaptive resonance theory. *Proceedings of the International Conference on Mathematics and Engineering Techniques in Medicine and Biological Sciences* (METMBS '02), CD, CSREA Press, ISBN 1-892512-39-4, H.R. Arabnia (Ed.), Las Vegas, NV, pp. 230-235.

Nikkilä, J., P. Törönen, S. Kaski, J. Venna, E. Castrén, and G. Wong. (2002). Analysis and visualization of gene expression data using self-Organizing maps. *Neural Networks* 15 (8-9): 953-966.

Pal, N.R., J.C. Bezdek (1995). On cluster validity for the fuzzy c-means model. *IEEE Transactions on Fuzzy Systems* 3(3): 370-379.

Quackenbush, J. (2002). Microarray data normalization and transformation. *Nature Genetics Supplement* 32: 496-501.

Reich, M., Ohm, K., Tamayo, P., Angelo, M., Mesirov, J.P. (2004) GeneCluster 2.0: An advanced toolset for bioarray analysis. Bioinformatics 2004; doi:10.1093/bioinformatics/bth138

Ressom, H., D. Wang, and P. Natarajan (2003). Clustering gene expression data using adaptive double self-organizing map. *Physiological Genomics* 14: 35-46.

Rezaee, M.R., B.P.F. Lelieveldt, J.H.C. Reiber (1998). A new cluster validity index for the fuzzy c-means. *Pattern Recognition Letters* 18: 237-246.

Su, M., and H. Chang (2001). A new model of self-organizing neural networks and its application in data projection. *IEEE Transactions on Neural Networks* 12: 153-158.

Somogyi, R. (1999). Making sense of gene-expression data. *Pharmainformatics*, 17-24.

Sugiyama, A. and M. Kotani (2002). Analysis of gene expression data by using self-organizing maps and k-means clustering. *Proceedings of the 2002 International Joint Conference on Neural Networks*, Honolulu, HI, USA, pp. 1342-1345.

Tamayo, P., D. Slonim, J. Mesirov, Q. Zhu, S. Kitareewan, E. Dmitrovsky, E.S. Lander, and T.R. Golub (1999). Interpreting patterns of gene expression with self-organizing maps: Methods and application to hematopoietic differentiation. *Proc. Natl. Acad. Sci. USA* 96: 2907-2912.

Tibshirani, R., G. Walther, and T. Hastie. (2000). Estimating the number of clusters in a dataset via the gap statistic. *Tech. Rep. 208*, Dept. of Statistics, Stanford University, Stanford, CA, USA.

Tomida, S., T. Hanai, H. Honda, T. Kobayashi (2002). Analysis of expression profile using fuzzy adaptive resonance theory. *Bioinformatics* 18(8): 1073-1083.

Törönen, P., M. Kolehmainen, G. Wong. 1999. Analysis of gene expression data using self-organizing maps. *FEBS Letters* 451(2): 142-146.

Ultsch, A. (1993). Self-organizing neural networks for visualization and classification. In Opitz, O., B. Lausen, and R. Klar (Editors). *Information and Classification*, Springer-Verlag, Berlin, pp. 307-313.

Xie, X.L., G. Beni (1991). A validity measure for fuzzy clustering. *IEEE Transactions on Pattern Analysis and Machine Intelligence* 13(8): 841-847.

Yen, J. and R. Langari (1999). *Fuzzy Logic: Intelligence, Control, and Information*. Prentice Hall, Upper Saddle River, NJ.

Yueng, K.Y., D.R. Haynor, and W.L. Ruzzo (2001a). Validating clustering for gene expression data. *Bioinformatics* 17: 309-318.

Yeung, K.Y., C. Fraley, A. Murua, A.E. Raftery, and W.L. Ruzzo (2001b). Model-based clustering and data transformations for gene expression data. *Bioinformatics* 17: 977-987.

In: Bioinformatics: New Research
Editor: Peter V. Yan, pp. 27-54

ISBN 1-59454-242-2

Chapter II

Computational Approaches for Deciphering the Transcriptional Regulatory Network by Promoter Analysis

Ping Qiu
Bioinformatics Group and Discovery Technology Department at Schering-Plough Research Institute, 2015 Galloping Hill Road, Kenilworth, New Jersey 07033
Email: ping.qiu@spcorp.com
Tel: 908 740 4145

Abstract

The rapid accumulation of complete genome sequences and the advance of high-throughput expression profiling technology have made the computational approach to the study of transcription regulation networks attractive and feasible. In this chapter, computational approaches to deciphering the transcriptional regulatory network, including promoter prediction, transcription factor binding site identification, combinatorial regulatory element predictions, transcription factor target gene identification and the attempt to reconstruct the global regulatory network are discussed. The role of comparative genomics in transcription regulatory region analysis is also reviewed.

Keywords: transcriptional regulatory network, transcription factor (TF), comparative genomics, phylogenetic footprinting, computational, transcription factor binding site (TFBS), promoter

1. Introduction

With the completion of the draft human genome sequence, focus has shifted from sequencing to functional genomics, whose goal is not merely to assign genes into functional categories, but also to provide a comprehensive understanding of genetic networks. Regulation of transcription is a key component of this network, thus the elucidation of gene regulation networks has become one of the greatest challenges in the post-genome-sequencing era. Regulation of gene transcription is crucial for the function and development of all organisms. Each cell is the product of gene expression programs involving the regulated transcription of thousands of genes. The regulation of gene expression involves a complex regulatory network. DNA-binding transcription factors (TFs) are one of the important components of this network. TFs usually bind to specific, short DNA sequence motifs of ~5-25 bp in the *cis*-regulatory region of a gene (promoter and enhancer) to activate or repress its transcription in response to changes in the environment, as well as during development. Knowledge of the transcription factor binding sites (TFBSs) bound by all TFs encoded in a genome can provide the information necessary to construct models for transcriptional regulatory networks.

Although computational methods for identifying exons are becoming quite powerful, systematic identification of non-coding functional regulatory elements remains a daunting task, although significant progress has been made recently in this area. The emergence of several new technologies has accelerated the field in recent years. First, high-throughput sequencing methodologies have allowed the sequencing of the complete genomes of a large variety of species, including human (International Human Genome Sequencing Consortium 2001), mouse (Mouse Genome Sequencing Consortium 2002), rat (http://genome.ucsc.edu/cgi-bin/hgGateway?org=rat), pufferfish (Aparicio et al. 2002), and chimpanzee (http://www.nature.com/nsu/031208/031208-9.html), with the sequencing of additional vertebrate genomes well underway (Winslow and Boguski 2003). Thus, genome-wide comparisons and phylogenetic footprinting, methods based on the assumption that functional regulatory motifs are conserved across species, have become feasible endeavors. Second, high-throughput expression profiling technologies, such as microarray (genechip) and serial analysis of gene expression (SAGE), have allowed the rapid parallel analysis of expression levels of tens of thousands of genes in a single assay. The underlying assumption of using microarray technology in regulatory region analysis is that a set of co-regulated genes usually share a similar set of regulatory motifs. Third, mass spectrometric identification of gel separated proteins has allowed the state of a cell to be characterized on the proteomic level. Fourth, large-scale chromatin immuno-precipitation (ChIP), which allows genome-wide location analysis of TF-binding *in vivo*, has offered an additional powerful tool in dissecting global regulatory networks (Ren et al. 2000). Lastly, since promoters, enhancers, suppressors, insulators, and locus control regions all have been shown to be associated with DNase HS sites (Gross and Garrard 1988), most recently, Crawford et al. (2004) reported a method for rapidly recovering all gene regulatory elements in a specific tissue or cell line by the cloning of DNase HS sites. This approach has the advantage of taking chromatin context into account by digesting nucleosome-free regions of the genome, allowing for identification of both ubiquitous and tissue-specific regulatory elements. This high-throughput technique will be a valuable addition to the growing collection of tools that can be used to globally identify gene regulatory elements.

In this chapter, recent advances in the computational approach to the identification of promoters, transcription factor binding sites, combinatorial regulatory elements and transcription factor target genes is discussed. I will also discuss the attempts to reconstruct the global regulatory network in simple eukaryote organisms and the role of comparative genomics in regulatory region analysis.

2. Identification of Promoters

The first step towards the identification of a TFBS is finding the promoter. The core promoter is a minimum promoter region that is capable of initiating basal transcription. It contains transcription start site (TSS) and typically spans from -60 to +40 relative to the TSS. Some of the promoters contain TATA-box located 30 bp upstream of the TSS. The core promoter region serves as the recognition site for the basal transcription apparatus, which comprises RNA polymerase II and several auxiliary factors. The region 200–300 bp immediately upstream of the core promoter constitutes the proximal promoter. The proximal promoter usually contains TFBSs, which are responsible for transcription regulation. The distal part of the promoter (enhancer/silencer elements) is located further upstream and may also include transcription factor binding sites. This distal part of the promoter are not discussed in this review.

Despite the importance of promoters, the ability to identify them is far less advanced than the ability to identify coding regions, especially for mammalian promoters. Finding promoters in a mammalian genome is complicated by the diverse nature of promoters. Mammalian promoters may be tens of kilobases upstream of the coding region due to the existence of non-coding leading exons (Schef et al 2001). Promoters are very diverse and even well-known signal motif sequences are not always conserved. For example, the TATA box is found in only about 75% of vertebrate RNA PolII promoters, and another conserved sequence motif, the CCAAT box, which lies upstream of the TATA box, is present in only about half of vertebrate promoters (Mount 2001). Each gene also contains a set of a unique combination of TFBSs in the promoter that determines its temporal and spatial expression. The human genome contains about 1,850 distinct TFs (Venter et al 2001), each of which binds to a specific TFBS, and their combinatorial pattern permutations are immense. All promoter prediction methods have to rely on combinations of those subtle features, none of which is really promoter-specific.

Computational Methods for Predicting Promoters

A number of computational methods for predicting promoters have been developed over the last several years. In general, algorithms can be classified into two groups. First, the signal-based approach, relies on the recognition of relatively conserved signals and conserved spacing among patterns such as the TATA box, CCAAT box, and TFBS using neural network, genetic algorithm (PROMOTER2.0) (Knudsen 1999) or using a weight matrix-based approach (ProScan) (Prestridge 1995). Second, the content-based approach, depends on content difference that can distinguish promoter sequences from non-promoter sequences, such as triplet base-pair preferences around TSSs, hexamer frequencies in consecutive 100-bp upstream regions using either the linear discriminant function (such as programs TSSG and TSSW (Solovyev and Salamov 1997)) or quadratic discriminant analysis (CorePromoter) (Zhang 1998). However, although these programs correctly predicted 13-54% of the promoters of tested genes, each program also predicted a number of false positive promoters and the level of false positive (FP) predictions appears to be unacceptably high. A recently developed system, PromoterInspector (Scherf et al 2000), which is based on context features extracted from training sequences by an unsupervised learning technique, was reported to produce a considerably reduced level of false positive recognition, compared with those of other publicly available promoter recognition programs. A true positive:false positive ratio of 2.3 was obtained using sequences from the review by J.W. Fickett (Fickett and Hatzigeorgiou 1997), surpassing the best ratio of 0.6 that was reported for TSSG. PromoterInspector is considered to be a breakthrough in the area of promoter prediction.

However, the main focus in each of the methods described above is to detect so-called 'promoter regions,' rather than locating the positions of TSSs. At least in more complex species, it appears to be common for genes to have several different transcription start sites, which may be active under different conditions. Several studies were designed specifically to tackle this problem and predict the location of TSS. The algorithms in this category are Eponine (Down and Hubbard 2002) and Dragon Promoter Finder (Dragon PF; Bajic et al 2002, 2003). These algorithms were compared with PromoterInspector and both reported better overall performance on the data sets that they used. PromH (Solovyev and Shahmuradov 2003) uses linear discriminant functions that take into account conservation features and nucleotide sequences of promoter regions in pairs of orthologous genes, which resulted in improvement of TSS prediction.

CpG Islands and Promoter Prediction

Another approach to identify promoters depends on the fact that many vertebrate promoter regions are associated with CpG islands. The likelihood of finding any dinucleotide in a given DNA sequence is 1/16 or ~6%. However, in humans, the measured frequency of the CpG dinucleotide is very low, a phenomenon referred to CG suppression. A CpG island is a region where the occurrence of CpG is significantly higher or close to the expected frequency (~6%). CpG islands are believed to preferentially occur at the transcriptional start of genes, and it has been observed that CpG islands can be found around gene starts in approximately half of mammalian promoters (Cross and Bird 1995) and are estimated to be associated with ~60% of human promoters (Cross et al. 1999). Pedersen et al. (1999) suggested that CpG islands could represent a good global signal to locate promoters across genomes. At least in mammalian genomes, CpG islands are a good indicator of gene presence. Ioshikhes and Zhang (2000) described a method to discriminate between CpG islands in promoters and in other parts of the genome. By combining other methods of promoter identification with CpG island information, the sensitivity of a promoter identification protocol can be greatly enhanced. For example, Davuluri et al (2001) claimed that by including CpG information, they can successfully predict first exons 86% of the time, with a

17% false positive rate. Other algorithms using this CpG island information are CpG_Promoter (Ioshikhes and Zhang 2000); the system by Hannenhalli and Levy (2001); CpGProD (Ponger and Mouchiroud 2002).

The Transcript Mapping Approach in Promoter Localization

The computational prediction of promoters has been greatly aided by mRNA sequence information. With the number of finished genomes increasing and the accumulation of well annotated genes, several studies have tried to analyze promoter sequences upstream of TSSs by aligning full-length mRNA with their counterpart genomic sequences. This approach can achieve over 80% accuracy in promoter localization, which reduces the number of false positive promoter prediction immensely (Wang et al 2001; Qiu et al 2002; Trinklein et al 2003, Marino-Ramirez et al 2004). Yet, due to the incompleteness of full-length transcripts, a complementary approach, CONPRO has been developed by Liu and States (2002). CONPRO makes use of expressed sequence tags (ESTs) to anchor the position of a gene, and then a gene prediction program called GENSCAN (http://genes.mit.edu/GENSCAN.html) is used to identify the missing 5' exon of the gene. A gene model extending upstream of this aligned transcript anchor is then built and the region upstream of the 5'-most predicted exon is searched by TSSG, TSSW and PROSCAN, among others, for a candidate promoter. The authors claimed that CONPRO can identify promoters with very high confidence: it correctly detected promoters for nearly half of the human genes in the test set.

3. Prediction of Transcription Factor Binding Sites

Identification of TFBSs Using TFBS Sequence Profiles

After promoter regions are identified, it is then possible to search for *cis*-regulatory elements. Identification of TFBSs is important for gene prediction, functional characterization of newly discovered genes, as well as for understanding of regulatory network in the cell. Traditionally, DNA-binding specificity has been determined primarily with *in vitro* techniques such as DNase I footprinting and electromobility shift assay (EMSA) (Rooney et al 1995). However, these processes are very costly and time-consuming. Due to the large number and combinatorial nature of regulation and unlimited variety of cellular and environmental conditions, it is impractical to carry out any genome wide identification of TFBS experimentally. One common computational alternative for the identification of TFBSs involves screening genomic sequences for the presence of TFBS motifs that have already been identified. Because most TFs bind to short (5-25 base pairs), degenerate sequence motifs that occur very frequently in the human genome, a PWM (position weight matrix) or IUPAC (International Union of Pure and Applied Chemistry) string (Figure 1) is often used to summarize the binding specificity of these factors. TRANSFAC (http://transfac.gbf.de/TRANSFAC/) is a database of transcription factors, their binding sites, and TFBS sequence profiles generated from published literature and represented in PWM and IUPAC string

(Wingender et al 2001). The consensus sequences represented by IUPAC string or PWM in TRANSFAC can be used to search the genome for known TFBS elements. Several programs have been developed to perform searches based on PWM and IUPAC: SIGNAL SCAN (Prestridge 1996), MATRIX SEARCH (Chen et al 1995), Matinspector (Quandt et al 1995), ConsInspector (Frech et al 1993), TFSearch (Frech et al 1997), etc. While a PWM-based search is considered to be more sensitive, a major drawback of using PWM directly in identifying TFBSs is its high false positive rate. The false positive rate is particularly high when examining multicellular organism promoters, as only a small fraction of the predicted binding sites are functionally significant. This is because regulatory elements in multicellular organisms are often located far away from the region immediately upstream of coding sequence. Comparative genomics, a method for reducing the large number of false positives, has been used by many researchers and will be discussed below.

A	C	G	T	IUPAC Consensus
1	3	1	17	T
1	1	0	20	T
1	0	0	21	T
0	12	10	0	S
0	4	17	0	G
0	19	3	0	C
0	2	20	0	G
0	13	8	1	S

Figure 1. PWM and IUPAC consensus representations of the E2F binding site (from TRANSFAC 7.4, V$E2F_Q6) with matrix head (A C G T) and derived IUPAC consensus in the last column. IUPAC strings are often used to represent consensus sequences (TTTSGCGS in this case) of a TFBS which allows ambiguity, as S means C or G nucleotides. PWM usually contains entries formed by taking the logarithm of the ratio of the frequency that the nucleotide occurs in the corresponding position divided by the frequency that it occurs randomly. In this figure, the frequency of each nucleotide is shown for each position.

Identification of TFBSs Using Expression Profiling

The recent advancement of microarray technology and the availability of a large number of complete genome sequences make the use of computational methods to find potential functional TFBSs more robust. Genes can be classified into different clusters based on their expression patterns using various clustering algorithms. Genes in the same cluster are assumed to be co-regulated and therefore share common regulatory elements. Different methods can then be used to discover regulatory elements within the genes in the same cluster. Binding sites of known TFs and putative TFs can both be identified. The common feature of these methods is to search for overrepresented motifs in the collection of regulatory regions (van Helden et al 1998; Roth et al 1998). Popular programs that can perform this task are Consensus (Hertz and Stormo et al 1999), MEME (Bailey et al 1994), Gibbs Sampler (Lawrence et al 1993), DIALIGN (Morgenstern et al 1998), ANN-Spec (Workman and Stormo 2000), AlignACE (Roth et al 1998; Hughes et al 2000), PROJECTION (Buhler and Tompa 2002), MDScan (Liu et al 2002),YMF (Sinha and Tompa 2003) , and most recently, Clover (Frith et al 2004) and CompareProspector (Liu et al 2004). Most of the methodologies have been successfully demonstrated mainly in prokaryote and lower eukaryotic organisms. Elkon et al (2003) demonstrated that a similar approach (PRIMA) can also be applied to reveal transcriptional networks in human cells. Focusing on transcriptional mechanisms that control cell cycle progression, they revealed eight TFs whose binding sites are significantly overrepresented in promoters of genes whose expression is cell-cycle-dependent.

However, the correlation between gene cluster and regulatory motifs is imprecise for at least two reasons. First, not all co-regulated gene promoters share a common motif, due to the fact that some of the identified genes in a given cluster might in fact be secondary response genes. Second, the same motif can be found in the promoter regions of genes that are not co-regulated, due to the combinatorial nature of TFs. Therefore, partitioning the data into disjoint clusters will cause loss of information. Allocco et al estimated that even if the correlation between their expression profiles (across the 611 microarrays used in their study) is greater than 0.84, two genes only have a greater than 50% chance of sharing a common transcription factor (Allocco et al 2004). In order to circumvent the limitations of gene clustering based on expression profiles, Bussemaker et al (2001) used a regression model in which upstream motifs contribute additively to the log-expression level of a gene to predict statistically significant motifs. This method requires a single genome-wide set of expression ratios and the upstream sequence for each gene. Using publicly available expression data for *Saccharomyces cerevisiae,* they found that known motifs generally have high statistical significance and they also revealed several new putative regulatory elements, some of which plausibly control the early, transient induction of genes during sporulation. Another algorithm, called MobyDick, was designed for discovering multiple motifs from among a large collection of sequences, even without expression data (Bussemaker et al 2000). This method decomposed a set of DNA sequences into the most probable dictionary of motifs or words, which enables many *cis*-regulatory motifs to be extracted with high statistical significance from intergenic regions in the yeast genome without other empirical information.

Computationally Linking TFs with Unknown TFBSs

Few of the methods described above attempt to link computationally discovered regulatory motifs that are not previously known with the TFs that bind to them. Approaches taken by Birnbaum et al (Birnbaum 2001) and Zhu et al (2002) promised to provide this missing information. Based on the assumption that in some cases, the mRNA level of TFs and their target genes are correlated, Birnbaum et al established a link between TFs and motifs by decomposing promoter regions into '7-mers', followed by correlating the composite expression pattern of all genes containing each 7-mer with the TF expression pattern. A TFcentric clustering algorithm developed by Zhu et al took an opposite approach, that is to use a particular TF expression pattern to identify *cis*-regulatory motifs. If a particular TF is chosen as a seed for expression clustering, then some of the genes in the cluster should contain the regulatory motif to which the seed TF binds. By using a Gibbs sampling algorithm to identify shared *cis*-regulatory elements in promoters of clustered genes, at least one of the discovered motifs would be the site bound by the original seed TF. Use of this method allowed the correct identification of previously characterized binding site motifs of four of eight TFs that are known to regulate cell cycle and sporulation in *Saccharomyces cerevisiae*, and the prediction of some unknown TF binding sites (Zhu et al 2002).

Although these two approaches both demonstrated success, they are both limited by the common underlying assumption that expression profiles of TFs correlate with the expression profiles of their target genes. Generally, expression profiling analysis of genes requires that the expression levels of those genes fluctuate in different conditions, while in fact the expression levels of TF genes as compared with those of other gene classes are usually low, and any fluctuations in the expression levels of TF genes may not be detectable against background fluctuation levels. Finally, many TFs may be constitutively expressed, but strictly controlled post-transcriptionally.

Functiona-Network-Based Approach to Discovering Novel TFBSs

To facilitate the identification of TFBSs, researchers make use of more than genome sequence and expression profiling information. Ettwiller et al. (2003) combined functional information such as protein-protein interactions or metabolic networks with genome information in *S. cerevisiae* and developed a new scoring method to predict *cis*-regulatory motifs in the upstream regions of genes. The rationale behind this is that proteins rarely act alone and they usually associate with others and form a functional group to perform a given task. All the essential proteins in the functional group need to be present at the same time and be regulated in a synergic fashion by some common TFs. This mechanism is especially true in prokaryotes, but has also been found true in specific cases in eukaryotes (Niehrs and Pollet 1999). For example, yeast genes coding for proteins involved in the metabolism of galactose are regulated by the same TFs, GAL4/GAL80 (Klar and Halvorson 1974). This method is complementary to gene expression (microarray) based clustering: if a gene can not be assigned to any common cluster due to a number of different regulatory pressures, it can still be associated with other genes in a functional network.

Biophysical-Property-Based Approach to Finding TFBSs

A novel approach to identifying TFs that bind to specific DNA sequences, based on structural information of the protein-DNA complex, is described by Mandel-Gutfreund et al (2001). It has already been shown that specific recognition between a TF and its DNA target is achieved by stereo-chemical complementarity between the amino acids of the TF and the DNA nucleotides. The proposed computational scheme uses crystallographic information to define the set of amino acid-nucleotide contacts between the proteins of a given DNA-binding protein family and their DNA targets. The compatibility of a given TF with a putative regulatory DNA sequence is then evaluated by knowledge-based parameters of amino acid-nucleotide interactions. This method has been successfully demonstrated when applied to known TF-DNA interactions. Djordjevic et al (2003) described yet another physical-property-based approach to TFBS discovery, based on the estimate of sequence-sequence binding energy of a given TF. The authors claimed that the new algorithm QPMEME (Quadratic Programming Method of Energy Matrix Estimation) is more appropriate for the analysis of TFs with highly variable known binding sites, that is, TFs that bind with low specificity under physiological conditions. In contrast with the widely used PWM method, this approach correctly describes saturation in the TF/DNA binding probability, which results in a significant improvement in the number of expected false positives, particularly in the ubiquitous case of low-specificity factors. In the strong binding limit, the algorithm is related to the "support vector machine" approach to pattern recognition. The QPMEME algorithm was applied to the identification of the potential regulatory binding sites in *Escherichia coli* for the set of TFs collected in the DPInteract database (http://arep.med.harvard.edu/dpinteract/). The QPMEME algorithm allows identification of likely RNA polymerase (RNAP) binding sites, including the RNAP-70 sites, which is highly nontrivial because of the strong variability of those sites in E. coli. Djordjevic et al also provided predictions for the location and modality of numerous cAMP-receptor protein (CRP) binding sites using this method.

4. Identification of Combinatorial TF Modules

Combinatorial Regulation of Transcription

Genes are rarely controlled by a single TF (Buchler et al 2003). Rather, accumulating evidence suggests that specific combinations of TFs are required to achieve the complex differential expression of genes in higher organisms through combinatorial regulation of transcription (Figure 2). Combinatorial regulation of transcription makes the organism much more efficient by allowing the use of a limited number of TFs to create numerous combinations of regulators that are modulated by diverse sets of conditions

The structural basis for combinatorial regulation exists in the organization of multiple TFBSs into modules in the promoters of each gene, usually a few hundred base pairs upstream of the TSS site. Each gene contains in its promoter a unique combination of TFBSs that determine the gene's temporal and spatial expression pattern. One of the best-studied examples is that of composite NFAT/AP-1 sites, in which it was demonstrated that these two factors bind cooperatively to activate cytokine gene expression (Cockerill et al 1995). Therefore, identifying combinatorial TF modules is one of the important steps in understanding the complex architecture of the transcriptional regulation network.

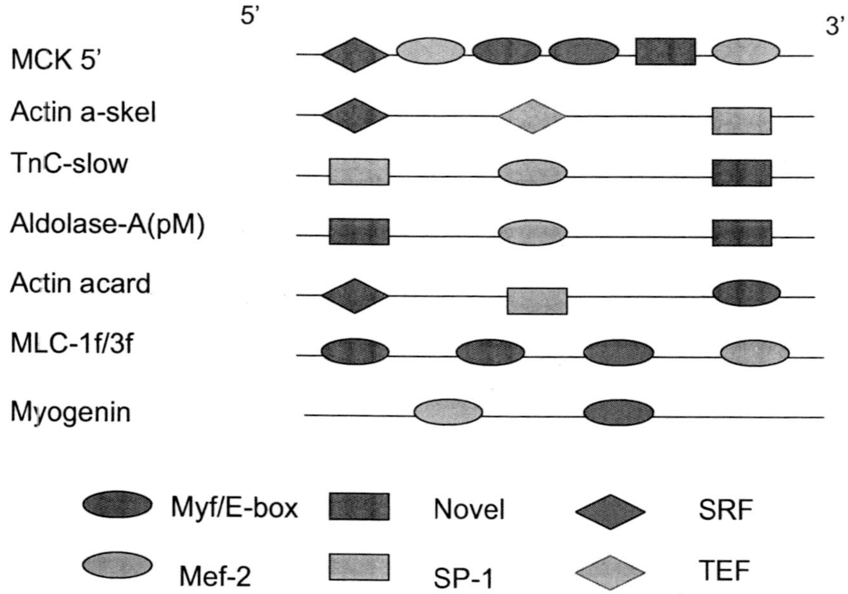

Figure 2. Genes are rarely controlled by a single TF. Rather, accumulating evidence suggests that specific combinations of TFs are required to achieve the complex temporal and spatial expression of a given gene. For example, studies have indicated that specific combinations of TFs are required to achieve muscle-specific expression. An example of functional TFBSs within 200bp of TSS in several muscle genes is shown (Wasserman and Fickett 1998).

Computational Methods of Identifying TF Synergism

One effort to document all combinatorial elements is TRANSCompel (Kel et al 2000; Kel-Margoulis et al 2002). TRANSCompel is a database which provides published information on composite elements. Composite elements are two closely situated binding sites for distinct TFs, within a particular gene for which the cooperative action between the TFs has been confirmed by experimental results. Klingenhoff et al (1999) developed a method, FastM, that combines a search algorithm for individual TFBSs with a distance correlation function to detect genes containing composite elements taken from TRANSCompel. However, the effectiveness of TRANSCompel is still limited by its small size: release 7.4 (2004) contains only 388 entries.

In order to sidestep the limitations of TRANSCompel, several groups have devised different computational approaches to detect TF synergism. One approach depends on the notion that a pair of TFs acting synergistically will have a higher frequency of corresponding *cis*-elements that co-localize on the promoter region than random occurrence (Qiu et al 2002, Hannenhalli and Levy 2002). The identified hits were partially validated by published experimental evidence or TRANSCompel in both approaches. While the previous two studies were performed on human genome, a similar approach was by taken by Bulyk et al (2004) to predict sets of two or more TFBSs that co-regulate downstream genes in the E.coli genome. For five predictions, knockouts with mutated replacements of the predicted binding sites were created. RT-PCR indicated that at least one of the genes immediately downstream from each of the binding site knockouts exhibits a significant change in mRNA expression. However, these methods can only detect composite elements consisting of known TFs with known PWMs.

A second approach, Co-Bind (for COoperative BINDing), uses Gibbs sampling strategy to model the cooperativity between two TFs, and to define PWMs for identified binding sites (Guhathakurta and Stormo 2001). Co-Bind has been demonstrated to be useful in discovering new synergistic regulatory sites and could potentially be extended to model TF synergism consisting of more than two factors. Since this approach is based on modeling sequence motif synergism without the need of prior knowledge of TFs that bind to the motifs, one limitation of this approach is that the connection between binding site motifs discovered and the corresponding TFs is not established. Another limitation is that the sequence motif length needs to be specified as input during the analysis.

Expression Profiling Analysis in Identifying TF Combinations

Pilpel et al (2001) first used high-throughput expression profiling technology to identify novel TF combinations in the promoters of the yeast *S. cerevisiae*. Their approach involves screening genomic sequences against a database of known and putative regulatory motifs to identify genes containing each motif. The effect of each motif on gene expression is then evaluated by examining the expression profiles of genes containing this motif. For each motif or combination, an expression coherence score, a measure of the overall similarity of the expression profiles of all the genes containing that motif in several different conditions, is calculated. A pair of motifs is considered synergistic if the expression coherence score of genes containing both motifs in their promoters is significantly higher than that of genes containing either motif alone. By virtue of generating a motif-association map, it is possible to provide a global view of transcription networks using this approach. Banerjee et al (2003) integrated genome-wide gene expression data and chromatin immunoprecipitation (ChIP-chip, for determining downstream targets of TFs *in vivo*) data and combined the results with statistical analysis to discover more biologically relevant synergistic interactions between different TFs. The assumption is that if two TFs are cooperative, they should both bind (either directly or through another DNA-binding protein) to the promoters of their target genes and the expression profiles of these target genes would be similar. If they are not cooperative, the TFs will either bind independently or not bind at all to the promoters and the expression profiles will likely not be coherent overall. However, the analysis has only been applied in the relatively simple organism yeast in both of these studies.

5. Cross-Species Genome Comparison in Regulatory Region Analysis

The methods discussed thus far are capable of identifying likely TFBSs via the alignment of regulatory regions of co-expressed genes or by statistical analysis of over-represented motifs. Such methodology is quite successful when applied to genomic analysis of single-cell organisms such as yeast, because most regulatory elements are located within 200-500 bp upstream of a given TSS. However, in multicellular organisms like vertebrates, regulatory elements are not necessarily located immediately upstream of the coding region, and can be found upstream or downstream of the gene and in introns. Furthermore, regulatory sequences in multicellular organisms may be spread over tens or even hundreds of kilobases. Consequently, searches for over-represented motifs and sequence alignment strategies will return a high frequency of false positive results.

Resources for Comparative Promoter Analysis

Comparative genomics (also referred to as phylogenetic footprinting) has proven useful for identifying functional elements in the genome. This approach relies on the assumption that functional sequences such as coding regions and regulatory modules are more conserved evolutionarily than nonfunctional regions. Comparative sequence analyses have been shown to facilitate the identification of both coding (Flicek et al 2003; Alexandersson et al 2003) and functional non-coding sequences (Loots et al 2000, 2002; Wasserman et al. 2000; Elnitski et al 2003; Kellis et al 2003). Giardine et al (2003) developed a relational database to contain whole genome sequence alignments between human and mouse with extensive annotations of the human sequence, which allows complex queries to be made. Several algorithms have been developed for cross-species sequence comparison. Some are based on local alignment, for example BLAST (Altschul et al 1990; Schwartz et al 2000); MultiPipMaker (Schwartz 2003); BBA (Zhu et al 1998); and DBA (Jareborg et al 1999). Others are based on global alignment: CLUSTALW (Thompson et al 1994), VISTA (Mayor et al 2000), AVID (Bray et al 2003) and LAGAN (Brudno et al 2003). Instead of only being limited to cross-species sequence comparison, other programs are designed specifically for discovery of putative TFBSs using comparative genomics. Examples of programs in this category are rVISTA (*Loots* et al 2002) and FootPrinter (Blanchette et al 2002). Most recently, Lenhard et al. (2003) devised a flexible suite of methods (ConSite) for the identification and visualization of conserved TFBSs. The system reports putative TFBSs that are not only located in conserved regions but also located as pairs of sites in equivalent positions in alignments between two orthologous sequences, which resulted in a significant reduction of noise and increase of specificity of predicted TFBSs over other methods. Liu et al (2004) developed a sequence-motif-finding algorithm called CompareProspector, which extends Gibbs sampling by biasing the search in regions conserved across species. Using human–mouse comparison, CompareProspector identified known motifs for TFs Mef2, Myf, Srf, and Sp1 from a set of human-muscle-specific genes. CompareProspector outperformed many other pure motif-finding programs, demonstrating the power of comparative genomics-based biased sampling in complex eukaryotic regulatory element identification.

Advantage of Phylogenetic Footprinting

Phylogenetic footprinting has been used to identify regulatory control elements with considerable success. (Hardison et al 1997; Oeltjen et al 1997; Hardison 2000; Loots et al 2000; Wasserman et al 2000; Krivan and Wasserman 2001; Loots et al 2002; Blanchette et al 2002; Qiu et al 2003, Dickmeis et al 2004) . The major advantage of phylogenetic footprinting over the single genome, multigene approach discussed above is that the latter method requires a reliable set of co-regulated genes. In contrast, phylogenetic footprinting is capable of identifying regulatory elements specific even to a single gene, as long as they are sufficiently conserved across species. Therefore phylogenetic footprinting is especially useful when only a small set of high-quality co-regulated genes are available. Phylogenetic footprinting of a set of co-regulated genes can substantially reduce the size of the sequence to be searched for functional sites (Figure 3; Qiu et al 2003). For instance, phylogenetic footprinting of human and mouse promoters has revealed that 17% of conserved sequences (over 60% identity) in the 5,000 bp upstream of a TSS contain about 90% of experimentally conserved TFBSs (Qiu et al 2003).

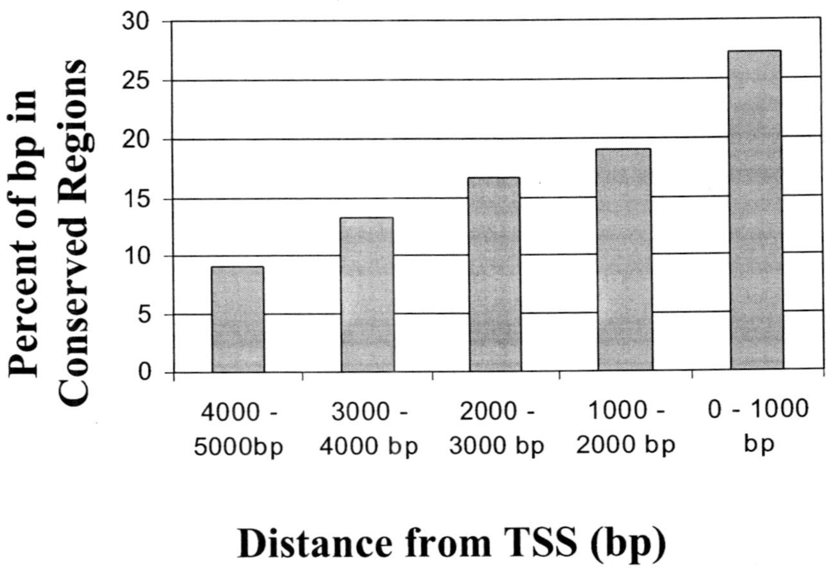

Figure 3. Distribution of percentage of base pairs located in the conserved (above 60% identity) human-mouse promoter region. (Qiu et al 2003). The overall conservation is higher in the most proximal 5' region (0-1000bp) in comparison to the most distal region (4000-5000bp). The majority of functional sites is located in the conserved regions. Cross-species comparison can substantially reduce the size of the promoter regions to be searched for functional sites and make the statistical computational analysis of the functional units more sensitive and specific.

The sequences of rodent genomes have been particularly useful in phylogenetic footprinting. Wasserman et al (2000) reported that 98% (74/75) of experimentally defined binding sites of skeletal-muscle-specific TFs are confined to the 19% of the conserved region among human and rodent in a set of skeletal muscle specific genes, and were able to identify all three known major muscle-specific TFs (MYF, SRF and MEF2) . Additionally, by taking a similar phylogenetic footprinting approach in conjunction with a TRANSFAC PWM search and statistical analysis, Qiu et al identified all three known parathyroid hormone (PTH)-responsive TFs (AP1, RUNX2, CREB), and generated a list of other potential TFs involved in the PTH pathway (Qiu et al 2003).

Multi-Species Genome Comparison

Even pairwise genome comparison combined with TFBS prediction and statistical analysis has produced promising results. Multi-species comparison has been shown to be more specific in terms of conserved region identification (Margulies et al 2003; Thomas et al 2003). By analyzing a set of sequences orthologous to a 1.8Mb fragment on human chromosome 7q31 that were generated from 11 non-human vertebrates (chimpanzee, baboon, cat, dog, cattle, pig, rat, mouse, chicken, fugu and tetraodon), Margulies et al were able to show that none of the individual pairwise comparisons alone came close to identifying all of the MCSs (Multi Species Conserved Sequences). Use of rodent sequences resulted in the detection of the greatest number of MCS bases, as well as the largest fraction of non coding sequences. Non-human primate sequences are not useful for MCS detection. Forty percent of the human genome sequence forms alignments with the mouse genome, which is much higher than the amount of mammalian genome estimated to be under active selection (~ 5%) (Mouse Genome Sequencing Consortium 2002). This suggests that pairwise sequence comparison alone might not be sufficient for precisely identifying the small fraction of the mammalian genome that is functionally important.

Network-Level Comparison

In the studies described above, one of the important requirements is that the regulatory regions from different species can be aligned by multiple sequence alignment algorithms. However, more distant phylogenetic comparisons will not meet this requirement, given the relatively short length of functional TFBSs and the large number of insertion/deletion events within regulatory regions. In more complex multicellular organisms, orthologous regulatory elements may exist tens of kilobases away from the TSS of a gene. Pritsker et al (2004) described a method that is based on the notion that each TF regulates the expression of many genes (~30-200) in the genome and the conservation of global gene expression between two closely related species requires most of these TF target genes to maintain their regulation. The homologous function of the whole regulatory system requires that the genes regulated by a TF in one organism should also be regulated by the same TF in the closely related and physiologically similar phylogenetic neighbor. This network-level conservation represents a system-level constraint on functional TFBSs and it does not depend on global alignments, or even the availability of sequences from multiple species. To look for significant intra-genomic conservation of binding sites, they used the hypergeometric distribution (Tavazoie et al. 1999) to assess the significance of overlap between the set of genes which harbor the top scoring motifs in the two species. This algorithm requires only a fraction (12%) of the sequences of another species and was able to find 71% of known TFBSs in the yeast *S. cerevisiae*.

6. Identification of Functional Clusters of TFBSs and TF Target Gene Identification

Identification of TFs that control the expression of a given gene is important, yet equally important in a pursuit of an understanding of the transcriptional regulatory network is to be able to predict downstream genes that are responsive to a set of TFs.

General Approaches

The notion of TFBS coordinate or close positioning has been used widely to identify target genes that are regulated by similar mechanisms (Wasserman and Fickett 1998; Wagner 1999). While many methods for the identification of TF target genes have been reported, they all share several common features. First, most of the methods derive a set of TFBS elements from a set of co-regulated genes or a set of genes with similar functions; the individual binding elements are then combined into one recognition module/model. The module/model is then used in a search against the genome or genes with similar expression profiles. Second, the phylogenetic footprinting approach is used to either reduce the size of the genomic region to be searched for a certain regulatory module, or to increase the sensitivity/specificity of the model building. Third, TF binding specificity is often expressed by a consensus IUPAC string, but PWM is used more often. Studies show that 95% of the highest scoring hits identified by PWM for the liver-specific TF HNF-1 can be bound by HNF-1 *in vitro* (Tronche 1997), suggesting that a high-quality PWM can effectively identify sequences that can be bound by a specific TF (Fickett 1996). Many of the approaches reported use PWM to search for TFBSs. Finally, high-throughput expression profiling data such as that obtained from microarrays and SAGE are also used in many of these methods.

From TFBS Modules/Models to Target Gene Identification

The results obtained thus far are very promising. A protocol developed by Wasserman and Fickett (1998) generated PWMs for the well-characterized muscle factors MEF-2, TEF and Myf. Their analysis of known regulatory regions of skeletal-muscle-specific genes revealed that multiple muscle-specific sites are concentrated in their regulatory regions. Using logistic regression analysis, Wasserman et al derived a model that allowed them to identify genes that are likely to exhibit muscle-specific expression and resulted in meaningful predictions.

Additionally, Kel et al (2001) studied the structural features of the 5' regulatory regions of cell-cycle-related genes, looking for other key TFBSs around the binding site of E2F (a key cell cycle regulator). A TFBS module containing E2F was identified, and this E2F composite module was found at high frequency and in close proximity to the TSSs of vertebrate cell-cycle-related genes. Application of E2F modules resulted in the identification of 319 new genes that might be involved in the cell cycle. The authors were able to verify *in vivo* binding of E2F for a small percentage of the promoters predicted by their method using chromatin immunoprecipitation assay.

A method reported by Halfon et al (2002) is based on a single detailed model – the *Drosophila* dorsal mesodermal enhancer (the *eve* MHE) which contains five key TFBSs. Using this model, they tried to identify sequence elements with the co-occurrence of the same combination of TFs described in the model in the whole genome. They also demonstrated that from the sequence alignment of the search results, they were able to derive additional potential TFBSs and confirmed some of the predictions empirically. The authors also suggest that their simple model-based approach, if combined with expression profiling and phylogenetic footprinting, will allow genome-wide characterization of functionally related *cis*-regulatory elements, a functional step toward understanding the genetic regulatory networks involved in development.

By using published DNA binding specificity data for five TFs active in the early *Drosophila* embryo and making PWMs, Berman et al (2002) identified genomic regions containing unusually high concentrations of predicted binding sites for these factors. A significant fraction of these binding site clusters overlaps known regulatory modules that are regulated by these factors. In addition, many of the remaining clusters are adjacent to genes expressed in a pattern characteristic of genes regulated by these factors.

Frith et al (2002) developed a general method called 'cluster of motifs E-value tool' (COMET) to detect local concentrations of *cis*-element motifs, using predetermined matrix representations of the *cis*-elements, and the statistical significance of these motif clusters. The program takes as input a set of sequences to search and a set of user-specified motifs in the form of count matrices. It then finds optimal scoring motif clusters in the sequences. They made novel target gene predictions of TFs associated with muscle using this approach.

Based on the A* procedure which is an optimal heuristic graph search algorithm, Aerts et al (2003) developed a generic algorithm (ModuleSearcher) to find the best scoring combination of TFBSs (CRM, cis-regulatory modules) within a sequence window in a given co-regulated gene set. The search was performed in the conserved regions between human and mouse. Given a predicted CRM or with a user-defined CRM known from the literature, another algorithm ModuleScanner performs genomic searches to find possible target genes. The validity of a set of putative targets was checked using Gene Ontology annotations.

Lastly, Liu et al (2003) used logistic regression models of the promoters of 62 known NF-kappa-B-regulated immune genes to derive TFBS patterns. By means of the comparative genomics approach, these patterns were used to scan a set of 6,440 previously identified human promoters. The analysis predicted 28 NF-kappa-B-related genes, 19 of which have a known function; 18 of the 19 are regulated by NF-kappa-B. The analysis also predicted nine novel putative NF-kappa-B-regulated immune genes that were confirmed with available SAGE data. This method of predicting gene function, based on characteristic patterns of TF binding, evolutionary conservation, and expression studies, can be applicable to finding genes with other functions.

Previous algorithms discussed in this section share one common limitation. They all need a well-defined set of known modules for the training of the discriminant function. However the experimental data is too sparse to provide such a positive training set, and one can obtain a sufficient number of literature-derived regulatory modules in only a few cases. To circumvent=the training data set problem, another algorithm, MSCAN, developed by Johansson et al (2003), is based on the statistical significance of clusters of binding sites. It takes a set of TF binding models represented by PWM, a significance threshold and a genomic sequence as input. Using dynamic programming, the most significant cluster of putative binding sites within a window of sequence is identified and those windows are reported. The performance of this algorithm was assessed on two curated collections of regulatory regions: one each for liver-specific expression and skeletal-muscle-cell-specific expression. While such an approach is unlikely to surpass the performance of those incorporating positive training sets, it does provide an alternative that can accelerate characterization of regulatory regions within the genome.

Current Problems in TF Target Gene Identification Approaches

Although all these methods drastically improve the likelihood of identifying target genes for a given TF, all of them nonetheless have their limitations. One common problem of all these computational prediction approaches is the fairly large amount of false positive results, though various approaches (phylogenetics footprinting, statistical analysis and model building) have been implemented to minimize the false positive ratio. Second, very little empirical validation of hits was performed in the analyses described above. Yet the computational method provides a systematic test on all genes potentially regulated by a certain TF and a framework for continued analysis of the regulation network. With the advent of large-scale sequencing projects, it is becoming increasingly essential that *in vivo* validation needs to be combined with the computational approach in order to understand the transcriptional regulatory networks that control cell growth in, and development of, multicellular organisms.

7. Reconstructing Regulatory Networks

Understanding transcriptional regulatory networks is crucial to the understanding of fundamental cellular processes. With the availability of large quantities of high throughput genomic data, reconstructing regulatory networks is rapidly evolving into one of the major research topics in computational biology and has become one of the central tasks in the postgenomic era. A regulatory network can be reconstructed based on annotated genome information, well curated databases and research literature. Yet despite the limited resources and incompleteness of these data types, the utilization of the high-throughput data types (genome-wide expression profiling and large-scale ChIP) in combination with promoter sequence analysis has been shown to provide a powerful platform for regulatory network reconstruction (De Jong 2002; Lee et al 2002; Wang et al 2002), especially for refining and expanding particular subcomponents of known regulatory networks.

Most attempts so far to understand transcriptional regulatory networks have focused on simple organisms such as *E.coli* and *S. cerevisiae* and many advances have been made. One strategy infers global networks directly from genome-wide microarray data (D'Haeseleer et al. 2000; de Jong 2002; Lee et al. 2002; Herrgard et al 2003; Kwon et al 2003; Segal et al 2003). For example, by employing support vector machine (SVM), Qian et al (2003) developed an approach to predict the targets of a transcription factor by identifying subtle relationships between their expression profiles. SVM is a form of supervised machine learning. Qian et al used a training set to learn in advance which gene pairs have a regulatory relationship. The first gene in a pair is a TF, while the second is the target gene it potentially regulates. After the training stage, the machines determine probabilities for each TF-target pairing and these probabilities, with appropriate thresholds, can then be used to construct parts of a regulatory network. They applied this SVM to predict the regulatory targets for 36 TFs in the *S. cerevisiae* genome based on microarray expression data under many different physiological conditions. Sixty-three percent of predicted TF-target relationships were confirmed through cross-validation. The regulatory network constructed based on these data is comparable to that generated from the recent genome-wide ChIP-chip experiments (Horak et al 2002; Lee et al 2002). However, due to the enormous number of potential regulatory network structures that are generated, the network reconstruction is still a daunting task. An approach to overcome the problem of purely data-driven reconstruction methods would be to start with established regulatory network structures and use the new data sets to refine and expand these structures. To evaluate the validity of these approaches, Herrgard et al (2003) examined the consistency between known genome-wide regulatory network structures and extensive gene expression data collections in *E. coli* and *S. cerevisiae*. They found that the consistency of the network elements is influenced by both structural features of the network, such as the number of regulators acting on a target gene, and by the functional classes of the genes involved in a particular element. Their results suggest that targeted gene expression profiling data can be used to refine and expand particular subcomponents of known regulatory networks that are sufficiently decoupled from the rest of the network.

However, using expression alone is not sufficient for network constructing as demonstrated by previous methods. It is more beneficial to also incorporate other information such as protein-protein interaction data, scientific literatures and TF binding site data generated from promoter analysis. Haverty et al (2004) developed a computational method named CARRIE for transcriptional regulatory network inference. This method combined microarray analysis and TFBS analysis. First, microarray data were used to reveal the genes that respond to a given stimulus. Clusters of co-regulated group were formed in this step. If there were TFs in the group, they are proposed to regulate the observed expression changes of the other genes. Second, they identify TFs with binding sites that are statistically over-represented in the promoter regions of the co-regulated cluster of genes. Even if their expression levels do not change upon stimulation, these TFs are also predicted to regulate the group. Transcription networks were further constructed based on information derived from the previous two steps. They applied CARRIE to six sets of publicly available microarray experiments on *S. cerevisiae*. The networks generated by CARRIE are cohesive in terms of the biological function of the genes involved after comparing with gene ontology biological process information.

Starting from building functional modules, Wang et al (2002) proposed a systematic approach to reconstruct transcription networks in *S. cerevisiae* using a variety of information. First they identified the conserved DNA regulatory motifs in the promoter region recognized by a particular TF and then further identified all the genes likely to be directly regulated by this TF using an expression-weighted profile method. Then they determined which transcription modules (TF and its target gene) are activated/deactivated under particular experimental conditions. Last, they inferred interaction between coactivated transcription modules by identifying genes shared by them and other annotation information, such as protein-protein interaction and the hierarchy of known signaling pathway.

The regulatory relationships inferred from expression data sets derived from experiments whose parameters include time course, cell cycle and environmental perturbation have limitations and sometimes are questionable, since they are not based on comprehensive experimental data designed specifically to elucidate transcription regulatory networks and can therefore only produce information on co-regulation of expression, rather than hierarchical dependency. To rigorously and precisely identify novel and complex gene regulatory networks from *de novo* expression data sets, Aburatani et al (2003) reported a systematic and integrated strategy of expression experiments on genomic deletion of yeast on 118 genes with known involvement in transcription regulation. Using a static Boolean network model algorithm, which is based on a multi-level digraph approach and can handle large sets of expression data and analyze large-scale gene regulatory networks at high speed, they were able to infer gene expression regulatory relationships and validate some of their findings with existing database information as well as through biological experimentation.

8. Conclusion

The rapid accumulation of the genomic sequences of different species and the huge amount of expression profiling data are making computational analysis of transcription regulation more and more attractive (Markstein and Levine 2002). Currently, most microarray experiments are designed to address specific problems such as target gene identification or the diagnosis of certain diseases. However, one of the final goals of expression analysis is to decipher the transcriptional regulation of the entire genome and reconstruct the global regulatory network. This task cannot be achieved by expression profiling alone, since transcriptional regulation is a complex and condition-dependent network and microarray analysis can only capture a small portion of the overall picture. Microarray analysis combined with *cis*-regulatory element analysis will provide the better chance to decipher the regulatory network. Microarray information can also be used to validate and improve TF binding motif prediction.

Generally, individual TFBS hits generated by PWM or IUPAC strings are too abundant to be analyzed in full, but combining such information with microarray analysis, phylogenetic footprinting, combinatorial model building, and statistical analysis will bring the output to a manageable scale for further experimental validation. Despite all the methods developed so far, computationally deciphering the regulatory network completely is far from reality due to the complexity of transcription regulation (especially in multicellular organisms), lack of experimental evidence, and the inherent imperfectness of computational algorithms. Full reconstruction of regulatory networks will rely on a combination of approaches that can be described as 'bottom-up' (based on descriptions of individual interactions and regulons in the literature or regulation modules inferred from genome wide data) and 'top-down' (based on large systemic data sets), with targeted experimentation to successfully resolve inconsistencies between the two. The systematic integration of diverse data types, together with the development of progressively more sophisticated computation algorithms for promoter prediction, regulatory element identification and the accumulation of databases of genes and TFs (such as TRANSFAC and TRANSCompel, among others) will yield synergistic, additional information that is not available through any of the individual resources, and thus provide an integrated platform for deciphering the transcriptional regulatory network.

References

Aburatani S, Tashiro K, Savoie CJ, Nishizawa M, Hayashi K, Ito Y, Muta S, Yamamoto K, Ogawa M, Enomoto A, Masaki M, Watanabe S, Maki Y, Takahashi Y, Eguchi Y, Sakaki Y, Kuhara S. (2003) Discovery of novel transcription control relationships with gene regulatory networks generated from multiple-disruption full genome expression libraries. *DNA Res*. 10: 1-8.

Aerts S, Van Loo P, Thijs G, Moreau Y, De Moor B.(2003) Computational detection of cis - regulatory modules. *Bioinformatics*.19(Suppl 2):II5-II14

Alexandersson M, Cawley S, Pachter L. (2003) SLAM: cross-species gene finding and alignment with a generalized pair hidden Markov model. Genome Res. 13: 496-502

Allocco DJ,Kohane IS and Butte AJ.(2004) Quantifying the relationship between co-expression, co-regulation and gene function BMC *Bioinformatics* 5:18

Altschul SF, Gish W, Miller W, Myers EW, Lipman DJ. (1990) Basic local alignment search tool. *J Mol Biol* 215:403-10

Aparicio S, Chapman J, Stupka E, Putnam N, Chia JM, Dehal P, Christoffels A, Rash S, Hoon S, Smit A et al (2002) Whole-genome shotgun assembly and analysis of the genome of Fugu rubripes. *Science*. 297: 1301-10.

Bailey TL, Elkan C. (1994) Fitting a mixture model by expectation maximization to discover motifs in biopolymers. *Proc Int Conf Intell Syst Mol Biol* 2: 28-36

Bajic VB, Seah SH, Chong A, Krishnan SP, Koh JL, Brusic V. (2003) Computer model for recognition of functional transcription start sites in RNA polymerase II promoters of vertebrates. *J Mol Graph Model* 21: 323-332

Bajic, VB, Seah, SH, Chong, A., Zhang, G., Koh, JLY, and Brusic, V. (2002) Dragon Promoter Finder: Recognition of vertebrate RNA Polymerase II promoters. *Bioinformatics* 18: 198-199

Banerjee N, Zhang MQ. (2003) Identifying cooperativity among transcription factors controlling the cell cycle in yeast. *Nucleic Acids Res*. 31:7024-31.

Berman BP, Nibu Y, Pfeiffer BD, Tomancak P, Celniker SE, Levine M, Rubin GM, Eisen MB. (2002) Exploiting transcription factor binding site clustering to identify cis-regulatory modules involved in pattern formation in the Drosophila genome. *Proc Natl Acad Sci USA* 99: 757-762

Birnbaum K, Benfey PN, Shasha DE. (2001). cis element/transcription factor analysis (cis/TF): a method for discovering transcription factor/cis element relationships. *Genome Res*. 11: 1567-73.

Blanchette, M. and Tompa, M. (2002) Discovery of regulatory elements by a computational method for phylogenetic footprinting. *Genome Res*.12: 739-748.

Bray N., Dubchak I. and Pachter, L. (2003) AVID: a global alignment program. *Genome Res*. 13: 97-102.

Brudno M, Do CB, Cooper GM, Kim MF, Davydov E, Green ED, Sidow A, Batzoglou S, NISC Comparative Sequencing Program. (2003) LAGAN and Multi-LAGAN: efficient tools for large-scale multiple alignment of genomic DNA. *Genome Res.* 13:721-31.

Buchler NE, Gerland U, Hwa T. (2003). On schemes of combinatorial transcription logic. *Proc Natl Acad Sci USA* 100:5136-5141

Buhler J and Tompa M. Finding motifs using random projections.(2002) *J Comput Biol* 9: 225-42

Bulyk ML, McGuire AM, Masuda N and Church GM. (2004) A Motif Co-Occurrence Approach for Genome-Wide Prediction of Transcription-Factor-Binding Sites in Escherichia coli. *Genome Research* 14:201-208

Bussemaker HJ and Li H, Siggia ED. (2000) Building a dictionary for genomes: identification of presumptive regulatory sites by statistical analysis. *Proc Natl Acad Sci* 97:10096-100.

Bussemaker HJ, Li H and Siggia ED.(2001) Regulatory element detection using correlation with expression. *Nat Genet* 27: 167-71

Chen QK, Hertz GZ, Stormo GD.(1995) MATRIX SEARCH 1.0: a computer program that scans DNA sequences for transcriptional elements using a database of weight matrices. *Comput Appl Biosci.* 11:563-6.

Cockerill PN, Bert AG, Jenkins F, Ryan GR, Shannon MF, Vadas MA. (1995) Human granulocyte-macrophage colony-stimulating factor enhancer function is associated with cooperative interactions between AP-1 and NFATp/c. *Mol Cell Biol* 15: 2071-9

Crawford GE, Holt IE, Mullikin JC, Tai D, National Institutes Of Health Intramural Sequencing Center, Blakesley R, Bouffard G, Young A, Masiello C, Green ED, Wolfsberg TG, Collins FS. (2004) From the Cover: Identifying gene regulatory elements by genome-wide recovery of DNase hypersensitive sites. *Proc Natl Acad Sci U S A.* 101:992-7.

Cross SH, Clark VH, and Bird AP (1999) Isolation of CpG islands from large genomic clones. *Nucleic Acids Res.* 27: 2099-2107.

Cross, S.H. and Bird, A.P. (1995) CpG islands and genes. *Curr. Opin. Genet. Dev.* 5: 309-314

Davuluri RV, Grosse I, Zhang MQ. (2001) Computational identification of promoters and first exons in the human genome. *Nat Genet* 29: 412-7

de Jong H. (2002) Modeling and simulation of genetic regulatory systems: a literature review. *J Comput Biol.* 9: 67-103

D'Haeseleer, P., Liang, S., and Somogyi, R. (2000) Genetic network inference: From co-expression clustering to reverse engineering. *Bioinformatics* 16: 707-726

Dickmeis T, Plessy C, Rastegar S, Aanstad P, Herwig R, Chalmel F, Fischer N, Strahle U. (2004) Expression Profiling and Comparative Genomics Identify a Conserved Regulatory Region Controlling Midline Expression in the Zebrafish Embryo. *Genome Res.* 14: 228-238

Djordjevic M, Sengupta AM, Shraiman BI. (2003) A biophysical approach to transcription factor binding site discovery. *Genome Res.* 13: 2381-90.

Down, T.A. and Hubbard, T.J.(2002) Computational detection and location of transcription start sites in mammalian genomic DNA. *Genome Res* 12:458-461

Elkon R, Linhart C, Sharan R, Shamir R, Shiloh Y. (2003) Whole-genome discovery of transcription factor binding sites by network-level conservation. *Genome Res.* 14: 99-108.

Elnitski L, Hardison RC, Li J, Yang S, Kolbe D, Eswara P, O'Connor MJ, Schwartz S, Miller W, Chiaromonte F. (2003) Distinguishing regulatory DNA from neutral sites. *Genome Res*. 13: 64-72.

Ettwiller LM, Rung J, Birney E (2003) Discovering novel cis-regulatory motifs using functional networks, *Genome Res*. 13: 883-895.

Fickett JW(1996) Coordinate positioning of MEF2 and myogenin binding sites. *Gene* 172, GC19-32

Fickett JW, Hatzigeorgiou AG (1997) Eukaryotic promoter recognition. *Genome Res* 7: 861-878.

Flicek P, Keibler E, Hu P, Korf I, Brent MR. (2003) Leveraging the mouse genome for gene prediction in human: from whole-genome shotgun reads to a global synteny map. *Genome Res*. 13: 46-54.

Frech K, Herrmann G, Werner T. (1993) Computer-assisted prediction, classification, and delimitation of protein binding sites in nucleic acids. *Nucleic Acids Res*. 21: 1655-64.

Frech K, Quandt K, Werner T. (1997) Finding protein-binding sites in DNA sequences: the next generation. *Trends Biochem Sci* 22, 103-4

Frith M, Spouge JL, Hansen U and Weng Z (2002) Statistical significance of clusters of motifs represented by position specific scoring matrices in nucleotide sequences. *Nucleic Acids Res*. 30:3214-24.

Frith MC, Fu Y, Yu L, Chen J, Hansen U and Weng Z (2004) Detection of functional DNA motifs via statistical over-representation. *Nucleic Acids Res*. 32:1372-1381

Giardine B, Elnitski L, Riemer C, Makalowska I, Schwartz S, Miller W, Hardison RC. (2003) GALA, a database for genomic sequence alignments and annotations. *Genome Res*. 13: 732-41.

Gross DS, Garrard WT. (1998) Nuclease hypersensitive sites in chromatin. *Annu Rev Biochem*. 57:159-97.

GuhaThakurta, D. and Stormo, G.D. (2001) Identifying target sites for cooperatively binding factors. *Bioinformatics* 17, 608-621

Halfon MS, Grad Y, Church GM, Michelson AM.(2002) Computation-based discovery of related transcriptional regulatory modules and motifs using an experimentally validated combinatorial model. *Genome Res* 12: 1019-28

Hannenhalli S and Levy S (2001) Promoter prediction in the human genome. *Bioinformatics* 17 Suppl 1, S90-96

Hannenhalli S and Levy S (2002). Predicting transcription factor synergism. *Nucleic Acids Res* 30: 4278-4284

Hardison R, Slightom JL, Gumucio DL, Goodman M, Stojanovic N and Miller W (1997). Locus control regions of mammalian beta-globin gene clusters: Combining phylogenetic analyses and experimental results to gain functional insights. *Gene* 205: 73-94.

Hardison, R.C. (2000). Conserved noncoding sequences are reliable guides to regulatory elements. *Trends Genet*. 16: 369-372.

Haverty PM, Hansen U, Weng Z. (2004) Computational inference of transcriptional regulatory networks from expression profiling and transcription factor binding site identification. *Nucleic Acids Res*. 32:179-88

Herrgard MJ, Covert MW, Palsson BO (2003) Reconciling gene expression data with known genome-scale regulatory network structures. *Genome Res*. 13: 2423-34.

Hertz, G.Z. and Stormo, G.D.(1999). Identifying DNA and protein patterns with statistically significant alignments of multiple sequences. *Bioinformatics* 15: 563-577.

Horak CE, Luscombe NM, Qian J, Bertone P, Piccirrillo S, Gerstein M, Snyder M. (2002) Complex transcriptional circuitry at the G1/S transition in Saccharomyces cerevisiae. *Genes Dev*. 16: 3017-33.

Hughes, J., Estep, P., Tavazoie, S. & Church, G. (2000). Computational identification of cis-regulatory elements associated with groups of functionally related genes in Saccharomyces cerevisiae. *J. Mol. Biol.* 296, 1205-1214.

International Human Genome Sequencing Consortium. (2001) Initial sequencing and analysis of the human genome. *Nature*. 409: 860-921.

Ioshikhes, I.P., Zhang, M.Q.(2000) Large-scale human promoter mapping using CpG islands. *Nat Genet* 26:61-63

Jareborg N, Birney E, Durbin R. (1999) Comparative analysis of noncoding regions of 77 orthologous mouse and human gene pairs. *Genome Res* 9: 815-24

Johansson O, Alkema W, Wasserman WW, Lagergren J. (2003) Identification of functional clusters of transcription factor binding motifs in genome sequences: the MSCAN algorithm. *Bioinformatics*. 19 Suppl 1: I169-I176.

Kel AE, Kel-Margoulis OV, Farnham PJ, Bartley SM, Wingender E, Zhang MQ. (2001) Computer-assisted identification of cell cycle-related genes: new targets for E2F transcription factors. *J Mol Biol* 309, 99-120

Kel OV, Romashchenko AG, Kolchanov NA,Wingender E and Kel A (2000) COMPEL: a database on composite regulatory elements providing combinatorial transcriptional regulation. *Nucleic Acids Res*. 28, 311-315

Kellis M, Patterson N, Endrizzi M, Birren B, Lander ES. (2003) Sequencing and comparison of yeast species to identify genes and regulatory elements. *Nature*. 423: 241-54.

Kel-Margoulis OV, Kel AE, Reuter I, Deineko IV, Wingender E. (2002) TRANSCompel: a database on composite regulatory elements in eukaryotic genes. *Nucleic Acids Res* 30: 332-334

Klar AJ, Halvorson HO. (1974) Studies on the positive regulatory gene, GAL4, in regulation of galactose catabolic enzymes in Saccharomyces cerevisiae. *Mol Gen Genet*. 135: 203-12.

Klingenhoff A, Frech K, Quandt K, Werner T. (1999) Functional promoter modules can be detected by formal models independent of overall nucleotide sequence similarity. *Bioinformatics* 15: 180-186

Knudsen, S. (1999). Promoter2.0: for the recognition of PolII promoter sequences. *Bioinformatics* 15: 356-361

Krivan, W. and Wasserman, W.W. (2001). A predictive model for regulatory sequences directing liver-specific transcription. *Genome Res*.11, 1559-1566.

Kwon AT, Hoos HH, Ng R. (2003) Inference of transcriptional regulation relationships from gene expression data. *Bioinformatics*. 19: 905-12.

Lawrence CE, Altschul SF, Boguski MS, Liu JS, Neuwald AF, Wootton JC. (1993) Detecting subtle sequence signals: a Gibbs sampling strategy for multiple alignment. *Science* 262: 208-14

Lee TI, Rinaldi NJ, Robert F, Odom DT, Bar-Joseph Z, Gerber GK, Hannett NM, Harbison CT, Thompson CM, Simon I, Zeitlinger J, Jennings EG, Murray HL, Gordon DB, Ren B,

Wyrick JJ, Tagne JB, Volkert TL, Fraenkel E, Gifford DK, Young RA. (2002) Transcriptional regulatory networks in Saccharomyces cerevisiae. *Science*. 298: 799-804.

Lenhard B, Sandelin A, Mendoza L, Engstrom P, Jareborg N, Wasserman WW (2003) Identification of conserved regulatory elements by comparative genome analysis. *J Biol.* 2:13.

Liu XS, Brutlag DL, Liu JS.(2002) An algorithm for finding protein-DNA binding sites with applications to chromatin-immunoprecipitation microarray experiments. *Nat Biotechnol* 20, 835-9

Liu Y, Liu XS, Wei L, Altman RB and Batzoglou S. (2004) Eukaryotic Regulatory Element Conservation Analysis and Identification Using Comparative Genomics *Genome Res.* 14:451-458

Liu, R, McEachin, RC, States, DJ (2003) Computationally identifying novel NF-kappa B-regulated immune genes in the human genome, *Genome Res.* 13:654-661.

Liu, R. and States, D.J.(2002). Consensus promoter identification in the human genome utilizing expressed gene markers and gene modeling. *Genome Res* 12: 462-469

Loots, G.G., Locksley, R.M., Blankespoor, C.M., Wang, Z.E., Miller, W., Rubin, E.M., and Frazer, K.A. (2000). Identification of a coordinate regulator of cytokines 4, 13, and 5 by cross-species sequence comparisons. *Science* 288:136-140.

Loots, G.G., Ovcharenko, I., Pachter, L., Dubchak, I. & Rubin, E.M.(2002) rVista for comparative sequence-based discovery of functional transcription factor binding sites *Genome Res.*12: 832-839.

Mandel-Gutfreund Y, Baron A, Margalit H. (2001). A structure-based approach for prediction of protein binding sites in gene upstream regions. *Pac Symp Biocomput*, 139-150

Margulies EH, Blanchette M, Haussler D, Green ED; NISC Comparative Sequencing Program. (2003) Identification and characterization of multi-species conserved sequences. *Genome Res.* 13: 2507-18.

Marino-Ramirez L, Spouge JL, Kanga GC, and Landsman D (2004) Statistical analysis of over-represented words in human promoter sequences. *Nucleic Acids Res.* 32: 949 - 958.

Markstein, M and Levine M. (2002) Decoding cis-regulatory DNAs in the Drosophila genome. *Curr Opin Genet Dev* 12: 601-606

Mayor C, Brudno M, Schwartz JR, Poliakov A, Rubin EM, Frazer KA, Pachter LS, Dubchak I. (2000) VISTA : visualizing global DNA sequence alignments of arbitrary length. *Bioinformatics* 16:1046-7

Morgenstern B, Frech K, Dress A, Werner T. (1998) DIALIGN: finding local similarities by multiple sequence alignment. *Bioinformatics*. 14:290-4.

Mount, D.W. (2001) In *Bioinformatics, pp337-380,* Cold Spring Harbor Laboratory Press

Mouse Genome Sequencing Consortium. (2002) Initial sequencing and comparative analysis of the mouse genome. *Nature*. 420: 520-62.

Niehrs C, Pollet N. (1999) Synexpression groups in eukaryotes. *Nature*. 402: 483-7.

Oeltjen, J.C., Malley, T.M., Muzny, D.M., Miller, W., Gibbs, R.A. & Belmont, J.W. (1997). Large-scale comparative sequence analysis of the human and murine Bruton's tyrosine kinase loci reveals conserved regulatory domains. *Genome Res*. 7: 315-329.

Pedersen, A.G., Baldi, P., Chauvin, Y., and Brunak, S. (1999). The biology of eukaryotic promoter prediction—A review. *Comput. Chem*. 23: 191-207

Pilpel Y, Sudarsanam P, Church GM.(2001) Identifying regulatory networks by combinatorial analysis of promoter elements. *Nat Genet* 29, 153-9

Ponger, L. and Mouchiroud, D. (2002) CpGProD: Identifying CpG islands associated with transcription start sites in large genomic mammalian sequences. *Bioinformatics* 18: 631-633

Prestridge DS (1995). Predicting Pol II promoter sequences using transcription factor binding sites. *J Mol Biol* 249, 923-32

Prestridge DS.(1996) SIGNAL SCAN 4.0: additional databases and sequence formats. *Comput Appl Biosci.* 12:157-60.

Pritsker M, Liu YC, Beer MA, Tavazoie S. (2004) Whole-genome discovery of transcription factor binding sites by network-level conservation. *Genome Res.* 14: 99-108.

Qian J, Lin J, Luscombe NM, Yu H, Gerstein M. (2003) Prediction of regulatory networks: genome-wide identification of transcription factor targets from gene expression data. *Bioinformatics.* 19: 1917-26.

Qiu P, Ding W, Jiang Y, Greene J, Wang L.(2002) Computational analysis of composite regulatory elements. *Mamm Genome* 13: 327-332.

Qiu P, Qin L, Sorrentino RP, Greene J, Wang L (2003).Comparative promoter analysis and its application in analysis of PTH-regulated gene expression. *J Mol Biol* 326: 1327-1336

Quandt K, Frech K, Karas H, Wingender E, Werner T. (1995) MatInd and MatInspector: new fast and versatile tools for detection of consensus matches in nucleotide sequence data. *Nucleic Acids Res.* 23:4878-84.

Ren B, Robert F, Wyrick JJ, Aparicio O, Jennings EG, Simon I, Zeitlinger J, Schreiber J, Hannett N, Kanin E, Volkert TL, Wilson CJ, Bell SP, Young RA. (2000) Genome-wide location and function of DNA binding proteins. *Science* 290: 2306-2309

Rooney, J.W., Sun, Y.L., Glimcher, L.H., Hoey, T. (1995). Novel NFAT sites that mediate activation of the interleukin-2 promoter in response to T-cell receptor stimulation. *Mol. Cell Biol.* 15: 6299-6310.

Roth FP, Hughes JD, Estep PW, Church GM. (1998) Finding DNA regulatory motifs within unaligned noncoding sequences clustered by whole-genome mRNA quantitation. *Nat Biotechnol* 16: 939-45

Scherf M, Klingenhoff A, Frech K, Quandt K, Schneider R, Grote K, Frisch M, Gailus-Durner V, Seidel A, Brack-Werner R, Werner T. (2001) First pass annotation of promoters on human chromosome 22. *Genome Res.* 11: 333-40.

Scherf M, Klingenhoff A, Werner T. (2000) Highly specific localization of promoter regions in large genomic sequences by PromoterInspector: a novel context analysis approach. *J Mol Biol* 297: 599-606

Schwartz S, Elnitski L, Li M, Weirauch M, Riemer C, Smit A, Green ED, Hardison RC, Miller W; NISC Comparative Sequencing Program. (2003) MultiPipMaker and supporting tools: Alignments and analysis of multiple genomic DNA sequences. *Nucleic Acids Res.* 31:3518-24.

Schwartz S, Zhang Z, Frazer KA, Smit A, Riemer C, Bouck J, Gibbs R, Hardison R, Miller W. (2000) PipMaker--a web server for aligning two genomic DNA sequences. *Genome Res* 10: 577-86

Segal E, Shapira M, Regev A, Pe'er D, Botstein D, Koller D, Friedman N. (2003) Module networks: identifying regulatory modules and their condition-specific regulators from gene expression data. *Nat Genet.* 34:166-76.

Sinha S, Tompa M. YMF (2003) A program for discovery of novel transcription factor binding sites by statistical overrepresentation. *Nucleic Acids Res.* 31: 3586-8.

Solovyev V and Shahmuradov I PromH: promoters identification using orthologous genomic sequences.(2003) *Nucleic Acids Res*. 31: 3540-3545.

Solovyev V, Salamov A. (1997) The Gene-Finder computer tools for analysis of human and model organisms genome sequences. Proc Int Conf Intell Syst Mol Biol 5:294-302

Tavazoie S, Hughes JD, Campbell MJ, Cho RJ and Church GM (1999) Systematic determination of genetic network architecture. *Nat. Genet*. 22: 281-285.

Thomas JW, Touchman JW, Blakesley RW, Bouffard GG, Beckstrom-Sternberg SM, Margulies EH, Blanchette M, Siepel AC, Thomas PJ, McDowell JC et al (2003) Comparative analyses of multi-species sequences from targeted genomic regions. *Nature*. 424: 788-93.

Thompson JD, Higgins DG, Gibson TJ. (1994) CLUSTAL W: improving the sensitivity of progressive multiple sequence alignment through sequence weighting, position-specific gap penalties and weight matrix choice. *Nucleic Acids Res* 22: 4673-80

Trinklein ND, Aldred SJ, Saldanha AJ, Myers RM. (2003) Identification and functional analysis of human transcriptional promoters. *Genome Res* 13, 308-12

Tronche F, Ringeisen F, Blumenfeld M, Yaniv M, Pontoglio M. (1997) Analysis of the distribution of binding sites for a tissue-specific transcription factor in the vertebrate genome. *J Mol Biol* 266: 231-245

van Helden, J., André, B., Collado-Vides, J. (1998). Extracting regulatory sites from the upstream region of yeast genes by computational analysis of oligonucleotide frequencies. *J. Mol. Biol*. 281: 827-842.

Venter JC, Adams MD, Myers EW, Li PW, Mural RJ, Sutton GG, Smith HO, Yandell M, Evans CA, Holt RA et al. (2001) The sequence of the human genome. *Science* 291:1304-51

Wagner, A. (1999) Genes regulated cooperatively by one or more transcription factors and their identification in whole eukaryotic genomes. *Bioinformatics* 15: 776-784

Wang L, Wu Q, Qiu P, Mirza A, McGuirk M, Kirschmeier P, Greene JR, Wang Y, Pickett CB, Liu S. (2001) Analyses of p53 target genes in the human genome by informatic and microarray approaches. *J. Biol. Chem*. 276: 43604-43610.

Wang W, Cherry JM, Botstein D, Li H. (2002) A systematic approach to reconstructing transcription networks in Saccharomycescerevisiae. *Proc Natl Acad Sci U S A*. 99:16893-8.

Wasserman, W. and Fickett, J.W. (1998) Identification of Regulatory Regions which confer Muscle-Specific Gene Expression. *J Mol Bio* 278:167-181.

Wasserman, W.W., Palumbo, M, Thompson, W., Fickett, J.W. & Lawrence, C.E. (2000). Human-mouse genome comparisons to locate regulatory sites. *Nat. Genet*. 2: 225-228

Wingender, E., Chen, X., Fricke, E., Geffers, R., Hehl, R., Liebich, I., Krull, M., Matys, V., Michael, H., Ohnhauser, R., Pruss, M., Schacherer, F., Thiele, S. & Urbach, S. (2001). The TRANSFAC system on gene expression regulation. *Nucleic Acids Res*. 29: 281-283

Winslow, R.L. and Boguski, M.S. (2003) Genome informatics: current status and future prospects. *Circ Res* 92, 953-961

Workman, C.T. and Stormo, G.D. (2000). ANN-Spec: A method for discovering transcription factor binding sites with improved specificity. *Pac. Symp. Biocomput*. 467-478.

Zhang, M.Q. (1998) Identification of human gene core promoters in silico. *Genome Res*., 8:319-326

Zhu J, Liu JS, Lawrence CE. (1998) Bayesian adaptive sequence alignment algorithms. *Bioinformatics* 14: 25-39.

Zhu Z, Pilpel Y, Church GM. (2002) Computational identification of transcription factor binding sites via a transcription-factor-centric clustering (TFCC) algorithm. *J Mol Biol.* 318: 71-81.

Table 1. Web addresses of programs cited in this chapter

Program	Web Address	Reference
Promoter prediciton		
PROMOTER2.0	http://www.cbs.dtu.dk/services/Promoter/	Knudsen et al 1999
ProScan	http://bimas.dcrt.nih.gov/molbio/proscan/	Prestridge et al 1995
TSSW	http://www.softberry.com/berry.phtml?topic=promoter	Solovyev and Salamov 1997
CorePromoter	http://argon.cshl.org/genefinder/CPROMOTER	Zhang et al 1998
PromoterInspector	http://www.genomatix.de/cgi-bin/promoterinspector/promoterinspector.pl	Scherf et al 2000
CpG-Promoter	ftp://cshl.org/pub/science/mzhanglab/ioshikhes	Ioshikhes and Zhang 2000
CONPRO	http://stateslab.bioinformatics.med.umich.edu/conpro/	Liu et al 2002
Eponine	http://www.sanger.ac.uk/Users/td2/eponine/	Down and Hubbard 2002
DPF	http://sdmc.krdl.org.sg:8080/promoter/	Bajic et al 2002, 2003
CpGProD	http://pbil.univ-lyon1.fr/software/cpgprod.html	Ponger and Mouchiroud 2002
FirstEF	http://www.cshl.org/mzhanglab/	Davuluri et al 2001
PromH	http://www.softberry.com/berry.phtml?topic=promh	Solovyev and Shahmuradov 2003
TFBS finding		
SIGNAL SCAN	http://bimas.dcrt.nih.gov/molbio/signal	Prestridge 1996
MATRIX SEARCH	http://bimas.dcrt.nih.gov/molbio/signal	Chen et al 1995
Matinspector	http://www.genomatix.de/software_services/software/MatInspector/matinspector.html	Quandt et al 1995
TFSearch	http://www.cbrc.jp/research/db/TFSEARCH.html	French et al 1997
ConsInspector	http://www.gsf.de/biodv/consinspector.html	Frech et al 1993
Over-represented Motif/TFBS finding		
MEME	http://meme.sdsc.edu/meme/website/meme.html	Bailey et al 1994
Gibbs Sampler	http://bayesweb.wadsworth.org/gibbs/gibbs.html	Lawrence et al 1993
DIALIGN	http://www.gsf.de/biodv/dialign.html	Morgenstern et al 1998
ANN-Spec	http://www.cbs.dtu.dk/services/DNAarray/ann-spec.html	Workman and Stormo 2000
AlignACE	http://atlas.med.harvard.edu/cgi-bin/alignace.pl	Roth et al 1998
PROJECTION	http://www.cse.wustl.edu/~jbuhler/projection.html	Buhler and Tompa 2002
MDScan	http://bioprospector.stanford.edu/MDscan/	Liu et al 2002
MobyDick	http://genome.ucsf.edu/mobydick/	Bussemaker et al 2000
PRIMA	http://www.cs.tau.ac.il/~rshamir/prima/PRIMA.htm	Elkon et al 2003
YMF	http://bio.cs.washington.edu/software.html	Sinha and Tompa, 2003
Clover	http://zlab.bu.edu/clover/	Frith et al 2004
MSCAN	http://tfscan.cgb.ki.se/cgi-bin/MSCAN	Johansson et al 2003
ModuleSearcher/ ModuleScanner	http://www.esat.kuleuven.ac.be/~dna/BioI	Aerts et al 2003
Genome comparison		
BLAST	http://www.ncbi.nlm.nih.gov/BLAST/	Altschul et al 1990
PIPMaker	http://bio.cse.psu.edu/cgi-bin/pipmaker?basic	Schwartz et al 2000
MultiPipMaker	http://bio.cse.psu.edu/cgi-bin/multipipmaker	Schwartz 2003
BBA	http://www.bioinfo.rpi.edu/applications/bayesian/bayes/bayes_ali	Zhu et al 1998

Program	Web Address	Reference
	gn12.pl	
DBA	http://www.ebi.ac.uk/Wise2/doc_wise2.html	Jareborg et al 1999
CLUSTALW	http://www.ebi.ac.uk/clustalw/	Thompson et al 1994
VISTA	http://www-gsd.lbl.gov/vista/	Mayor et al 2000
AVID	http://baboon.math.berkeley.edu/avid	Bray et al 2003
LAGAN	http://lagan.stanford.edu/lagan_web/index.shtml	Brudno et al 2003
Conserved TFBS finding		
rVISTA	http://teapot.jgi-psf.org/ovcharen/rvista/index.html	Loots et al 2002
FootPrinter	http://abstract.cs.washington.edu/~blanchem/FootPrinterWeb/FootPrinterInput.pl	Blanchette et al 2002
ConSite	http://mordor.cgb.ki.se/cgi-bin/CONSITE/consite/	Lenhard et al 2003
CompareProspector	http://compareprospector.stanford.edu	Liu et al 2004

In: Bioinformatics: New Research
Editor: Peter V. Yan, pp. 55-80
ISBN 1-59454-242-2

Chapter III

Application of Computational Biology in Understanding Emerging Infectious Diseases: Inferring Biological Function for S-M Complex of SARS-CoV

Xiu-Feng Wan[1*], Demet Ataman[2], and Dong Xu[1,2**]

[1] Digital Biology Laboratory, Computer Science Department, University of Missouri-Columbia, Columbia, MO 65211, USA.

[2] UT-ORNL Graduate School of Genome Science and Technology, Oak Ridge, TN 37831, USA.

Abstract

Bioinformatics can play a special role in studying emerging infectious diseases, where a fast characterization of the diseases is often urgently needed before they are widespread. In this chapter, we described a computational framework for fast modeling of emerging infectious diseases, including five components: (1) gene survey of the biological sequences related to the emerging diseases; (2) biological problem definition; (3) computational analyses of each gene sequence, which may include molecular characterization, structure prediction, phylogenetic analysis, and regulatory motif prediction; (4) literature review; (5) inference of the biological mechanism and hypothesis for experimental testing. We selected Severe Acute Respiratory Syndrome coronavirus (SARS-CoV) as an example to illustrate the computational framework. SARS-CoV is a most recently emerging coronavirus causing the worldwide SARS pandemic. It is a novel coronavirus, which is similar in genome organization but distantly related to previously characterized coronaviruses in gene sequences. Among the identified Open Reading Frames (ORFs), replicase ORF1ab, spike [S], envelope [E], membrane [M] and nucleocapsid [N] are found in other known coronaviruses with a conserved genome organization. In addition to this common genome organization, this novel virus also has a number of nonstructural proteins with unknown functions. We first computationally surveyed all the ORFs within SARS-CoV, and then predicted the cleavage sites between S1 and S2.

* Current Address: Department of Microbiology, Miami University, Oxford, OH 45056. E-mail: wanx@muohio.edu
** Corresponding author: xudong@missouri.edu.

According to the literature, M and S proteins play an important role in the processing of assembly, attachment, and fusion for coronavirus-host interaction. However, there has not been a systematically description about the mechanism of the M and S proteins. Although the cellular roles of the S and M proteins are known, it requires structural information to understand the molecular mechanisms of how these two proteins perform their functions. The protein structure of either the M protein or the S protein has not been solved. Questions remains include: (1) How S1 protein interacts with the associated human receptor? (2) How the S protein interacts with M protein? (3) What is the role of the S-M complex in virus fusion? (4) What are the other possible roles of the M protein in the virus infection besides its role in cell assembly? In this chapter, we only focused on question 2. We first performed the molecular characterization of S and M proteins. Then we predicted the three-dimensional structures for the S and M proteins and the potential human receptor N-aminopeptidase. We further illustrated how the S-M complex assembles based on correlated mutation analysis. In the end, hypotheses about the S-M complex were proposed based on our computational results and previous experimental results.

Color graphics are presented at the end of the chapter.

Introduction

Importance of Studying the Emerging Disease, SARS

Throughout the human history, emerging infectious diseases have been shown to threaten our civilization. Two remote examples are the "Black Death" and "flu" epidemic. In the 14th century, the Black Death killed more than one third of the population in Europe. More than 20 million people were killed by the great influenza epidemic of 1918, which was caused by H_1N_1 influenza virus A. Recently, a growing list of emerging infectious diseases were detected and reported. The diseases include Legionaires' disease, *Clostridium difficile* antibiotic-associated colitis, Toxic Shock Syndrome, Hemolytic Uremic Syndrome and Thrombotic Thrombocytopenic Purpura deriving from food borne infection, Human Immunodeficiency Syndrome (AIDS), Bovine Spongiform Encephalopathy, Chronic Wasting Disease of cervids, Hantavirus Pulmonary Syndrome, and West Nile virus encephalitis (Feldmann *et al.* 2002; Maki 2003).

In 2003, a new unusual pneumonia, Severe Acute Respiratory Syndrome (SARS), attacked us as "a new apocalyptic horseman" (Maki 2003), which was caused by a novel coronavirus, SARS-CoV (Ksiazek *et al.* 2003). After the first case of this disease was identified in November 2002 in Guangdong Province, China, this disease spread to more than 32 countries and areas around the world. Until August 7, 2003, 8422 persons worldwide have been infected by SARS, with the vast majority occurred in Mainland China (5,327 infected; 349 deaths), Hong Kong (1,755; 300), Taiwan (665; 180), Canada (251, 41), Singapore (238; 33), and Vietnam (63; 5). There were about 33 cases but no deaths in the United States (see the "WHO SARS case summary", http://www.who.int/csr/sars/). This disease resulted in mortality of 11% in general. Mortality in persons older than 60 years was reported to be more than 40% (Donnelly *et al.* 2003). In addition, the economic loss caused by SARS reached billions of dollars. Most recently, the SARS has been reported to occur again in Beijing, P. R. China and one death has been associated with this disease (http://www.who.int).

This new disease is unique among the numerous types of community-acquired pneumonia for the following reasons: (1) it is extremely contagious. Among the earlier cases, there are more than 50% infections occurred in the health care workers. (2) The early laboratory diagnosis is difficult. The early virus isolation was hard, RT-PCR is not effective for early detection, and the early seroreversion happened even about 3 weeks after infection (Sampathkumar *et al.* 2003). (3) SARS has a longer incubation period (an average of 6.4 days) than other respiratory viruses (generally 2 to 3 days) (Donnelly *et al.* 2003). (4) SARS-CoV can survive for hours on environmental surfaces, and it can spread fast by droplets spread in respiratory particles with diameters less than 10 μM, which can reach more than 2 meters in space (Donnelly *et al.* 2003). (5) Similar to other RNA viruses, SARS-CoV showed a very rapid mutation. Genomic sequencing showed the strains isolated from different infections are significantly different, even when the infections in the same area were examined (Ruan *et al.* 2003).

The SARS has been gradually under control since July 2003 although occasional cases still occurred around the world. However, we still face the potential challenges from this disease that could be extraordinarily severe:

(1) SARS-CoV may be a genetic recombinant virus from human and/or animals (Maki 2003; Guan *et al.* 2003). The genetic evidence and phylogenetic studies showed SARS-CoV is a remote strain from other known coronaviruses (Rota *et al.* 2003; Marra *et al.* 2003; Drosten *et al.* 2003; Ruan *et al.* 2003). The molecular mechanisms of this virus are poorly understood. Even the functions of most individual ORFs are not known. The routine laboratory work alone will take a long time to accomplish this task. Without understanding of gene functions and molecular mechanisms, the drug and vaccine development will be very difficult.

(2) The evidence showed SARS-associated coronaviruses may spread throughout the population of domestic and market animals (Guan *et al.* 2003). The roof rat was also hypothesized to be a transmission vector of SARS (Ng 2003). This provides a potential channel to create new species of coronaviruses besides the rapid mutants generated within SARS-CoV. The new species may be more harmful and deadly. Even if they are not harmful to humans, they may cause severe diseases among domestic animals, which could be a big loss to the farming industry.

(3) SARS-CoV may have established a significant reservoir in the human population and it may come back from time to time as shown in the recent emergence of the SARS case in Beijing, P. R. China (http://www.who.int/). This virus reservoir can also serve to provide seeds for the generation of new more severe virus strains as SARS-CoV evolves.

Current Understanding of SARS-CoV

SARS-CoV is a novel coronavirus, which is similar in genome organization but distantly related to previously characterized coronaviruses in gene sequences (Rota *et al.* 2003; Marra *et al.* 2003; Yu *et al.* 2003). Among the identified ORFs, replicase ORF1ab, spike [S], envelope [E], membrane [M], and nucleocapsid [N] are found in other known coronaviruses with a conserved genome organization. In addition to this common genome organization, this novel virus also has a number of nonstructural proteins with unknown functions (Rota *et al.* 2003; Marra *et al.* 2003; Zeng *et al.* 2003).

The current understanding about the life cycle of SARS virus is as follows (Figure 1):

1. The infection starts with the binding of the S protein of the SARS virus to a human cell surface receptor. The SARS virus diffuses into the human cell by receptor-mediated endocytosis or by membrane fusion with the plasma membrane (Blau and Holmes 2001; Bosch *et al.* 2003). Then the viral genome enters the cytoplasma.
2. The positive stranded genomic RNA of SARS virus translates RNA-dependent RNA polymerase. The replication complexes generate new genomic RNA and sub-genomic mRNAs, which encode the new viral proteins, including the three main structural proteins of SARS virus, i.e., S, M, and N proteins (An *et al.* 1998; Sethna and Brian 1997; Baric and Yount 2000). The N protein is synthesized in the cytoplasm free ribosome and assembled with the genomic RNA to form RNP (ribonucleoprotein). The M and S proteins are synthesized on the Rough Endoplasmic Reticulum (RER) and form the M-S complex, which then are transported into the Golgi complex.
3. The RNP attaches to the host cell membrane, where the S and M proteins have previously assembled (M-S complex). The RNP buds into the lumen of the vesicle. Finally, the membrane bound RNP and its radiating spikes detach and come to be free in the lumen as an immature virion (Zhang *et al.* 2003). These particles will be transported through Golgi apparatus, where they become mature in a denser and more icosahedral form (Risco *et al.* 1996 & 1998; Salanueva *et al.* 1999).
4. Finally, the mature virions gather in large vesicles and released onto the cell surface to start the cycle again.

Much but incomplete information has been obtained about coronaviruses. Since the first coronavirus was isolated from chickens in 1937, more than 15 species of coronaviruses have been identified in different hosts including human, cattle, pig, rodent, cat, dog and bird. Some coronaviruses are very important veterinary pathogens. For example, the coronaviruses in chickens causes infectious bronchitis, which has always been a big problem for the poultry industry around the world. Generally the human coronavirus (human-CoV) infection is mild and common. Human-CoV infection occurs often in children. More than 30% of common colds in humans are caused by Human-CoV mainly from strain 229E and OC43 (Holmes 2003). However, many human coronaviruses may have not been isolated because of the difficulty of their *in vitro* culture. There have been very rare reports about cross species infection for coronaviruses (Holmes 2003). The lack of understanding of SARS-CoV has shown that our knowledge about the coronavirus family is very limited. Since no good model animal to characterize SARS-CoV has been found, it will be very challenging and time-consuming to characterize this novel emerging coronavirus.

As a new coronavirus family member, SARS-CoV forms a new (fourth) subgroup of coronaviruses. Until May 14, 2004, more than 150 SARS CoV genomes have been deposited in the NCBI database (http://www.ncbi.nlm.nih.gov/genomes/SARS/SARS.html). The genomes of two SARS CoV-like viruses isolated from animals have also been deposited into the database. Although S, E, M, N, and 3CL protease of SARS-CoV may have similar structures and functions to the ones in other coronaviruses, the associated amino acid sequence identities are less than 40-50% (Rota *et al.* 2003). The genomic sequence analysis showed SARS-CoV differs substantially from other known coronaviruses, whose sequences are much more similar to each other (Drosten *et al.* 2003; Marra *et al.* 2003; Rota *et al.* 2003). Genetic evidence shows that SARS-CoV may be a recombinant virus from human and animal (Maki 2003; Guan *et al.* 2003). However, the parent sources are still unknown. This suggests that SARS-CoV has gone through a substantial evolution from other known coronaviruses. This novel coronavirus may possess many unique unknown features.

In this chapter, we first give a description about the computational framework for emerging disease and then give an example about how to apply this framework in modeling SARS-CoV, especially inference of the biological roles of the S-M complex.

Computational Framework

The rapid characterization of an emerging disease will provide invaluable information in the prevention and control of the disease. Thus, computational studies may be particularly important for emerging diseases, where understanding of the diseases is often urgently needed before their widespread. Compared to the lab bench work, computational methods can provide a relatively fast and efficient approach to derive theoretical models based on experimental data, to simulate/predict biological processes and to provide working hypotheses for rational designs of new experiments. It usually takes years and months to characterize a single protein experimentally. However, it only takes about hours, minutes, or even seconds to infer the biological functions once the computational model is constructed for the specific requirement. Hence, a good computational framework can play important roles in the research of emerging diseases.

Figure 2 illustrates our computational framework for modeling an emerging disease. (1) We survey genes and get general pictures about an emerging disease. (2) We identify the significant questions to solve by combining current knowledge related to the emerging disease. (2) To target the biological questions, we perform different computational analyses, which may include: A. Molecular Characterization: Molecular characterization may include sequence comparison, transmembrane domain prediction, and coiled-coil region prediction. B. Structure Prediction: The structure prediction may provide useful information of understanding protein function and designing drugs. If the structure prediction is hard, we can predict the protein contact regions, which can help provide information about protein-protein contact information. C. Phylogenetic Analysis: The phylogenetic analysis may provide the evolutional relationship of query genes. D. Other Analyses. The other related analyses can be regulatory motif prediction, codon usage bias analysis, and so on. (4) We need to do the literature review and summarize the computational analysis. (5) In the end, the biological functions will be inferred. At this stage, the hypothesis may be generated for biologists to test using experimental approaches. We can define new biology problems and initiate another similar computational inference procedure iteratively.

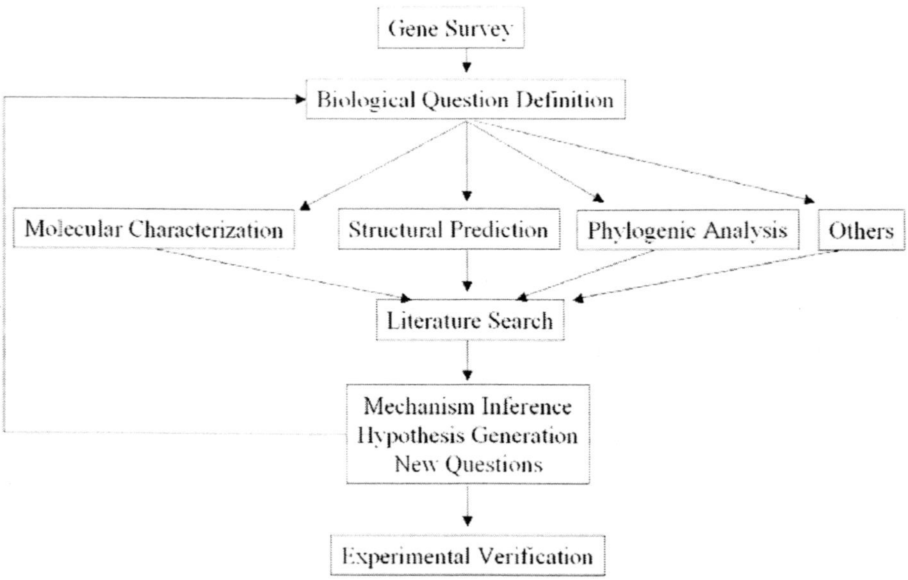

Figure 2. Computational framework for modeling an emerging disease

A central aspect of the computational framework is protein structure prediction. Protein structures provide the basis for functional studies of proteins on the molecular level. Traditionally, protein structures are solved using X-ray crystallography or NMR methods. It could take months or even years to solve one structure, which could cost hundreds of thousands dollars. An alternative approach for protein structure solution is through computational modeling and prediction. Existing prediction methods fall into two main classes: (a) *ab initio* methods and (b) comparative modeling methods – predictions based on identified structural relationship with known structures. A key advantage of computational methods is their efficiency – the solution time will be in days, hours or even minutes rather than months or years. Although computational techniques are yet to consistently produce structures with the same quality of experimental methods, the best comparative modeling techniques (including both threading and homology-based modeling) can often generate backbone structures with an accuracy of 4Å RMSD for a large class of proteins (Koehl & Levitt 1999), as demonstrated in the CASP predictions. With this level of prediction accuracy, we expect that highly useful functional information can be derived. We will be mainly using threading-based methods for protein 3D structure predictions in this proposed study.

Protein threading is a computational technique for protein backbone structure prediction (Bowie *et al.* 1991; Bryant & Lawrence 1993). It makes a structural fold prediction from the amino-acid sequence by recognizing a native-like fold of a query protein (if there is any) in a database of experimentally determined structures. The identified folds and predicted structures (even not highly accurate) could provide a significant amount of information about the proteins' functions and give useful guidance to experimentalists to conduct further experiments for functional investigation. Recognition of native-like fold is typically achieved by finding an optimal placement (*alignment*) of residues in the query sequence (sequential order maintained; deletions and insertions allowed) onto residue positions of each structural fold in the database, and by identifying those sequence-fold alignments that are statistically significant. For each statistically significant alignment, the placed positions of the query sequence's residues are predicted to be the backbone positions in its structure. Generally speaking, core (α-helix or β-strand) residues are expected to have more accurate predictions than loop residues, since the former tend to be conserved among structures of the same fold, while the latter may not be (Bryant & Lawrence 1993). Statistics from the PDB Web site (http://www.rcsb.org/pdb/holdings.html) shows that about 90% of the proteins submitted to the PDB database (Westbrook et al. 2000) share similar folds to structures already in PDB. This suggests that many of these protein structures are potentially solvable by computational techniques like protein threading. Though it may be an over-estimate that threading may apply to 90% of proteins because of the biased sampling from the protein space since people tend to solve the "easy" proteins first; and membrane proteins are clearly under-represented in PDB, it is generally believed that 60-70% of new proteins are potentially solvable using threading-based prediction methods (Montelione & Anderson 1999).

We mainly used our in-house tool PROSPECT (PROtein Structure Prediction and Evaluation Computer Toolkit) (Xu & Xu 2000) for structure prediction of SARS-CoV proteins. For a query SARS-CoV protein sequence, PROSPECT can effectively recognize native-like folds in the PDB database by finding an optimal sequence-structure alignment, and make a backbone structure prediction based on the recognized native-like folds and the calculated optimal threading alignment. Compared to other threading programs, PROSPECT has two unique features: (1) it guarantees to find the globally optimal alignment between a query sequence and a template structure for an energy function consisting of the following additive terms: (1a) a mutation energy, (1b) a singleton energy, (1c) a pairwise contact energy, and (1d) a penalty for alignment gaps; and does so efficiently (Xu *et al.* 1998; Xu & Xu 2000); and (2) it allows a user to easily incorporate experimental data as constraints in the threading process, and guarantees to find the globally optimal threading under the specified constraints. The advantage of having a rigorous threading algorithm has been demonstrated in our CASP3 (Xu *et al.* 1999) and CASP4 (Xu *et al.* 2001a) predictions. PROSPECT has been extended to a pipeline (http://compbio.ornl.gov/proteinpipeline/) that includes other related computational analysis tools, such as (a) preprocessing of protein sequences, which includes signal peptide prediction, protein type prediction (membrane or soluble), protein domain partition, (b) secondary structure prediction, (c) fold recognition, and (d) atomic structural model generation. (Shah *et al.* 2003; Guo *et al.* 2004).

During the following section, we are going to model SARS-CoV based on this computational framework: (1) computational survey of all the ORFs in SARS-CoV; (2) literature search to define the problems; (3) computational analysis: (A) molecular characterization of S and M proteins; (B) structural prediction of S, M, and the potential receptor N-aminopeptidase; (C) contact region prediction between S and M proteins using correlated mutation; (4) biological mechanisms inference for the S-M complex by combination of current knowledge about the S-M complex.

Computational Modeling of SARS

Computational Survey of All ORFs in SARS-CoV

A step towards characterizing the genes in SARS-CoV is an in-depth computational analysis of protein structure and function. We used the PROSPECT pipeline to survey the 11 ORFs in SARS-CoV strain Urbani, one of the first SARS-CoV genomes (Rota *et al.* 2003). Table 1 shows part of our survey results, which give the possible signal peptide and trans-membrane regions for each ORF. The different columns in Table 1 show the gene identification/gene name, number of amino acids, the number of homologs in SwissProt, the cleavage site of the predicted signal peptide (two boundary residues and prediction confidence), and predicted trans-membrane segments (primary helix means that the helix is stable in membrane by itself; the secondary helix requires interacting other trans-membrane helix/helices to keep it stable in membrane).

Table 1. A computational survey of all the ORFs in SARS-CoV

ORF	Protein length	Swiss-Prot entry	Signal P (start…end, *p*)	Trans-membrane
AAP13450 (X5)	84	-	-	Soluble protein
AAP13449 (X4)	122	-	15…16, 0.637	Membrane protein Secondary helix: 1-23; Primary helix: 96-117
AAP13448 (X3)	63	-	39…40, 0.106	Membrane protein Primary helix: 12-34
AAP13447 (X2)	154	-	-	Soluble protein
AAP13446 (X1)	274	1	61…62, 0.435	Membrane protein Primary helix: 40-62, 77-99; Secondary helix: 108-130
AAP13445 (N)	422	18	-	Soluble protein
AAP13444 (M)	221	12	39…40, 1.000	Membrane protein Primary helix: 46-68, 78-100; Secondary helix: 14-36
AAP13443 (E)	76	-	43…44, 0.880	Membrane protein Primary helix: 11-33, 37-59
AAP13441 (S)	1,255	18	13…14, 0.421	S1 domain: Soluble protein S2 domain: Membrane protein Primary helix: 531-553
AAP13440 (nonstructural polyprotein)	2,695	9	-	Soluble protein
AAP13439 (nonstructural polyprotein)	4,382	2	-	16 helices

Biological Problem Definition: Significance of Studying the Biological Roles of S-M Complex

Previous studies demonstrated that the N-terminal subunit (S1) of the S protein forms the surface knob-like structure of the spike, and the C-terminal subunit (S2) forms the stem-like structure beneath the knob (de Groot *et al.* 1987). The cleavage of the S protein depends on individual coronaviruses. The cleavage process is essential for the infectivity and cell fusion in many group-II coronaviruses, whereas it may not be necessary for other coronaviruses. It has been shown that the S protein is involved in various functions. The S1 domain was reported to be involved in mediating the attachment to the host cell receptors (Kubo *et al.* 1994; Suzuki & Taguchi 1996). The S2 domain was found to be important for viral entry into cells and virus fusogenic activity (Taguchi & Shimazaki 2000), although S1 was shown to affect the efficiency of virus entry (Krueger *et al.* 2001). It is very interesting that deletions in the S1 region may change the tissue tropism of the virus while not changing the receptor specificity of the virus. Previous reports show that the S1-receptor binding can induce conformational changes of heptad repeat regions in S2, which is similar to the conformational changes in HIV and influenza viruses (Matsuyama &Taguchi 2002; Eckert &Kim 2001).

As shown by co-immunoprecipitation, co-sedimentation, and immunofluorescence analyses (Opstelten *et al.* 1995a & 1995b), the M protein directs the incorporation of S protein into the particles by forming the M-S complex (Opstelten *et al.* 1995). The S protein is first transported to plasma membrane and then binds the M protein in the Golgi complex. It has been shown that the structural requirement for the M protein in the process of virus assembly is different from that in the M-S complex. Interruption of the amino-terminal or the carboxy-terminal tail did not interfere with the M-S complex formation. However, deletion of the first two or the last two trans-membrane segments of the triple-spanning protein in the M protein, which is known not to affect the structure of the globular part of the protein, interrupts in the M-S complex formation (de Haan *et al.* 1999).

The M protein is a component of the viral envelope that plays a central role in incorporation of the S protein into the viral envelope. It is involved in the assembly of virus particles by the interactions with other viral proteins such as the E and S proteins in the endoplasmic reticulum Golgi intermediate compartment of the host cell. The M-S complex interacts with RNPs and leads to the formation of virus particles as the RNP buds into the ER.

Although the cellular roles of the S and M proteins are known, it requires structural information to understand the molecular mechanisms of how these two proteins perform their functions. However, the protein structure of either the M protein or the S protein has not been solved. Protein structure predictions for the S and M proteins may provide some clues for the following questions: (1) How S1 interacts with the associated receptor? (2) How the S protein interacts with the M protein? (3) What is the role of the S-M complex in virus fusion? (4) What are the other possible roles of the M protein in the virus infection besides its role in cell assembly?

Molecular Characterization of S and M Proteins

S protein: Through the transmembrane prediction of SOSUI (Hirokawa *et al.* 1998), the S protein has only a single primary helix with 23 amino acids (1201-1223, GFIAGLIAIVMVTILLCCMTSC C), which is located in the S2 region. The coiled-coil-like regions in S2 protein predicted by LearnCoil-VMF (Wolf *et al.* 1997) are shown in Figure 3.

Our computational analysis confirmed the early suggestion (Rota *et al.* 2003) that the S protein of SARS-CoV is not cleaved due to the lack of a cleavage signal. However, structurally the S protein of SARS-CoV probably still forms two loosely connected domains that have similar structures to S1 and S2 in other coronaviruses' S proteins with cleavage sites. To identify the boundary between the two domains, we searched homologs of the S protein of SARS-CoV in Swiss-Prot. If the homolog has a known cleavage site, we align the homolog with the S protein of SARS-CoV. We defined the aligned position of the S protein of SARS-CoV from the cleaved site of the homolog as the predicted cleavage site of the S protein of SARS-CoV. It turns out that the predicted cleavage sites based on different homologs are very similar, i.e., between 670th and 671st residues. This suggests that the first 670 residues will be in the S1 domain and the residues 671-1255 in the S2 domain.

M protein: We predicted the trans-membrane domains using SOSUI (Hirokawa *et al.* 1998). The average hydrophobicity of M protein is 0.41 (Figure 4). Three transmembrane regions with 23 amino acids were predicted as Helix I (14-36, QLLEQWNLVIGFLFLAWIMLLQF), Helix II (46-68, YIIKLVFLWLLWPVTLACF VLAV), and Helix III (78-100, GIAIAMACIVGLMWLSYFVASFR) (Figure 5). The Helix II and III are the primary helices (which mean that each helix can be stable in the membrane by itself) whereas the Helix I is the secondary helix (i.e., the helix is not stable by itself in the membrane and it can only be stable through interacting with other transmembrane helix). We did not find the coiled-coil-like regions in M protein through LearnCoil-VMF (Wolf *et al.* 1997).

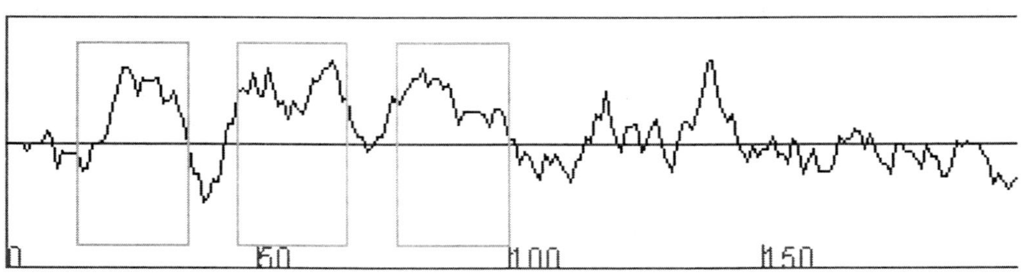

Figure 4. The hydrophobicity plot of the M protein.

Structural Prediction of S, M Proteins and the Potential Human Receptor N-Aminopeptidase

Structural Prediction of S and M Protein

We submitted the sequences of the M protein as well as the S1 and S2 domains to the PROSPECT pipeline (http://compbio.ornl.gov/proteinpipeline/). Table 2 summarizes the structure prediction results. The prediction results can be evaluated through Z-scores. Based on our previous experience, if the Z-score is above 10, the prediction is highly confident, and typically no manual assessment is needed. This is the case for the S2 domain. If the Z-score is less than 6, the prediction confidence level is low and manual analyses are necessary. For the M protein, our manual analyses indicated a good confidence level that the M protein adopts structural templates of 1boy or 1edha, both of which share the same structural fold, i.e., immunoglobulin (Ig)-like beta sandwich. Initial manual analyses did not yield a confident structure prediction for the S1 domain, and further studies are needed.

Interestingly, both the S2 domain and the M protein adopt the fold of Ig-like beta sandwich. The structural similarity suggests that the S2 domain and the M protein may be evolutionarily related through gene fusion and duplication, although their sequences do not have significant similarity anymore after the long period of evolution. Such a phenomenon often occurs among the proteins related to the same biological pathway (Murzin *et al.* 1995). Our results might explain how the M protein interacts with the S2 domain, for virus assembly: since the S2 domain with the fold of Ig-like beta sandwich can interact with the S1 domain, the M protein with the same fold can probably interact with the S1 domain in the mode. This suggests that the S1 domain may act as an on-off switch between the S2 domain and the M protein. Such a mechanism may suggest that the M protein could be also involved in the virus-host cell interaction. After we made the prediction, we found that our suggestion was supported by a recent study in the murine hepatitis coronavirus study, which showed the glycosylation of the M protein affected the interferogenic capacity of the virus (de Haan *et al.*2004).

Table 2. Structural analyses of the M and S proteins, and the N-aminopeptidase

PDB template (SARS-CoV ORF)	Z score	Class	Fold	Family	Function
1vfaa (S2)	15.45	All beta protein	Ig-like beta sandwich	V set domains (antibody variable domain-like)	It acts as mouse monoclonal antibody.
1boy (M)	<6	All beta protein	Ig-like beta sandwich	Fibronectin type III	It plays a role in initiating the cell-surface assembly and propagation of the coagulation protease cascade.
1edha (M)	<6	All beta protein	Ig-like beta sandwich	Cadherin	Cadherins are cell adhesion proteins interacting with themselves in a homophilic manner in order to connect cells.
1has6 (aminopeptidase)	73.62	Alpha/beta Protein	Zincin-like	Leukotriene A4 hydrolase catalytic domain	It hydrolyzes an epoxide moiety of leukotriene A4 to leukotriene B4. The enzyme also has some peptidase activity.

Table 2 shows the PDB code (and chain name in the fifth letter if available), the Z-score estimated from the PROSPECT pipeline, the structural class of the predicted fold, the category of fold and family, and the function of predicted structural template.

Independent of our study, Spiga *et al.* (2003) also predicted the structural of Spike protein of SARS-CoV. They predicted the S2 is an Ig-like beta sandwich structure with the template of *C. botulinum* neurotoxin B (pdb ID 1G9D), which is similar to our result. They also match S1 structure of SARS-CoV spike protein into the same template. Figure 7 is the template of *C. botulinum* neurotoxin B.

Structural Prediction of N-Aminopeptidase

N-aminopeptidases in many organisms act as a cell surface receptor for coronaviruses including TGEV, FIPV, FeCV, Human-CoV, and PRCV (Delmas *et al.* 1992; Tresnan & Homles 1998). It has been shown that the N-aminopeptidase interacts with the TGEV S protein in a specific manner (Delmas *et al.* 1992). However, the receptors may be different even for the coronaviruses of the same hosts. Human-CoV -229E uses hAPN as the virus receptor whereas Human-CoV-OC43 uses MHC I as its receptor (Yeager *et al.* 1992; Collins 1993). Bovine coronavirus (BCV) uses 9-O-actylneuraminic acid as its receptor (Schultze & Herrler 1993), and murine coronavirus use CEACAM as its receptor (Tan *et al.* 2002).

The aminopeptidases are a group of universal peptidase with various functions (Riemann *et al.* 1999; Wan *et al.* 2004a&b). For example, besides functioning in the cell adhesion and amino acid scavenging, this enzyme can serve as the receptor of Human CoV 229E as stated above. Although it is possible that SARS-CoV may utilize other receptors, the N-aminopeptidase or a similar structural fold of N-aminopeptidase might also be the receptor of SARS-CoV (Yu *et al.* 2003). Before predicting the human receptors for SARS-CoV systematically, we first predicted the structure of N-aminopeptidase as a basis for understanding its interaction with the S protein. As shown in Table 2, the structure prediction for N-aminopeptidase has a high Z score, which indicates a good confidence of the structure prediction. The graphic view of the predicted structural fold is shown in Figure 6.

Contact Region Prediction between S and M Proteins

Prediction of the contact residues between S and M proteins will generate the picture about how the two proteins form the S-M complex. Thus, we can generate a drug analog to block the interaction between S and M proteins thus intercept the life cycle of SARS-CoV. A common method for protein-protein interaction measurement is docking. Docking technique is a physical approach by minimizing the energy between two protein domains. It assumes that the physical principles underlying protein-protein interaction is the same as protein folding. It characterizes the protein-protein interface by rigorous scanning (Xu et al. 2001, Vakser & Aflalo 1994). However, it required high quality 3D structures of the query proteins. This will not be feasible for our problems, since both the structures of S and M protein are not available. Although we were able to model the M and S structures based on threading techniques as shown before, the structural quality for the M and S2 is probably not good enough for docking. An alternative method addressing the contact region correlated mutation approach. Here we will first describe correlated mutation and then illustrate the examples about application of correlated mutation in contact region prediction between S and M proteins.

Correlation Mutation

The rational for correlated mutation is based on the same physical principle as docking. When one residue mutates in one protein, the contact residue in the other protein often mutate accordingly and adapt to the fitness for the interaction between the two residues. Changes of amino acids within a single protein but not the interacting protein may result in the changes of the physical energy thus loosen contacts between two proteins. Especially, when the residue mutates from a negatively charge residue to a positively charged residue or vice versa, it may dramatically change the energetics of the protein-protein interaction. To maintain the functions of protein complex, the interacting proteins may mutate in a correlated manner to minimize physical energy. It is possible that more than one residue may complement the mutations within another protein sequence.

Different research efforts have been put to address the contact problems using correlation mutations. The prediction was based on the information derived from the occurrence of correlated mutations in similar proteins (Gobel *et al.* 1994; Shindyalov *et al.* 1994; Taylor & Hatrick 1994). The other features such as sequence conservation, sequence separation along the chain, alignment stability and residue-specific contact occupancy were incorporated into the contact prediction (Olmea & Valencia 1997). The neural network was employed to execute the prediction (Lund *et al.* 1997; Fariselli & Casadio 1999; Fariselli *et al.* 2001).

The correlated mutation score was calculated as the following (Gobel et al. 1994; Pazos *et al.* 1997). Given datasets $S = \{S_1, S_2, \ldots, S_k, \ldots, S_N\}$, and $S' = \{S'_1, S'_2, \ldots, S'_k, \ldots, S'_N\}$, the correlated mutation score is:

$$r_{ij} = \frac{1}{N^2} \sum_{kl} \frac{W_{kl}(S_{ikl} - u_i)(S_{jkl} - u_j)}{\sigma_i \sigma_j} \quad (1)$$

where N is the number of sequences, σ_i and σ_j is the standard deviation of similarities at alignment position i, W_{kl} is weight for sequence k and l, S_{ikl} is similarity for alignment position i between sequences k and l. S_i is the average similarity at alignment position i.

$$W_{kl} = 1 - \frac{I_{kl}}{L} \quad (2)$$

Where I_{kl} is the sequence identity between sequence k and l, and L is the length of the sequences. We can predict the contact region within a single protein in the same way by deem $S' = S$.

Contact Residue Prediction between S Protein and M Protein

As we mentioned in section 1, there are four families of coronaviruses. SARS-CoV is a novel member of coronaviruses belonging to family IV. We retrieved the coronaviruses with both S and M proteins in the databases, and table 3 lists the virus strains in our analysis. These viruses included 8 strains in family I, 7 strains in family II, 6 strains in family III, and 28 strains in family IV of SARS-CoV. Both the S protein and the corresponding M protein sequences in the same strain were extracted in the database. The S-M complex in each virus particle was considered as a unit.

The multiple sequence alignments were performed based on ClustalW (Thompson *et al.* 1994). By writing a C++ programming, we calculated the correlated mutation scores between the S and M sequences based on equation 1 and 2. PAM250 (Jones *et al.* 1992) was used for calculation of the alignment score between the S and M proteins. We used the strain sequence SARS-CoV Frankfurt 1strain (Thiel *et al.* 2003) as the query sequence. The discussion below is based on the position of the S and M proteins in this strain. The positions with gaps were ignored.

Table 3. Coronavirus sequences used for the contact residue study

Family	Virus Name	S Protein	M protein	Host
1	Feline Infectious Peritonitis Virus	138184	138771	Feline
1	Canine Coronavirus	549301	549376	Canine
1	Porcine epidemic diarrhea virus	19387577	19387580	Porcine
1	Porcine epidemic diarrhea virus	138181	465381	Porcine
1	Porcine epidemic diarrhea virus	138182	138769	Porcine
1	Porcine epidemic diarrhea virus	267339	138767	Porcine
1	Porcine epidemic diarrhea virus	31340517	138768	Porcine
1	Human coronavirus 229E	12175748	12175752	Human
2	Human coronavirus OC43	38018026	38018029	Human
2	Bovine coronavirus	138171	32699786	Bovine
2	Bovine coronavirus	138172	138763	Bovine
2	Equine coronavirus NC99	34398255	34398259	Equine
2	Murine hepatitis virus strain 2	6625763	32699770	Murine
2	Murine hepatitis virus strain ML-11	7739598	7739602	Murine
2	Rat sialodacryoadenitis coronavirus	9719318	9719322	Murine
3	Infectious Bronchitis Virus	138185	138772	Avian
3	Infectious Bronchitis Virus	14149035	14149039	Avian
3	Infectious Bronchitis Virus	14253130	14253134	Avian
3	Infectious Bronchitis Virus	138186	138773	Avian
3	Infectious Bronchitis Virus	138189	138775	Avian
3	Infectious Bronchitis Virus	138190	32699769	Avian
4	SARS-CoV	32187357	32187349	Human
4	SARS-CoV	38231929	38231930	Human
4	SARS-CoV	38231934	38231935	Human
4	SARS-CoV	38231939	38231940	Human
4	SARS-CoV	40457434	40457436	Human
4	SARS-CoV	40457450	40457454	Human
4	SARS-CoV	38505490	38505488	Human
4	SARS-CoV	38505499	38505497	Human
4	SARS-CoV	33285970	33285974	Human
4	SARS-CoV	33285982	33285986	Human
4	SARS-CoV	37576848	37576852	Human
4	SARS-CoV	33188328	33188332	Human
4	SARS-CoV	30795145	30795149	Human
4	SARS-CoV	30698329	30698333	Human
4	SARS-CoV	33411402	33411406	Human
4	SARS-CoV	33411417	33411421	Human
4	SARS-CoV	33411432	33411436	Human
4	SARS-CoV	33411447	33411451	Human
4	SARS-CoV	33411462	33411466	Human
4	SARS-CoV	30027620	30027623	Human
4	SARS-CoV	30275669	30275673	Human
4	SARS-CoV	33114193	33114197	Human
4	SARS-CoV	33114205	33114209	Human

Family	Virus Name	S Protein	M protein	Host
4	SARS-CoV	33114217	33114221	Human
4	SARS-CoV	30023954	30023958	Human
4	SARS-CoV	33578018	33578022	Human
4	SARS-CoV	31581505	31581509	Human
4	SARS-CoV	31416295	31416299	Human

We first performed the contact mapping between the positions between S proteins and between M proteins, respectively. Figure 8B is the correlated mutation profiling between the S proteins with a cutoff of 0.55, and Figure 8B is the correlated mutation profiling between M proteins with a cutoff of 0.55. The regions of S2 seem to fold by themselves and many regions are in contact with themselves. The residues with correlated score over 0.58 include 270, 272, 369, 525, 527, 531, 579, 700, 715, 716, 723, 726, 734, 749, 807, 808, 825, 845, 859, 885, 917, 929, 944, 947, 965, 980, 990, 994, 1006, 1036, 1049, 1075, 1087, 1097, 1129, 1172, 1175, 1185, 1213, 1217, and 1223. Most of these positions are located within the S2. Instead, in the M proteins (Figure 8B), the scores above its cutoff is 19, 53, 55, 70, 73, 81, 91, 96, 100, 107, 111, 131, 191, 193, 195, 201, 203, 219.

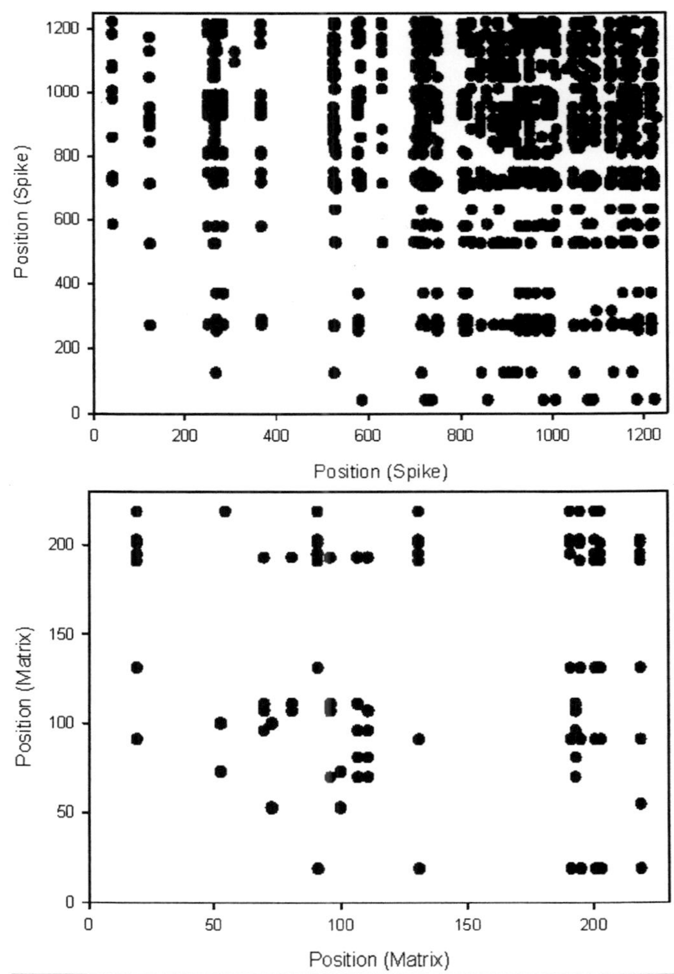

Figure 8. The correlated mutation profiling between the S and M proteins. A. S protein with cutoff 0.55. B. The M protein with cutoff 0.55.

Figure 9 shows the correlated mapping profiling with a cutoff of 0.55 between S and M proteins. From this figure, we can see the contact region is located between positions 40-100 of M protein (major positions 46, 53, 62, 73, 81, 100) and positions 800-1200 of S protein (major positions 16, 822, 869, 1036, 1075, and 1134).

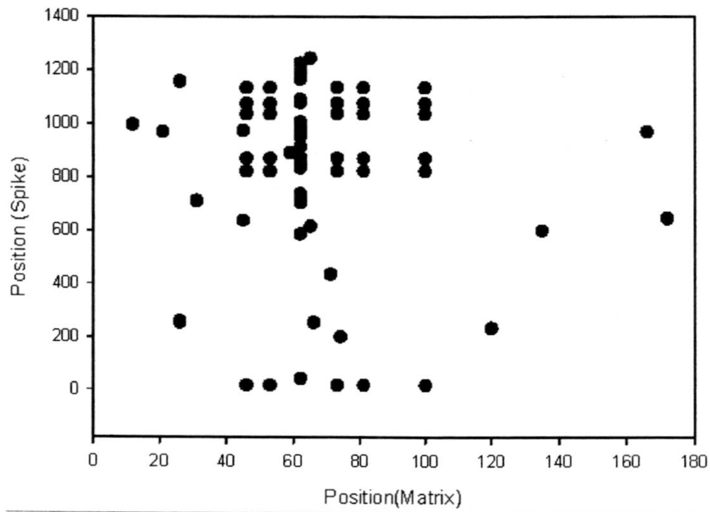

Figure 9. The correlated mutation profiling between S and M proteins with a cutoff of 0.55.

Inference of Biological Mechanisms of S-M Complex

S protein: As mentioned in the previous section, the N-terminal subunit (S1) of S protein forms the surface knob-like structure of the spike, and the C-terminal subunit (S2) forms the stem-like structure beneath the knob (de Groot *et al.* 1987). The S1 domain was reported to be involved in mediating the attachment to the host cell receptors (Kubo *et al.* 1994; Suzuki & Taguchi 1996). Recently, (Babcock *et al.* 2004) confirmed that the position 270 to 510 is required for binding human receptor. The S2 domain was found to be important for viral entry into cells and virus fusogenic activity (Taguchi & Shimazaki 2000), although S1 was shown to affect the efficiency of virus entry (Krueger *et al.* 2001). Previous reports show that the S1-receptor binding can induce conformational changes of HRs in S2, which is similar to the conformational changes in HIV and influenza viruses (Matsuyama & Taguchi 2002; Eckert & Kim 2001). The correlated mutation analysis showed the S2 may fold with each other (Figure 8A). The 3D structure modeling and the coiled-coil region prediction support this hypothesis.

M proteins: The above analysis showed that M protein has two primary helices and one secondary helix. Based on current understanding, only C tails of M protein is exposed to the interior face of the virion and interacts with the nucleocapsid and form the core (Escors *et al.* 2001). The M-M protein interaction analysis shows the tails of C may be able to fold by itself (Figure 8B). It shows that M proteins without part of the amphipathic domain or the hydrophilic C-terminal tail were still able to associate with assembly-competent M proteins, resulting in their coincorporation into VLPs. However, a mutant M protein in which all three transmembrane domains had been replaced lost this ability. Thus, the interaction between M proteins or M-S complex will have multiple contact sites, particularly at the transmembrane helices (de Haan *et al.* 2000). This is supported by a cluster of positions with high correlated mutation scores around Helix II and Helix III (Figure 8B), which may be involved in the contact between M molecules.

S-M complex: It was also the N-terminal or the carboxyl-terminal tail of M protein that did not interfere with the M-S complex formation. Instead, deletion of the first two or the last two trans-membrane segments of the triple spanning protein in M protein, which is known not to affect the structure of the globular part of the protein, interrupts in the M-S complex formation (de Haan *et al.* 1999). The above prediction shows the Helix II and Helix III of M protein may bind to the areas spanning both of the two predicted coiled-coil regions. Multiple residues are involved in forming the S-M complex. Interestingly, these positions are not overlapped M-M contact proteins.

Based on the above analysis, we can pursue a hypothesis: The interaction between multiple residues between region 40-100 of M protein (major positions 46, 53, 62, 73, 81, 100) and region 800-1200 of the S protein (major positions 16, 822, 869, 1036, 1075, and 1134) may form the S-M complex. By using positional mutation strategy, the laboratory experiments may verify this hypothesis. By design specific drug target one or more of these positions, the formation of S-M complex can be prohibited thus kill the SARS-CoV.

New computational questions may also be generated by the computational analysis at this stage. For example, are the contacted residues in the S-M complex still contacted when they form the membrane? If not, how do they dissociate during virus assembly?

Summary

In this chapter, we described a computational framework for modeling emerging disease. This framework can be composed of five components: (1) Gene survey of the sequences related to the emerging diseases; (2) biological problem definition; (3) computational analyses of the query sequences, which may include molecular characterization, structure prediction, phylogenetic analysis, and other analysis such as regulatory motif prediction; (4) literature review and summarize the solution to the problems; (5) inference the biological mechanism and possible generate further question and hypothesis for experimental testing.

We applied this computational framework in modeling SARS-CoV. By surveying the ORFs in SARS-CoV, we chose to predict the interaction between S and M complex as our main computational problem. Through transmembrane domain prediction, three-dimensional structural prediction, the interaction residues between S and M complex, we were able to define the putative contact regions between S and M proteins. The region 40-100 of M protein (major positions 46, 53, 62, 73, 81, 100) and region 800-1200 of the S protein (major positions 16, 822, 869, 1036, 1075, and 1134) may form the S-M complex. Further biological experiments could be designed to test these hypotheses. Based on the contact positions, we can design some protein homologs (small protein peptides) to compete with S or M proteins and block the S-M complex formation thus the virus assembly.

References

An, S., Maeda, A., and Makino, S. (1998) Coronavirus transcription early in infection. *J. Virol.* 72:8517-8524.

Babcock, G. J., Esshaki, D. J., Thomas, W. D. Jr, and Ambrosino, D. M., (2004) Amino acids 270 to 510 of the severe acute respiratory syndrome coronavirus spike protein are required for interaction with receptor. *J Virol.* 9:4552-60.

Baric, R. S., and Yount, B. (2000) Subgenomic negative-strand RNA function during mouse hepatitis virus infection. *J. Virol.* 74:4039-4046.

Blau, D. M., and Holmes, K. V. (2001) Human coronavirus HCoV-229E enters susceptible cells via the endocytic pathway. *Adv. Exp. Med. Biol.* 494:193-198.

Bosch, B. J., van der Zee, R., de Haan, C. A., and Rottier, P. J. (2003) The coronavirus spike protein is a class I virus fusion protein: structural and functional characterization of the fusion core complex. *J. Virol.* 77:8801-8811.

Bowie, J. U., Luthy, R., and Eisenberg, D. (1991) A method to identify protein sequences that fold into a known three-dimensional structure. *Science* 253:164-170.

Bryant, S. H. and Lawrence, C. E. (1993) An empirical energy function for threading protein sequence through the folding motif. *Proteins: Struct. Funct. Genet.* 16:92-112.

Collins, A. R. (1993) HLA class I antigen serves as a receptor for human coronavirus OC43. *Immunol. Invest.* 22:95-103.

de Groot, R. J., Luytjes, W., Horzinek, M. C., van der Zeijst, B. A. M., Spaan, W. J. M., and Lenstra, J. A. (1987) Evidence for a coiled-coil structure in the spike of coronaviruses. *J. Mol. Biol.* 196:963-966.

de Haan C. A., Stadler, K., Godeke, G. J., Bosch, B. J., Rottier, P. J. (2004) Cleavage inhibition of the murine coronavirus spike protein by a furin-like enzyme affects cell-cell but not virus-cell fusion. *J Virol.* 78:6048-6054.

de Haan, C. A., Smeets, M., Vernooij, F., Vennema, H., and Rottier, P. J. (1999) Mapping of the coronavirus membrane protein domains involved in interaction with the spike protein. *J. Virol.* 73:7441-7452.

de Haan, C. A., Vennema, H., and Rottier, P. J. (2000) Assembly of the coronavirus envelope: homotypic interactions between the M proteins. *J Virol.* 74:4967-4978.

Delmas, B., Gelfi, J., L'Haridon, R., Vogel, L. K., Sjostrom, H., Noren, O., and Laude, H. (1992) Aminopeptidase N is a major receptor for the entero-pathogenic coronavirus TGEV. *Nature* 357:417-420.

Donnelly, C. A., Ghani, A. C., Leung, G. M., Hedley, A. J., Fraser, C., Riley, S., Abu-Raddad, L. J., Ho, L. M., Thach, T. Q., Chau, P., *et al.* (2003) Epidemiological determinants of spread of causal agent of severe acute respiratory syndrome in Hong Kong. *Lancet* 361:1761-1766.

Drosten, C., Preiser, W., Gunther, S., Schmitz, H., and Doerr, H. W. (2003) Severe acute respiratory syndrome: identification of the etiological agent. *Trends Mol. Med.* 9:325-327.

Eckert, D. M. and Kim, P. S. (2001) Mechanisms of viral membrane fusion and its inhibition. *Annu Rev Biochem.* 70:777-810.

Escors, D., Ortego, J., and Enjuanes, L. (2001) The membrane M protein of the transmissible gastroenteritis coronavirus binds to the internal core through the carboxy-terminus. *Adv. Exp. Med. Biol.* 494:589-593.

Fariselli, P. and Casadio, R. (1999) A neural network based predictor of residue contacts in proteins. *Protein Eng.* 12:15-21.

Fariselli, P., Olmea, O., Valencia, A. and Casadio, R. (2001) Prediction of contact maps with neural networks and correlated mutations. *Protein Eng.* 14:835-843.

Feldmann, H., Czub, M., Jones, S., Dick, D., Garbutt, M., Grolla, A., and Artsob, H. (2002) Emerging and re-emerging infectious diseases. *Med. Microbiol. Immunol. (Berl).* 191:63-74.

Gobel, U., Sander, C., Schneider, R. and Valencia A. (1994) Correlated mutations and residue contacts in proteins. *Proteins* 18:309-317.

Guan, Y., Zheng, B. J., He, Y. Q., Liu, X. L., Zhuang, Z. X., Cheung, C. L., Luo, S. W., Li, P. H., Zhang, L. J., Guan, Y. J., *et al.* (2003) Isolation and Characterization of Viruses Related to the SARS Coronavirus from Animals in Southern China. *Science* 302:276-278.

Guo, J. T., Ellrott, K., Chung, W. J., Xu, D., Passovets, S., and Xu, Y. PROSPECT-PSPP: An Automatic Computational Pipeline for Protein Structure Prediction. *Nucleic Acid Research* 32:W522-525.

Hirokawa T, Boon-Chieng S, and Mitaku S. (1998) SOSUI: classification and secondary structure prediction system for membrane proteins. *Bioinformatics* 14:378-379.

Holmes, K. V. (2003) SARS-associated coronavirus. *N. Engl. J. Med.* 348:1948-1951.

Jones, D. T., Taylor, W. R., Thornton, J. M. (1992) The rapid generation of mutation data matrices from protein sequences. *Comput Appl Biosci.* 8:275-82.

Koehl, P. and Levitt, M. (1999). A brighter future for protein structure prediction. *Nature Struct. Biol.* 6:108-111.

Krueger, D. K., S. M. Kelly, D. N. Lewicki, R. Ruffolo, and T. M. Gallagher. (2001) Variations in disparate regions of the murine coronavirus spike protein impact the initiation of membrane fusion. *J. Virol.* 75:2792-2802

Ksiazek, T. G., Erdman, D., Goldsmith, C. S., Zaki, S. R., Peret, T., Emery, S., Tong, S., Urbani, C., Comer, J. A., Lim, W., *et al.* SARS Working Group. (2003) A novel coronavirus associated with severe acute respiratory syndrome. *N. Engl. J. Med.* 348:1953-1966.

Kubo, H., Yamada, Y. K. and Taguchi, F. (1994) Localization of neutralizing epitopes and the receptor-binding site within the amino-terminal 330 amino acids of the murine coronavirus spike protein. *J. Virol.* 68:5403-5410

Lund, O., Frimand, K., Gorodkin, J., Bohr, H., Bohr, J., Hansen, J., and Brunak, S. (1997) Protein distance constraints predicted by neural networks and probability density functions. *Protein Eng.* 10:1241-1248.

Maki, D. G. (2003) SARS: 1918 revisited? The urgent need for global collaboration in public health. *Mayo Clin. Proc.* 78:813-816.

Marra, M. A., Jones, S. J., Astell, C. R., Holt, R. A., Brooks-Wilson, A., Butterfield, Y. S., Khattra, J., Asano. J. K., Barber, S. A., Chan, S. Y., *et al.* (2003) The Genome sequence of the SARS-associated coronavirus. *Science* 300:1399-1404.

Matsuyama, S., and Taguchi, F. (2002) Receptor-induced conformational changes of murine coronavirus spike protein. *J Virol.* 76:11819-11826.

Montelione, G. T. and Anderson, S. (1999) Structural genomics: keynote for a human proteome project. *Nature Struct. Biol.* 6:11-12.

Murzin, A. G., Brenner, S. E., Hubbard, T., and Chothia, C. (1995) SCOP: a structural classification of proteins database for the investigation of sequences and structures. *J. Mol. Biol.* 247:536-540.

Ng, S. K. (2003) Possible role of an animal vector in the SARS outbreak at Amoy Gardens. *Lancet* 362:570-572.

Olmea, O. and Valencia, A. (1997) Improving contact predictions by the combination of correlated mutations and other sources of sequence information. *Fold Des.* 2:S25-32.

Opstelten, D. J., Raamsman, M. J., Wolfs, K., Horzinek, M. C., and Rottier, P. J. (1995a) Coexpression and association of the spike protein and the membrane protein of mouse hepatitis virus. *Adv. Exp. Med. Biol.* 380:291-297.

Opstelten, D. J., Raamsman, M. J., Wolfs, K., Horzinek, M.C., and Rottier, P. J. (1995b) Envelope glycoprotein interactions in coronavirus assembly. *J. Cell Biol.* 131:339-349.

Pazos, F., Olmea, O., and Valencia, A. (1997) A graphical interface for correlated mutations and other protein structure prediction methods. *Comput Appl Biosci.* 13:319-321.

Riemann, D., Kehlen, A., and Langner, J. (1999) CD13--not just a marker in leukemia typing. *Immunol. Today.* 20:83-88.

Risco, C., Anton, I. M., Enjuanes, L., and Carrascosa, J. L. (1996) The Transmissible gastroenteritis coronavirus contains a spherical core shell consisting of M and N proteins. *J. Virol.* 70:4773-4777.

Risco, C., Muntion, M., Enjuanes, L., and Carrascosa, J. L. (1998) Two types of virus-related particles are found during transmissible gastroenteritis virus morphogenesis. *J. Virol.* 72:4022-4031.

Rota, P. A., Oberste, M. S., Monroe, S. S., Nix, W. A., Campagnoli, R., Icenogle, J. P., Penaranda, S., Bankamp, B., Maher, K., Chen, M. H., *et al.* (2003) Characterization of a novel coronavirus associated with severe acute respiratory syndrome. *Science* 300:1394-1399.

Ruan, Y. J., Wei, C. L., Ee, A. L., Vega, V. B., Thoreau, H., Su, S. T., Chia, J. M., Ng, P., Chiu, K. P., Lim, L., *et al.* (2003) Comparative full-length genome sequence analysis of 14 SARS coronavirus isolates and common mutations associated with putative origins of infection. *Lancet* 361:1779-1785.

Salanueva, I. J., Carrascosa, J. L., and Risco, C. (1999) Structural maturation of the transmissible gastroenteritis coronavirus. *J. Virol.* 73:7952-7964.

Sampathkumar, P., Temesgen, Z., Smith, T. F., and Thompson, R. L. (2003) SARS: epidemiology, clinical presentation, management, and infection control measures. *Mayo Clin. Proc.* 78:882-890.

Schultze, B. and Herrler, G. (1993) Recognition of N-acetyl-9-O-acetylneuraminic acid by bovine coronavirus and hemagglutinating encephalomyelitis virus. *Adv. Exp. Med. Biol.* 342:299-304.

Sethna, P. B., and Brian, D. A. (1997) Coronavirus genomic and subgenomic minus-strand RNAs copartition in membrane-protected replication complexes. *J. Virol.* 71:7744-7749.

Shah, M., Passovets, S., Kim, D., Ellrott, K., Wang, L., Vokler, I., LoCascio, P., Xu, D., and Xu, Y. (2003) A computational pipeline for protein structure prediction and analysis at genome scale. *Bioinformatics,* 19:1985-1996.

Shindyalov, I. N., Kolchanov, N. A., and Sander, C. (1994) Can three-dimensional contacts in protein structures be predicted by analysis of correlated mutations? *Protein Eng.* 7:349-358.

Spiga, O., Bernini, A., Ciutti, A., Chiellini, S., Menciassi, N., Finetti, F., Causarono, V., Anselmi, F., Prischi, F., Niccolai, N. (2003) Molecular modelling of S1 and S2 subunits of SARS coronavirus spike glycoprotein. *Biochem Biophys Res Commun.* 310:78-83

Stadler, K.,Masignani V.,Eickmann M.,Becker S.,Abrignani S.,Klenk H.,Rappuoli R., (2003) SARS — beginning to understand a new virus, *Nature Reviews Microbiology* 1:209-218

Suzuki, H. and Taguchi, F. (1996) Analysis of the receptor binding site of murine coronavirus spike glycoprotein. *J. Virol.* 70:2632-2636

Taguchi, F. and Shimazaki, Y. K. (2000) Functional analysis of an epitope in the S2 subunit of the murine coronavirus spike protein: involvement in fusion activity. *J. Gen. Virol.* 81:2867-2871.

Tan, K., Zelus, B. D., Meijers, R., Liu, J. H., Bergelson, J. M., Duke, N., Zhang, R., Joachimiak, A., Holmes, K. V., and Wang, J. H. (2002) Crystal structure of murine sCEACAM1a[1,4]: a coronavirus receptor in the CEA family. *EMBO J.* 21:2076-2086.

Taylor, W. R. and Hatrick, K. (1994) Compensating changes in protein multiple sequence alignments. *Protein Eng.* 7:341-348.

Thiel, V., Ivanov, K. A., Putics, A., Hertzig, T., Schelle, B., Bayer, S., Weissbrich, B., Snijder, E. J., Rabenau, H., Doerr, H. W., Gorbalenya, A. E., and Ziebuhr, J. (2003) Mechanisms and enzymes involved in SARS coronavirus genome expression. *J. Gen. Virol.* 84:2305-2315.

Thompson, J. D., Higgins, D. G., and Gibson, T. J. (1994) CLUSTAL W: improving the sensitivity of progressive multiple sequence alignment through sequence weighting, position-specific gap penalties and weight matrix choice. *Nucleic Acids Res.* 22:4673-4680.

Tresnan, D. B. and Holmes, K. V. (1998) Feline aminopeptidase N is a receptor for all group I coronaviruses. *Adv. Exp. Med. Biol.* 440:69-75.

Vakser, I. A. and Aflalo, C. (1994) Hydrophobic docking: A proposed enhancement to molecular recognition technique. *Proteins: Struct. Funct. Genet.* 20:320-329.

Wan, X., Branton, S. L., Hanson, L. A., and Pharr, G. T. (2004b) Identification and initial characterization of an aminopeptidase gene in *M. gallinarum. Current Microbiology*, 48:32-38.

Wan, X., Branton, S. L., Hughlett, M. B., Hanson, L.A., and G. T. Pharr. (2004a) Expression and subcellular location of a leucine aminopeptidase of *Mycoplasma gallinarum. International Journal of Poultry Science* 3:70-74.

Westbrook, J., et al. (2000) The Protein Data Bank: unifying the archive. *Nucleic Acids Res.* 30:245-248.

Wolf, E., Kim, P. S., and Berger, B. (1997). MultiCoil: A Program for Predicting Two- and Three-Stranded Coiled Coils, *Protein Science* 6:1179-1189.

Xu, D., Baburaj, K., Peterson, C. B., and Xu, Y. (2001) A Model for the Three-Dimensional Structure of Vitronectin: Predictions for the Multi-Domain Protein from Threading and Docking. *Proteins: Structure, Function, and Genetics.* 44: 312-320.

Xu, D., Kim, D., Dam, P., Shah, M., Uberbacher, E. C., and Xu, Y. (2003) Characterization of protein structure and function at genome scale using a computational prediction pipeline. In "*Genetic Engineering, Principles and Methods*", edited by Setlow, J. K. 269-293.

Xu, Y., and Xu, D. (2000) Protein threading using PROSPECT: Design and evaluation. *Proteins: Struct Funct Genet* 40:343-354.

Xu, Y., Xu, D., and Uberbacher, E. C. (1998) An efficient computational method for globally optimal threading. *J. Comp. Biol.* 5:597-614.

Xu, Y., Xu, D., Crawford, O. H., Einstein, J. R., Larimer, F., Uberbacher, E. C., Unseren, M. A., and Zhang, G. (1999) Protein threading by PROSPECT: A prediction experiment in CASP3. *Protein Eng.* 12:899-907.

Yeager, C. L., Ashmun, R. A., Williams, R. K., Cardellichio, C. B., Shapiro, L. H., Look, A. T., and Holmes, K. V. (1992) Human aminopeptidase N is a receptor for human coronavirus 229E. *Nature* 357:420-422.

Yu, X. J., Luo, C., Lin, J. C., Hao, P., He, Y. Y., Guo, Z. M., Qin, L., Su, J., Liu, B. S., Huang, Y., *et al.* (2003) Putative hAPN receptor binding sites in SARS-CoV spike protein. *Acta Pharmacol. Sin.* 24:481-488.

Zeng, F. Y., Chan, C. W., Chan, M. N., Chen, J. D., Chow, K. Y., Hon, C. C., Hui, K. H., Li, J., Li, V. Y., *et al.* (2003) The complete genome sequence of severe acute respiratory syndrome coronavirus strain HKU-39849 (HK-39). *Exp. Biol. Med. (Maywood)* 228:866-873.

Zhang, Q. F., Cui, J. M., Huang, X. J., Lin, W., Tan, D. Y., Xu, J. W., Yang, Y. F., Zhang, J. Q., Zhang, X., Li, H., *et al.* (2003) Morphology and morphogenesis of severe acute respiratory syndrome (SARS)-associated virus. *Acta. Biochimica. Et. Biophysica. Sinica.* 35:587-591.

Acknowledgments

This research is supported in part by the US Department of Energy's Genomes to Life program (http://www.doegenomestolife.org) under project, "Carbon Sequestration in *Synechococcus* Sp.: From Molecular Machines to Hierarchical Modeling" (www.genomes-to-life.org). This work was also supported by the Laboratory Directed Research and Development Program of Oak Ridge National Laboratory, under Contract DE-AC05-00OR22725, managed by UT-Battelle, LLC.

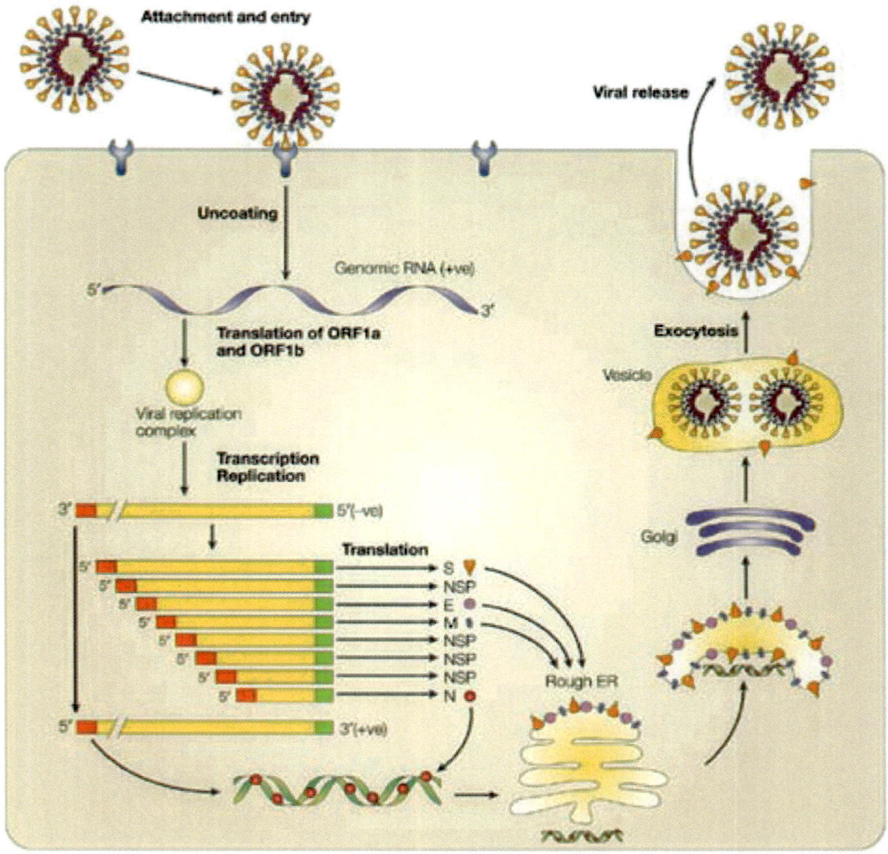

Figure 1. Life cycle of coronaviruses (with permission, adapted from Stadler *et al.* 2003, Nature Reviews Microbiology 1: 209-218)

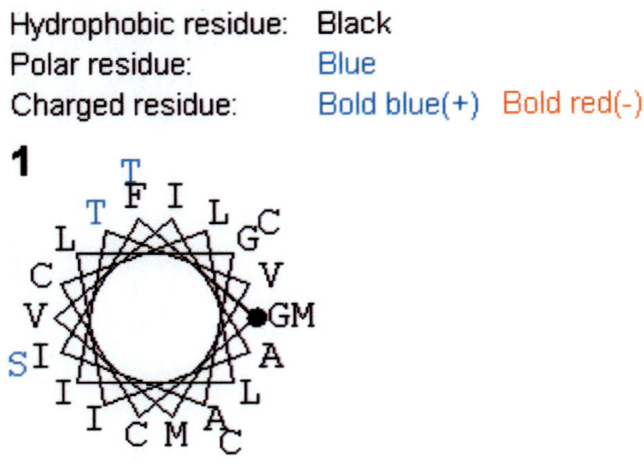

a

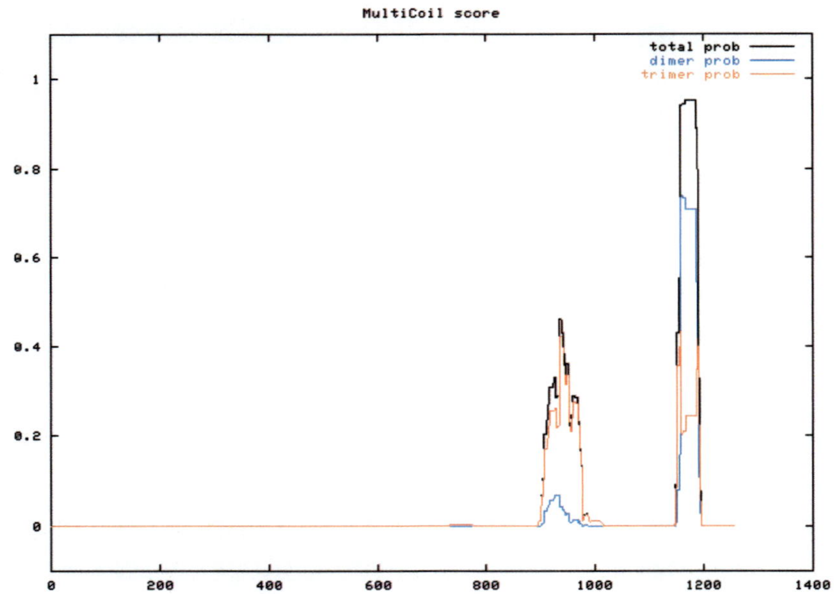

b

Figure 3. Molecular analysis of the S protein. A. The helical wheel diagram of the predicted transmembrane helix in the S protein. B. Coiled-coil-like region in S protein.

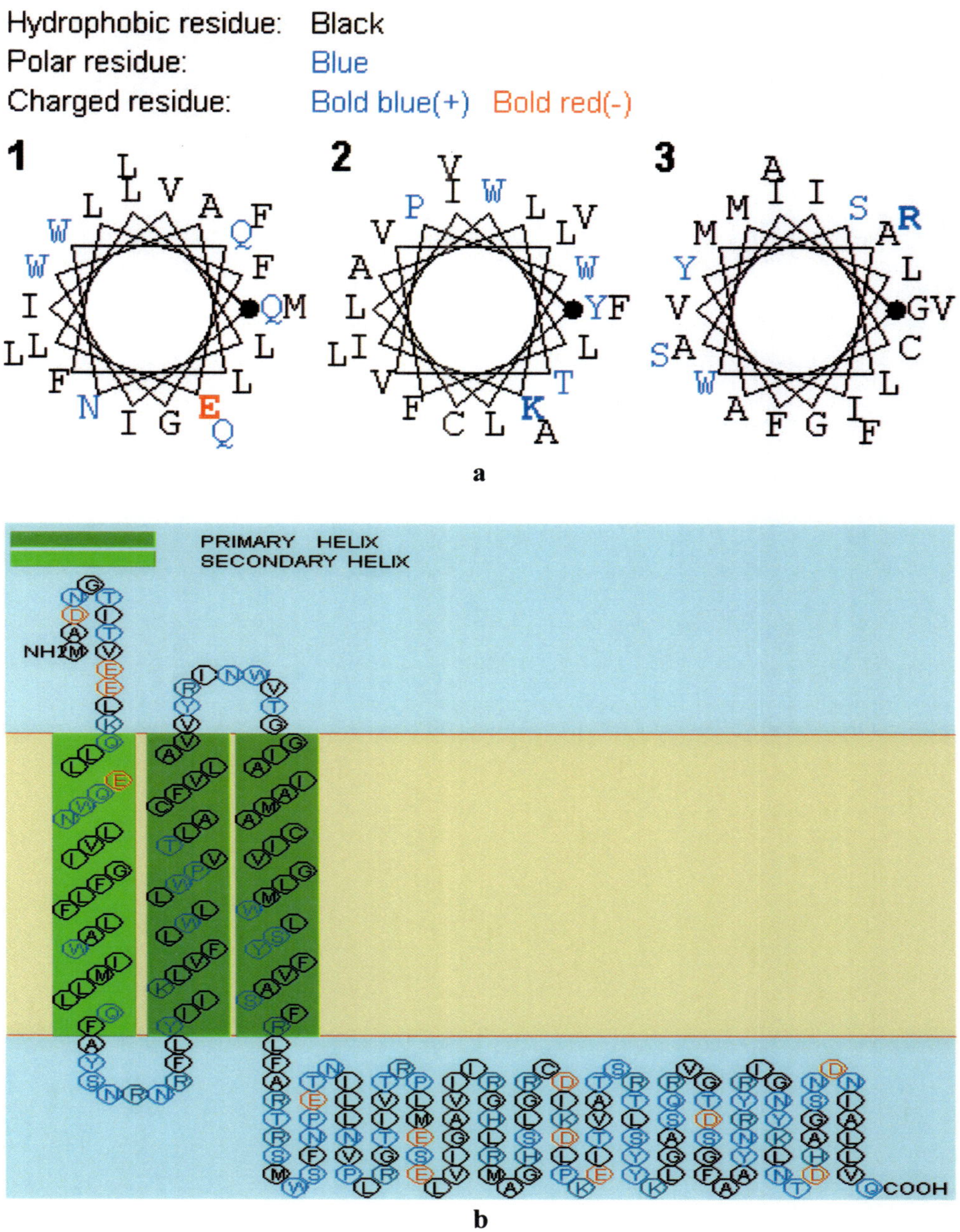

Figure 5. The transmembrane regions of the SARS-CoV M protein. A. Wheel diagram of the M protein; B. Transmembrane regions of the M protein predicted by SOSUI (Hirokawa *et al.* 1998).

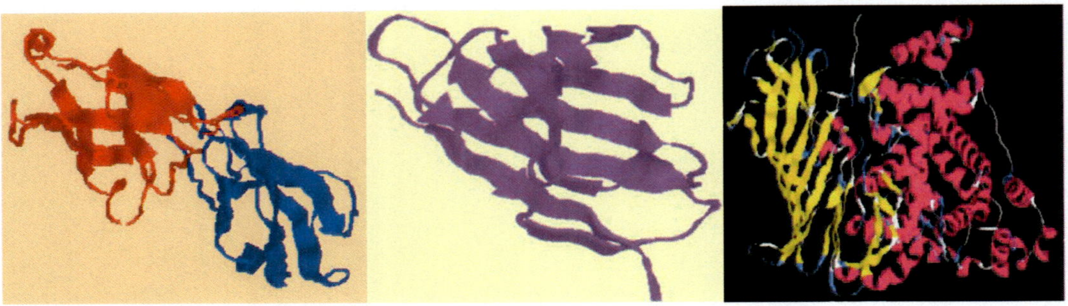

a b c

Figure 6. A. Structural template 1vfa for the S2 domain. B. Structural template 1edha for the M protein. C. Structural template 1hs6a for the N-aminopeptidase.

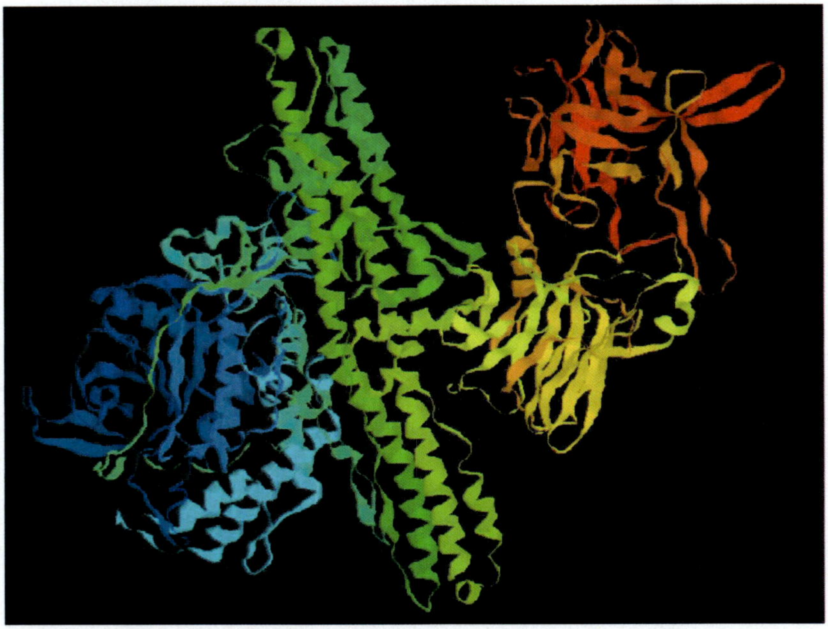

Figure 7. The 3D structure of *C. botulinum* neurotoxin B (pdb ID 1g9d).

In: Bioinformatics: New Research
Editor: Peter V. Yan, pp. 81-100
ISBN 1-59454-242-2

Chapter IV

Identification and Computer-Assisted Integration into Biological Pathways of Modulated Gene Expressions Patterns

***Franck Gadal*[1], *Anna Starzec*[2], *Christophe Bozic*[3], *Céline Pillot-Brochet*[3], *Sophie Malinge*[3], *Valérie Ozanne*[3], *Jérome Vicenzi*[3], *Laurent Buffat*[3], *Gérard Perret*[2], *Michel Crepin*[1] and *François Iris*[4]**

[1] Unité Inserm U 553, Hôpital St Louis, 75010 Paris, France and université Paris 13, France. 33 1 48 38 77 20, fax : 33 1 48 38 77 77.

[2] Laboratoire de pharmacologie clinique et expérimentale, faculté de médecine, université Paris 13, 93017 Bobigny cedex.

[3] Valigen, Tour Neptune, 92086 Paris La Défense, France.

[4] Ecole centrale de Paris, Grande voie des vignes 92295 Chatenay Malabry France and Bio-Modeling Systems, 26 Rue St Lambert, Paris 15, France.

Abstract

To understand the cellular mechanisms of malignant transformation induced by constitutive activation of the ras oncogene (Ha-ras) as well as by estrogens and anti-estrogens treatments, we used a subtractive hybridization method (VGID™) together with an integrative analytical procedure based upon literature databases in the form of extensive interaction graphs. We found 731 over- and under-expressed genes which, in the human MCF7-ras and MCF7 breast epithelial cell lines, are involved in the different aspects of tumoral transformation such as defined signaling pathways, cellular growth, protection against apoptosis, extracellular matrix and cytoskeleton remodeling. Integrative analysis led to the construction of physiological models defining cross talk and signaling pathway alterations which explicitly suggested mechanisms directly involved in tumor progression. The models further suggested points and means of intervention which could induce cell death in Ha-ras-transformed cells specifically. These hypotheses were directly tested in vitro and found to be largely correct, hence indicating that these new analytical and technological approaches allow the discovery of pathology-associated cellular mechanisms and physiologically defined targets leading to phenotype-specific pharmacological interventions.

Color graphics are presented at the end of the chapter.

Introduction

Over-expression of the ras family of oncogenes is associated with tumorigenicity, invasiveness and metastatic potential in a variety of human breast carcinomas (1) whereas in pathologies such as breast cancer, estrogens act as mitogenic factors and are important in tumor initiation and progression *in vitro* and *in vivo* (2-4). However, in contrast to organisms with fully sequenced and annotated genomes, DNA microarray technologies are of limited usefulness in identifying and measuring changes in mRNA levels originating from human genes, the expression of which are affected by Ha-ras constitutive activation and estrogens and anti-estrogens treatments. Here, a technological approach, free of a priori choices, was used in order to gather primary expression data, unbiased enough to allow successful integration with extensive published information. To investigate the mechanisms whereby Ha-ras activation leads to tumorigenic transformation and to explore how estrogens (E_2) and anti-estrogens (TAM) could regulate cell growth and tumor progression in breast cancer, we chose two human breast cell lines which only differ by constitutive activation of the Ha-ras oncogene. The MCF7 cell line, cloned from a pleural effusion of breast adenocarcinoma, is non-invasive and estrogens-growth-dependent and sensitive to TAM (5, 6), whereas the same MCF7 cells stably transfected with Ha-ras (MCF7-ras) are sensitive to, but not dependent upon, estrogens and can spontaneously form tumors after implantation in the nude mouse (6, 7). The patterns of differential expression associated with tumorigenic transformation were analyzed using the Valigen Gene IDentification (VGID™) process, a technology based on a modified subtractive hybridization method (8). The sequences differentially expressed in a "Tester" cDNA library are subjected to competitive hybridisation against an excess amount of "Driver" cDNA library (8) followed by selective trapping of all "Driver"' material, including sequences held in common by both "Tester" and "Driver", as well as single stranded "Tester" cDNA, thus avoiding the construction of normalized cDNA libraries. Several iterative rounds of subtraction and selective trappings result in an efficient and high enrichment of "Tester" specific sequences. This technology does not require specific probes or primers to isolate differentially expressed mRNAs, thus allowing identification of isoforms and unknown transcripts without having to predetermine the sequences to be investigated. Primary differential expression data and extensive published information were then integrated into detailed and experimentally testable biological models describing the mechanisms presumably implemented by Ha-ras constitutive activation and E_2/TAM effects, together with the points on which defined pharmacological intervention would specifically abrogate the tumorigenic phenotype.

The computational approach is based upon the weighted contextual indexation of the literature in terms of components and biological mechanisms associated with the systematic destruction of hypotheses arising from the injection of data into the indexed literature database (graph). The elements that result in a hypothesis being destroyed are in turn used to generate a new hypothesis which will then be submitted to the destructive process, and so on iteratively until a hypothesis which cannot be destroyed is obtained. This does not mean that the hypothesis is correct; it merely means that it is supported by the existing publicly accessible information. Undestroyed hypotheses are then merged into "metaypotheses" that are in turn subjected to the iterative destruction process. In this manner, one finally arrives at a theoretical biological model entirely supported by published information which provides directly testable explanations for as yet poorly understood mechanisms (8). Should the biological data arising from these tests demonstrate that the model is largely incorrect, this new data can now be injected into the process to correct the model. Although requiring a considerable amount of work, this process is surprisingly fast (months as opposed to years).

The integrative procedure we implemented consists of eight distinct steps (http://perso.club-internet.fr/fgadal). (i) Construction of an in silico relational graph encompassing all known functional interactions between genes, proteins and other small molecules recorded in the scientific literature pertaining to mammalian cellular and physiological mechanisms. (ii) Injection into the graph of the primary differential expression data set and extraction of the sub-graph containing the functional paths linking the data set components and identifying the biological elements associated with these paths. (iii) Integration of the resulting information into an initial model describing the pathways represented and the interactions governing pathway functions. (iv) Identification of the key genes and isoforms, absent from the primary data set, whose expression patterns govern cross-talk and functions within and between the pathways identified. (v) Construction of the appropriate DNA microarrays and direct verification of the expected expression patterns and expression levels. (vi) Reiteration of steps (ii) and (iii). (vii) Identification of the physiological intervention targets and intervention modes which should specifically affect Ha-ras transformed cells. (viii) Direct experimental verification of the model predictions. Thus, by combining subtractive hybridisations, cDNA microarrays and data integration, we were be able to highlight some of the interconnected mechanisms through which the Ha-ras oncogene and E_2 and/or TAM regulate tumor pregression.

Materials and Methods

Cell Culture

The epithelial cell line MCF7 was obtained from ATCC (Rockville, MD, USA) whereas MCF7-ras cell line, obtained from MCF7 cells transfected with the Ha-ras oncogene, was a generous gift from Dr Sommers (6). They were cultured routinely in GLUTAMAX I Dubelco's modified Eagle's medium (DMEM) (Gibco Invitogen) supplemented with 10% Fetal Calf Serum (FCS) (Gibco Invitogen), 50 µg/mL streptomycin (Gibco Invitogen) 50 UI/ml penicillin (Gibco Invitogen) at 37°C in 5%-CO_2 atmosphere. The experiments were carried out in phenol red-free DMEM (Gibco Invitogen) supplemented with 10% charcoal-treated FCS or 10% FCS respectively for MCF7 treated with E_2 and/or TAM and MCF7/MCF7ras experiments, 50 µg/ml streptomycin, 50 UI/ml penicillin and 2 mM L-glutamin (Gibco Invitogen). Regarding E_2 and TAM experiment, the MCF7 cells, divided into three batches, were incubated at 37°C in 5%-CO_2 atmosphere for 8 days. Then, one batch of MCF7 cells was stimulated with $1x10^{-8}$ M E_2 (Sigma Aldrich) for 15 h whereas the second batch was maintained in E_2-free medium. To explore E_2-associated differential expression, the VGID™ procedure was performed using cDNAs generated from batches 1 and 2. To explore TAM-associated differential expression, the third batch of MCF7 cells was incubated with $1x10^{-8}$ M E_2 and $1x10^{-7}$ M TAM (Sigma Aldrich) for 15 h and the VGID™ procedure was performed using cDNAs generated from batches 2 and 3.

cDNA Synthesis

Direct mRNA capture from lysed cells was performed using Dynabeads® mRNA™ direct kit (Dynal) according to the manufacturer's protocol. First strand cDNA synthesis was carried out as follows: 6 µl-aliquots of first strand synthesis mixure [10mM dNTP each (Promega), 0.1 M DTT and 5X first strand buffer (both from Life Technologies)], 500 ng of Dynabeads®-bound denatured mRNA and 200 units *Superscript* II (Life Technologies) were separately pre-incubated at 37°C for 1 min in a water bath, then mixed and incubated in a final volume of 30 µl at 37°C for 1 h. The first strand samples were then transfered to 170 µl of diluted second strand synthesis mixure [1X final *E. coli* DNA ligase buffer (New England Biolabs), 900 mM KCI (Sigma Aldrich), 20 mg/ml glycogen (Boehringer), 10 mM dNTP each, 10 U/µl *E. coli DNA ligase* (New England Biolabs), 2 U/µl *Rnase H* and 10 U/µl *E. coli DNA polymerase I*, all purchased from Promega] and incubated for 2 h at 16°C in a Perkin Elmer 9700 thermal cycler. The cDNA populations, still bound to Dynabeads, were then digested with Sau3A (4 U/µl; New England Biolabs) for 2 h at 37°C to generate the fragments of 256 base pairs in statistical length. The reaction was stopped by heating for 20 min at 65°C. The digested cDNAs were then ligated to adaptors and PCR was performed using adaptor specific primers in a Perkin Elmer 9700 thermal cycler, using 12 cycles of 95°C for 30 s, 55°C for 45 s, 72°C for 1 min, followed by 72°C for 7 min. The PCR products were purified using Qiaquick PCR purification kit (Qiagen) and utilised for VGID™ and/or micro-array experiments (see below).

Adapters and Oligonucleotides

Sequences of adapters (Cybergene) used in VGID procedure were as follows: BamHI adapter, 5'CTT AGA ACG AGA CGG ATC CT3' and 3'TT GAA TCT TGC TCT GCC TAG GAC TAGp5', BglII-bio adapter, bio 5'CCA GCT AAC ACC TAG ATC TC3' and 3'TT GGT CGA TTG TGG ATC TAG AGC TAGp5'. The fragments of cDNA ligated by this adapters were amplified with the corresponding oligonucleotides (Cybergene): BamHI primer, 5'AA CTT AGA ACG AGA CGG ATC CTG ATC3' and BglII-bio primer, bio 5'AA CCA GCT AAC ACC TAG ATC TCG ATC3'. The inserts were amplified with the primers pVG17 (– 74), 5'GCA AGG CGA TTA AGT TGG GTA3'and pVG17reverse (– 88), 5'CTT CCG GCT CGT ATG TTG TGT3'.

VGID™ Gene Identification Technology (See Patent n°6,221,585)

As previously described (8), VGID™ directly isolates over-expressed and under-expressed cDNA associated with the transition from a defined phenotypic state to another state within a congenic system. For the first denaturation – renaturation step, 300 ng of BamHI-ligated-amplified Tester was mixed with 1200 ng BglII-bio-ligated-amplified Driver. The mixture was ethanol-precipitated, resuspended in 4 μl of HEPES 0.5 M-EDTA 0.2mM) and overlaid with 20 μl of mineral oil, then denatured 5 min at 98°C and finally chilled on ice. The salt concentration was adjusted to 0.5 M with 1 μl of 2.5 M NaCl. After denaturation of 5 min at 98°C, the sample was allowed to anneal for 20 h at 65°C. After hybridization, the oil was removed. The sample volume was adjusted to 100 μl with 100 mM NaCl, 10 mM Tris HCl, pH 8, and mixed with 210 μl of streptavidin magnet beads (10mg/ml, Boehringer Mannheim) to recover tester single and double strand DNA as described by the manufacturer. This step was repeated to remove all biotinylated DNA. To recover of the tester double strand DNA, the supernatant, which contained unbiotinylated DNA, was incubated with 1.5 μg of Single Strand Binding Protein (SSB, Promega) for 30 min at room temperature. The sample was loaded onto a Millipore Micropure EZ membrane (which retained the proteins) and centrifuged for 1 min at 20,800 g at room temperature. The flow through was combined with 1200 ng of Driver and the next round of hybridization was set up as describe above. A total of 3 hybridization rounds were performed. DNA, recovered after the last round, was amplified by PCR as described above using 25 cycles and the BamHI primer. The sequences under-or over-expressed were cloned into a modified pUC19 vector (Gibco Invitogen).

Cloning

The vector used for the cloning step was a derivative of the pUC19 vector where polylinker EcoRI – HindIII was replaced by the 5'AATTCGGATCCA3' pVG17 sequence. In order to avoid the cloning of chimeric structures, the vector/insert DNA ratio used was 3:1. Vector (50 ng) was ligated to the recovered DNA and amplified after the subtraction in the presence of 1U of *ligase* (Boehringer) in a final volume of 10 μl overnight at 16°C. The ligation mixture was purified by Geneclean procedure (BIO 101) according to the manufacturer's recommendation and the 2-aliquot was used to transform 50 μl of MAX Efficiency DH10B cells (Gibco Invitogen). Transformation was performed by electroporation at 1800V using the EC100 Electroporator (E-C apparatus Corporation). Immediately after electroporation, 500 μl of SOC Medium were added. Cells were shaked for 1 h at 37°C and an aliquot was spread on LB plate containing 100μg/ml ampicillin.

Sequencing

Isolated colonies were picked in 150μl of LB with 100 μg/ml ampicillin in order to make glycerol stocks. 4μl of this solution were cycle-sequenced in a Perkin-Elmer thermal cycler with the *AmpliTaq Gold DNA* polymerase kit (Perkin Elmer) using 10 pmol of pVG17(-74) and pVG17rev(-88) primers in a final volume of 50 μl. A pre-PCR step, performed at 95°C for 13 min, allows the activation of the polymerase and the bacteria lysis. Each of the 40 PCR cycles included three segments: 95°C/30 s, 54°C/1 min, 72°C/2 min 30 s. The PCR products were sequenced without purification using the BigDye Terminator Cycle Sequencing kit and ABI Prism 3700 automatic DNA sequencer (Perkin Elmer Applied Biosystem).

Sequence Analysis

The clone sequences were analysed using in-house programs written in Perl. After removing the vector sequence, the repeats were masked and compared to public databases using the *blastn* and *blastx* programs. Significance of the similarities was checked at both the nucleic and protein level. DNA sequences were considered for further analysis when the level of similarity with known sequences was greater than 98%. At the protein level, significant similarity threshold was fixed as at least equal to 40%. The sequence data were then clustered using the *Fasta* software.

Microarray Construction

All the clones obtained from the subtraction process were studied using the microarray technology. Each clone was PCR-amplified in a final volume of 100 µl using 20 pmol of both primers pVG17 (-74) and pVG17rev (-88), 10 nmol of dNTPs and 1.5 U of *DyNazyme EXT*. After 13 min of enzyme activation at 95°C, forty cycles were carried out (95°C/30 s, 56°C/1 min, 72°C/1 min 30 s). A final incubation was performed for 7 min at 72°C. The PCR-products were purified with Multiscreen PCR Kit (Millipore) according to the manufacturer's instructions and concentrated under vacuum speedvac. The PCR-products, resuspended in 3X SSC, and eleven yeast genes used as internal control, were spotted in triplicate onto GAPS Amino Silane Coated Slides (Corning) with the GMS 417 arrayer (Genetic MicroSystem). The slides were UV cross-linked at 300mJ, prehybridized in a 50% formamide, 0.1% SDS, 1% BSA, 5X SSC buffer at 42°C for 1 h, then washed first in water, next in 95% ethanol and finally they were vacuum-dried.

Microarray Hybridization, Scanning and Data Acquisition

cDNA (500 ng) from MCF7-ras cells, MCF7 cells treated or not with E_2 or TAM were labelled by random priming with incorporation of Cyanine5-dUTP for the "Tester" DNA and Cyanine3-dUTP for the "Driver" samples, respectively. Then, the samples were mixed, concentrated by evaporation under vacuum and resuspended in prehybridization buffer, described above, with Denhardt's solution replacing BSA. The three-labelled cDNA mixtures (MCF7-ras cDNA mixed with MCF7 one, MCF7 cDNA mixed with MCF7 + E_2 one and MCF7 + E_2 cDNA mixed with MCF7 + E_2 + TAM one) were hybridised with the arrayed slides overnight at 42°C. The slides were then washed 5 min with 1XSSC-0.1% SDS, 3 min with 1X SSC, 3 min with 0.1X SSC, 1 min with water and finally 95% ethanol-dried and scanned (GenePix 4000A from AXON). Accurate differential measurements (final fluorescence ratios) were expressed as the average of nine independent assays where each sequence was arrayed in triplicate. Visualisation, quantification and gene expression analysis were performed using the GENEPIX 3.0 software. The data were normalized using the auto-normalisation method of Yang, Y. H., Dudoit, S., Luu, P., and Speed, T. (2000) (Normalization for cDNA Microarray Data). http://oz.Berkeley.EDU/users/terry/zarray/Html/normspie.html).

Bio-Path™ Integrative Process

The construction of an in silico relational graph encompassing all known functional interactions between genes, proteins and other small molecules recorded in the scientific literature was performed by the Bio-path™ software which allows the identification of all the neighbours for a physiological entity (here gene or protein) by means of the grammatical analyses of scientific articles. To perform the textual analysis of the relevant abstracts, we curated all the different names or descriptors available for one physiological entity into various databases such as Swiss-Prot, RevSeq and GeneBank. For each database, an exhaustive list of physiological entities name variations was constituted. We found 90.000 descriptors in the Swiss-Prot database, 24.000 in RevSeq and 100.000 in GeneBank which, after unification and coupling, corresponded to 54.710 descriptors available into the MEDLINE database (Fig. 1).

P43034 : LIS1

PLATELET-ACTIVATING FACTOR ACETYLHYDROLASE IB ALPHA SUBUNIT
EC 3.1.1.47
PAF ACETYLHYDROLASE 45 KDA SUBUNIT
PAF-AH 45 KDA SUBUNIT
PAF-AH ALPHA
PAFAH1B1
LISSENCEPHALY-1 PROTEIN
MDCR

Variations :
LIS1 → LIS-1
ALPHA → A
ACETYLHYDROLASE → ACETYL-HYDROLASE

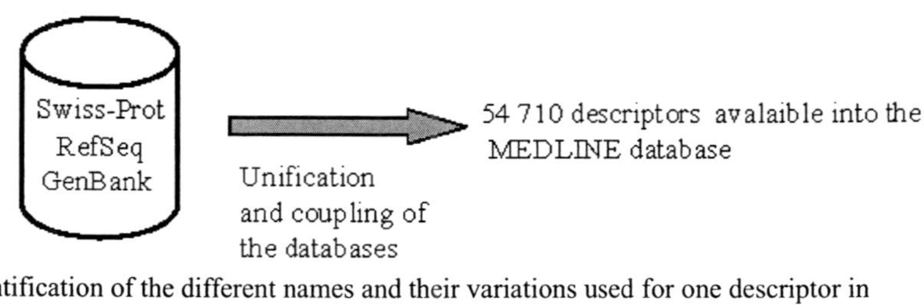

Figure 1. Identification of the different names and their variations used for one descriptor in several databases.

The next step consists in the construction of a listing representing all the verbs encountered in MEDLINE. We focused on verbal forms attached to interactions and regulations of physiological processes (such as "associate", "attach", "bind","activate", "inhibit", etc.) and biological activities (such as "acetylate", "phosphorylate", etc.) which corresponded to 1.066 verbs or verbal forms present in MEDLINE (Fig. 2). Finally, the software allowed to isolate from scientific articles sentences containing two descriptors and one predefined verb or verbal form, compile the results and connect physiological entities by a network of functional links (Fig. 3). To then generate the global relational graph encompassing all known functional interactions between physiological entities, the Bio-path™ software calculates the distance separating two entities as a ratio of the number of the sentences that connect two entities with a verbal form (Fig. 4). To obtain the biological model corresponding to the pathology of interest, the primary differential expression data sets generated by the VGID process are injected into the global graph. This generates a sub-graph containing the functional paths linking the data sets components and identifying the biological elements directly as well as indirectly associated with these paths (Fig. 5).

- **Interaction**
  - **<u>associate</u> - association, associated, associating, associative**
  - **<u>attach</u> - attached, attaching**
  - **<u>bind</u>, ...**
  - **<u>coprecipitate</u>, ...**
  - **<u>form a complex with</u>, ...**

  ...
- **Regulation**
  - **<u>activate</u> - activates, activating, activation, co-activate, inactivate, desactivate**
  - **<u>inhibit</u> - inhibits, inhibited, inhibitor, inhibitory**
  - **<u>regulate</u> - regulatory, regulation, regulating, upregulate, downregulate**
  - **<u>repress</u> ...**
  - **<u>stimulate</u> ...**

  ...
- **biochemical action**
  - **<u>acetylate</u> - acetylated, acetylating, acetylation**
  - **<u>degradate</u> ...**
  - **<u>phosphorylate</u> ...**

→ **1066 verbs available into MEDLINE database**

Figure 2. Verbs describing functional relationships between physiological entities.

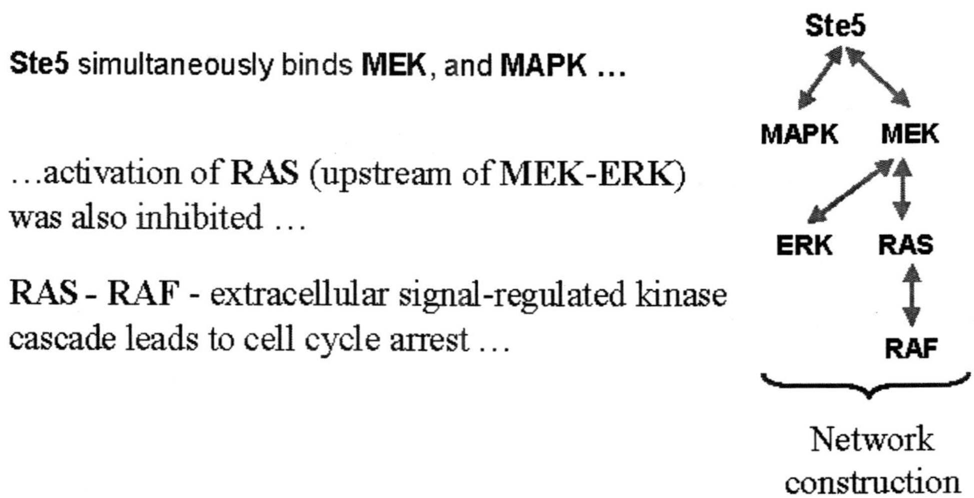

Figure 3. Abstracts analysis and constitution of a physiological network using descriptors and verbs lists.

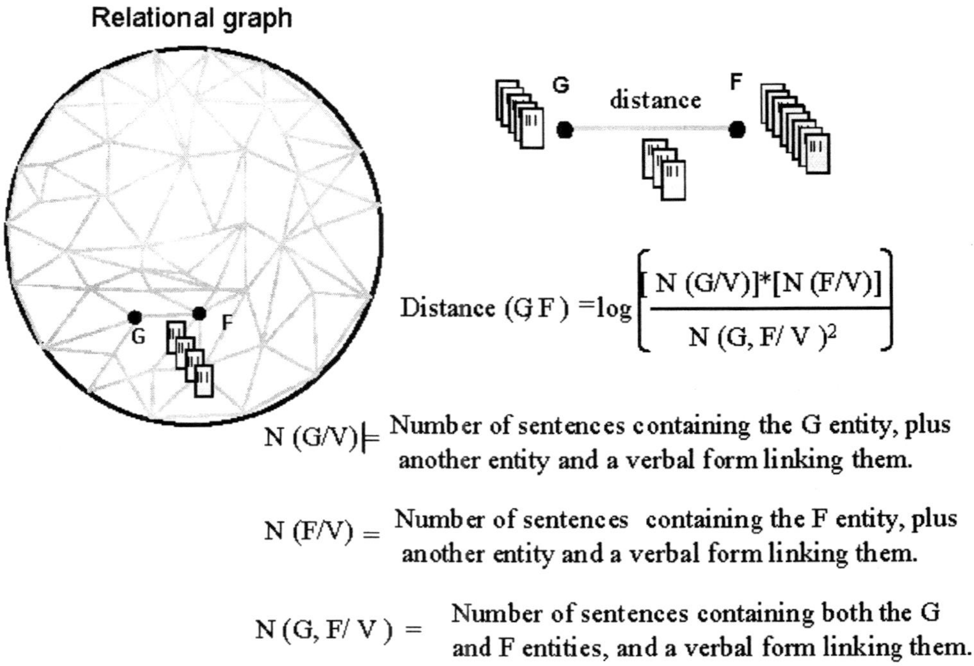

Figure 4. Definition of the distance between two entities

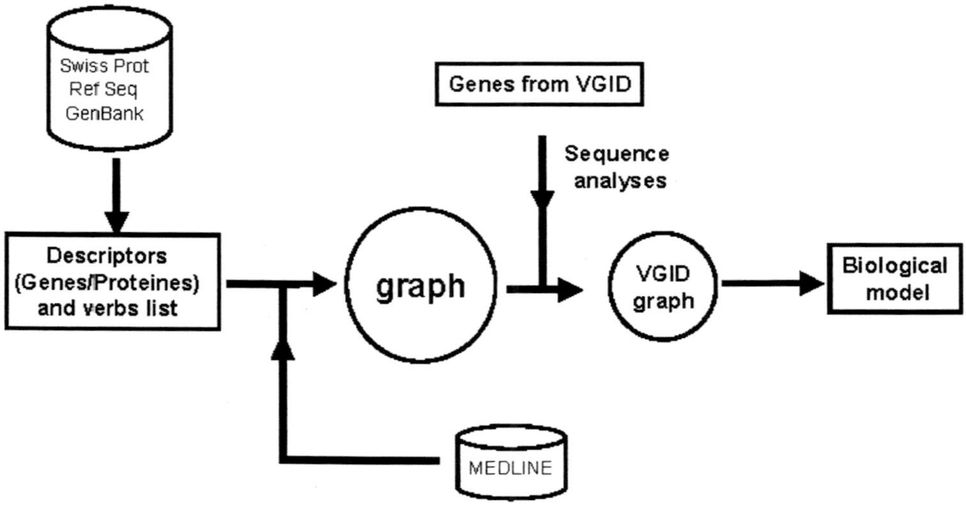

Figure 5. Global process identifying biological paths associated with differentially expressed genes.

Results

Subtractive Hybridization Process

The VGID™ subtractive hybridization process yielded 740 and 1005 cDNA inserts from the oncogene Ha-ras and E_2/TAM experiments, respectively, which were sequenced and cleaned using computer algorithms based in part on the recognition of the specific adaptors ligated to the cDNAs before cloning, thus eliminating empty vectors. The quality of the sequencing data was ascertained by bio-informatics analyses using the PHRED software. Sequence analysis revealed that the VGID™ data set contained 166 cDNA sequences found to be differentially expressed in MCF7-ras versus MCF7 cells. 28% of the total sequences were present more than twice while 63% were present at least twice. Of these, 106 corresponded to known transcripts encoding known functions, 41 to known transcripts/ESTs encoding unknown functions and 19 to new transcripts. Practically all the genes identified (over 95%) are known to have class II or class III expression levels (from 100 to less than 20 mRNA molecules/cell) (9) and most (over 80%) of these genes are known to be cancer associated and/or epithelium-associated. Furthermore, sequence analysis shown 565 cDNA sequences found to be differentially expressed in MCF7 versus MCF7 + E_2 and/or TAM cells, 47 of them were new transcripts. Microarray analyses confirmed both the patterns and levels of differential expression of the majority (~90%) of the genes identified as differentially expressed through utilisation of VGID™ (http//perso.club-internet.fr/fgadal).

Computer-Assisted Integrative Analyses

From the transcripts contained in the VGID™ data sets, the Bio-Path integrative process generates a classification of the neighbours functionaly associated with each transcript. This classification depends upon the number of sentences linking a defined verbal form, the transcript and the associated physiological entities. Finally, the results are weighed by, respectively, the type of verbal form used into the articles and the impact factor of the articles associated with the sentence. For example, figure 6 shows the entities most strongly associated with the gene CDK2, isolated through VGID, and provides information such as the number of functional neighbours (518) and the total number of articles (11822) from which this information was extracted. Here for instance, there were 358 articles linking cyclin A and CDK2 (Fig. 7). To evaluate the relevence of the neighbours classification and to understand the relationships between 2 entities, it is possible to read all the corresponding abstracts. But Bio-Path will sort out the abstracts from the MEDLINE databases according to the article's impact factor. Furthermore, it is possible to select a group of entities to identify the biological components presenting functional relationships with the selected group. In this manner, we can connect p27, CDK2 and CDK4 with a query based onCKS1/TGFβ (Fig 8).

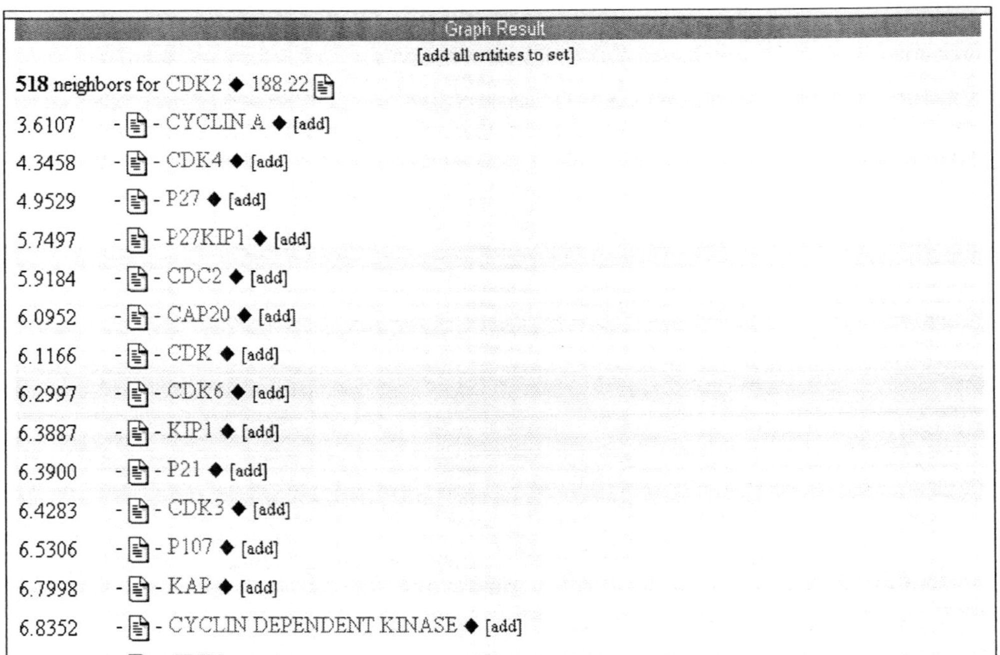

Figure 6. Display of the closest CDK2's neighbours identified through publication analyses. The weaker the score between 2 entities, the stronger their functional relationships. Here, cyclin A is the closest neighbour of CDK2.

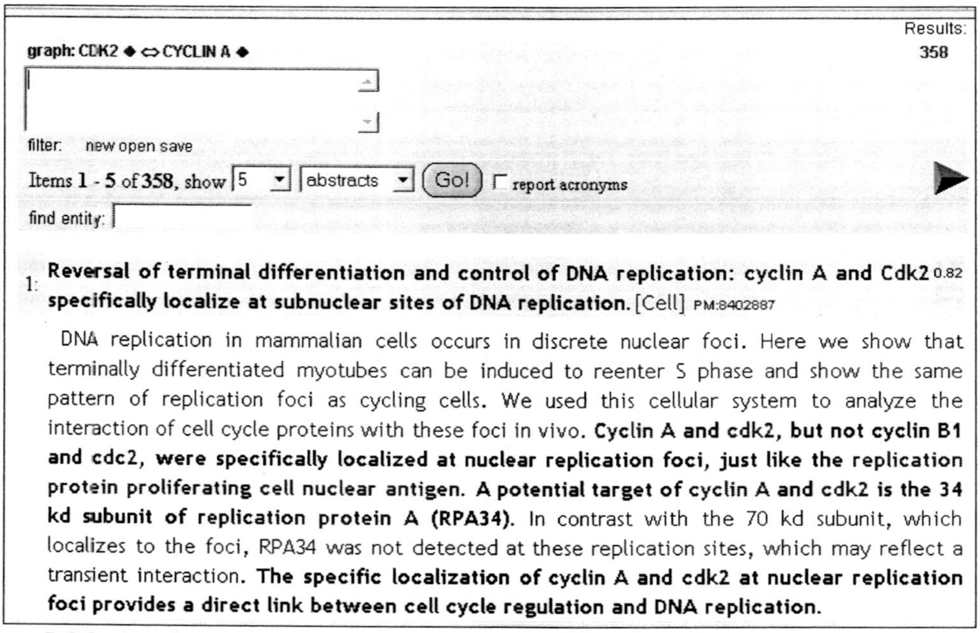

Figure 7. Selection of articles by Bio-Path. The biological entities are blue marked and the sentences containing the entities are bold marked.

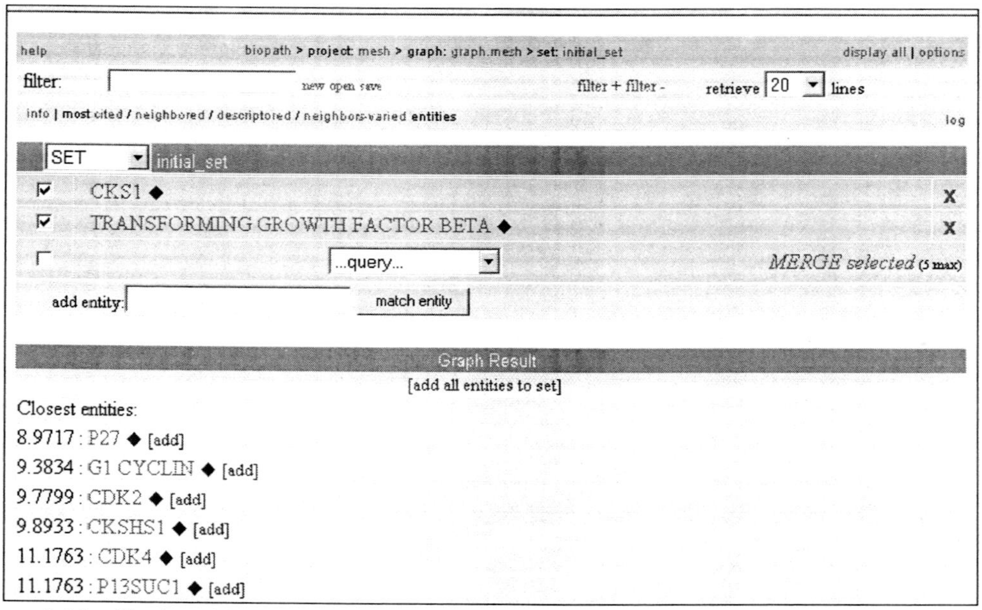

Figure 8. Identification of the closest entities associated with a query based on CKS1-TGFβ.

Table 1. Cellular mechanisms directly implicated in the Ha-ras transformation process

Broad functions	Genes	Accession number	VGID™ status	Microarray status (X fold expressed)
PKC activation and Ca^{2+} store mobilization.	DAGK ξ	NM_003646	↗	↗ 1.43 ± 0.29
	Reticulocalbin	NM_002901	↗	↗ 7.24 ± 0.29
	Rack 1	AF146043	↗	↗ 1.55 ± 0.10
	CaMKKβ	AF140507	↗	↗ 1.80 ± 0.17
	TCP 1θ	Z37164	↗	↗ 2.18 ± 0.23
	Annexin VI	NM_001155	↗	↗ 10.51 ± 1.35
Induction of PKC pathways	p38δ kinase	AF092535	↗	↗ 3.29 ± 0.76
	FKBP52	M88279	↗	↗ 1.37 ± 0.14
	DKK 1	AF177394	↘	↘ 8.33 ± 0.03
Cytoskeleton remodeling	STE 5	L01620	↗	↗ 1.12 ± 0.04
	LAR	Y00815	↗	↗ 1.34 ± 0.08
	NHE3RF	AF036241	↗	↗ 1.59 ± 0.13
	L-Plastin	NM_002298	↗	↗ 1.60 ± 0.12
	Thymosin β4.	M17733	↗	↗.1.20 ± 0.12
	ARP 3	NM_005721	↘	↘ 1.25 ± 0.1
	Profilin 1	NM_005022	↘	↘ 1.43 ± 0.2
	HSP 27	NM_001540	↘	↘ 1.30 ± 0.14
Cell surface proteins	ADAM 17	NM_003183	↗	↗ 2.03 ± 0.08
	ADAM 15	NM_003815	↗	↗ 2.30 ± 0.11
	67 LR	NM_002295	↗	↗ 2.03 ± 0.10
	PTK 7	NM_002227	↗	ND
	TGFβ-masking protein	AA134236	↘	ND
	Agrin/follistatin	AF016903	↘	↘ 1.33 ± 0.12
	Podocalixin	NM_005397	↘	ND
	Fibulin-1	NM_006487	↘	↘ 1.51 ± 0.07
	Caveolin 1	AF125348	↘	↘ 5.55 ± 0.18
	CD24	NM_013230	↘	↘ 1.25 ± 0.10
	Gnt IV	AB000616	↘	↘ 1.43 ± 0.14
	APR-3	NM_016085	↘	↘ 1.37 ± 0.07
	Hsp47/colligin	X61598	↗	↗ 1.33 ± 0.14
Survival mechanisms	HSP 70	M59828	↗	↗ 1.68 ± 0.28
	14.3.3. ε	U43430	↗	↗ 1.44 ± 0.09
	Bax-α	L22473	↘	↘ 1 ± 0.09
	MA-3	AA585361	↘	↘ 1.82 ± 0.05

Out of the 106 functionally characterized transcripts contained in the VGID data set, the 34 transcripts listed in the table played an important part in the integrative process, which led to the construction of a primary model of Ha-ras-dependent malignant transformation. The levels of expression indicate over-expression (upward pointing arrows) and under-expression (downward pointing arrows) in MCF7-ras as compared to MCF7. These expression patterns were qualitatively verified a posteriori by microarray expression analyses. ND corresponds to a detection failure.

Integrative analysis of the information embodied in the literature combined with the VGID and microarray results singled-out a set of 32 and 34 differentially expressed genes coding for proteins associated with broad cellular functions in the Ha-ras and E_2/TAM models respectively (Table 2, 3 and 4). Integrative analysis of the published information associated with the MCF7-ras data set indicated alteration in four different broad cellular mechanisms directly implicated in the Ha-ras-dependent transformation process (Table 2) such as (i) Cytoskeleton assembly, with the under-expression of actin-related complex 3 (Arp3), 27 kDa heat shock protein (Hsp27) and profilin, together with thymosin b4 and Leucocyte common Antigen Related protein (LAR) over- expression. (ii) Extra Cellular Matrix (ECM) dynamics, with the over-expression of ADAM 15 and 17, LAR, 67 Laminin Receptor (67LR), together with UDP-N-acetylglucosamine alpha1, 3-D-mannoside-beta1, 4-N-acetyl-glucosaminyltransferase (Gnt-IV), Fibulin-1 and Colligin/Hsp47 under-expression. (iii) Apoptosis regulation, with the over-expression of Hsp70 and 14.3.3.ε together with Bax-α and MA-3 under- expression. (iv) Cell growth stimulation, with activation of pathways dependent upon the p38 kinase (over-expression of rack-1, p38 delta and under-expression of Hsp27), Wnt (over- expression of Dickkopf-1 (DKK-1) and LAR) and inositol transduction signal (over-expression of the Calcium-calmodulin dependent protein kinase kinase β (CaMKKβ) and under-expression of profilin).

Table 2. Function and expression level of E_2 inducible genes

Broad functions	E_2 responsive genes	Accession number	VGID™ identification status	Microarray status (X fold expressed)	TAM inducible gene expression switching
PKC activation and Ca^{2+} store mobilization	DAGK ξ	U76549	↘	↘ 1.44 ± 0.02	↗ 2.03 ± 0.07
	Reticulocalbin	M26326	↘	↘ 1.72 ± 0.01	↗ 1.43 ± 0.03
	claudin 4	NM_001305	↘	↘ 1.74 ± 0.01	↗ 1.56 ± 0.05
	junction plakoglobin	AAH00441	↘	↘ 3.47 ± 0.07	-
	actin gamma	NM_001614	↘	↘ 1.29 ± 0.05	↗ 1.58 ± 0.02
	arp 2/3 complex, subunit 1B (41 kD)	AF006084	↘	↘ 1.60 ± 0.03	-
	beta catenin	X89448	↘	↘ 1.63 ± 0.04	-
	Hsp27	X54079	↗	↗ 1.90 ± 0.10	↘ 1.53 ± 0.01
ECM remodeling	USF2	Y07661	↘	↘ 1.44 ± 0.04	-
	HGFA I2	AB006534	↘	↘ 1.32 ± 0.03	↗ 1.31 ± 0.06
	pS2 protein	X00474	↗	↗ 4.93 ± 0.03	↘ 1.27 ± 0.02
	Cathepsin D	X05344	↗	↗ 3.16 ± 0.16	↘ 1.10 ± 0.05
Cell cycle progression	TGF-β	M60316	↘	↘ 4.09 ± 0.03	-
	c-myc oncogene	V00568	↗	↗ 1.57 ± 0.02	-
	Nm23-H2	L16785	↗	↗ 2.00 ± 0.02	-
	Cks1	NM_001826	↗	↗ 2.42 ± 0.05	-
	CDK2	X61622	↗	↗ 1.36 ± 0.05	-
	B-myb	X13293	↗	↗ 2.28 ± 0.02	-
	ASK	NM_006716	↗	↗ 2.06 ± 0.09	-
Catechols/quinone synthesis regulation	NAD(P)H menadione oxidoreductase	J03934	↘	↘ 1.30 ± 0.05	↗ 1.28 ± 0.01

Broad functions	E_2 responsive genes	Accession number	VGID™ identification status	Microarray status (X fold expressed)	TAM inducible gene expression switching
	UDP-glucuronosyltrans-ferase	M57951	↘	↘ 1.20 ± 0.10	-
	thiol specific antioxidant	Z22548	↘	↘ 1.56 ± 0.02	↗ 1.18 ± 0.04
	NADH dehydrogenase ubiquinone	NM_005006	↗	↗ 1.91 ± 0.09	↘ 1.33 ± 0.01.

The levels of expression indicate over-expression (upwards arrows) and under-expression (downwards arrows). These expression patterns were qualitatively and quantitatively verified by microarray expression analyses. Relative expression levels are indicated by arrows and x-fold. The last column indicates the genes whose expression is reverse by TAM treatment in MCF7 cells. In the "TAM inducible gene expression switching" column, "-" indicates that no switching effects were experimentally observed. Data for all VGID identified genes can be watch at this web site adress: http://perso.club-internet.fr/fgadal.

Integrative analysis of the published information associated with the E_2/TAM data set indicated that E_2 modulated the expression patterns of 23 genes (Table 3) involved in (i) Anchors and junction remodelling, with the under-expression of keratins 8 and 18, claudin 4, junction plakoglobin, actine γ, arp 2/3 complex and catenin β together with Hsp27 over-expression. (ii) ECM degradation, with the under-expression of USF2 and HGFA I2 together with pS2 and Cathepsin D over-expression. (iii) Cell cycle progression, including G1/S check point and S-phase regulation, with the over-expression of c-myc, NM23H2, Cks1, CDK2, B-myb and ASK together with TGFβ under-expression. (iiii) The synthesis of genotoxic metabolites, with the under-expression of NAD(P)H menadione oxidoreductase, UDP-glucuronosyltransferase and thiol specific antioxidant together with NADH dehydrogenase ubiquinone over-expression.

Table 3. Function and expression level of TAM responsive genes

Broad functions.	TAM responsive genes.	Accession number	VGID™ identification status.	Microarray status (X fold expressed).
Cytoskeletal remodeling.	profilin	J03191	↗	↗1.32 ± 0.05
Catechols/quinone synthesis regulation.	HSD17 B4	NM_000414	↗	↗1.24 ± 0.02
DNA repair	DDB-2	U18300	↘	↘1.27 ± 0.04
	XR-CC1	L34079	↘	↘1.44 ± 0.01
Active ER constitution	Hsp90	X15183	↘	↘1.37 ± 0.06
	immunophilin	M88279	↘	0
	REA	AF150962	↗	↗1.22 ± 0.02
Mitogenic pathway	ERK1	X60188	↗	↗1.49 ± 0.01
Growth factor.	TGF-α	AH003012	↘	↘2.14 ± 0.01

The levels of expression indicate over-expression (upwards arrows) and under-expression (downwards arrows). These expression patterns were qualitatively and quantitatively verified by microarray expression analyses. In the "microarrays status" column, "0" indicates failure to detect differential expression. Relative expression levels are indicated by arrows and x-fold. Data for all VGID identified genes can be watch at this web site adress: http://perso.club-internet.fr/fgadal.

In tumor cell, these four mechanisms are associated with the acquisition of a motile and invasive phenotype. TAM partly reversed the E_2-induced differential expression patterns and consequently restored most of the biological functions deregulated by E_2 (Table 3) except the mechanisms associated with cell cycle progression. Furthermore, we found that TAM affects the expression of 9 additional genes (Table 4) associated with: cytoskeletal remodelling (profilin), DNA repair (DDB-2 and XR-CC1), active estrogen receptor formation (Hsp90, immunophilin and REA) and growth factor synthesis and mitogenic pathways (ERK1 and TGFα).

The major advantages provided by integrative analyses reside in the possibility to decypher the links between the VGID isolated transcripts and the biological entities identified through the Bio-path analysis (neighboring studies). The resulting relational graph permits to reconstruct the functional mechanisms implemented in the MCF7 cancer cell in response to the activation of the Ha-ras oncogene and to E_2/TAM treatments. In this context, integrative analysis of the effects of E_2 treatment on the MCF7 cell line shows how E_2, in our experimental conditions, may induce, for example, cell cycle progression (Fig. 9) and genotoxic effects through the formation of estrogens-derived quinones (Fig. 10).

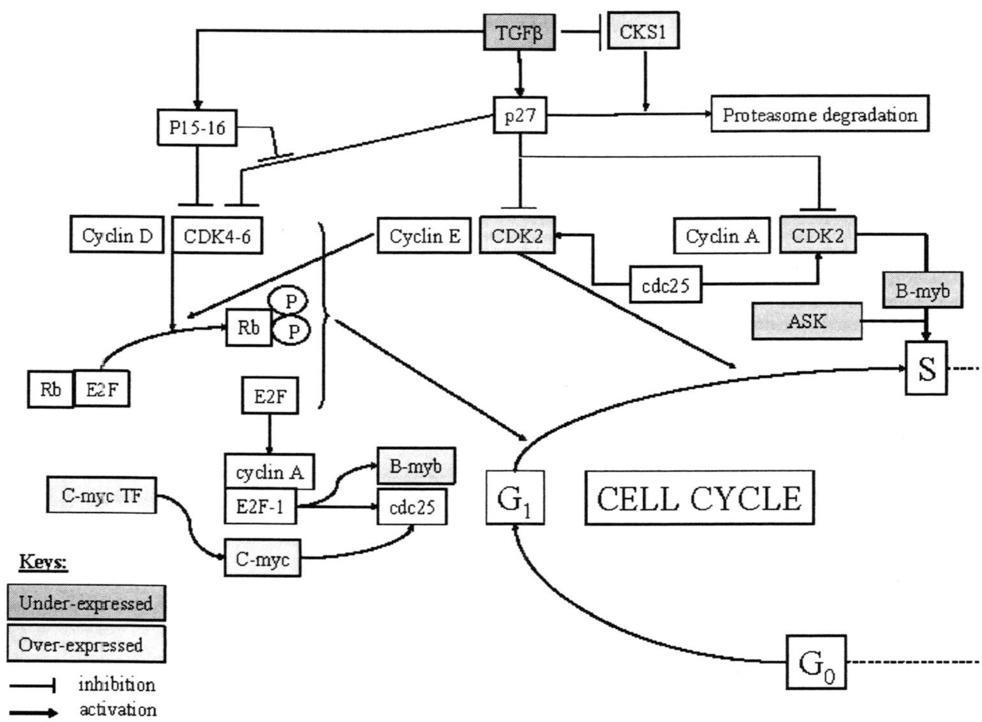

Figure 9. Evidence of cell cycle progression effects induced by E_2 treatment in MCF7 cells. The diagram was derived from the integration of published information associated with the genes under- and over-expressed in MCF7 cells in response to E_2. Boxes with plain color represent genes found to be differentially expressed using the VGID process and confirmed by cDNA microarrays analysis.

With respect to the Ha-ras model, the relational graph presented on figure 11 depicts the main cellular mechanisms suggested as the basis for Ha-ras dependent tumorigenic transformation of the MCF7 breast epithelial cell line. The diagram shows the consequences of the activation of the Ha-ras oncogene which, via a direct interaction with PLCε, appears to promote tumor progression through complex mechanisms leading to apoptosis down regulation, cell cycle progression deregulation, and ECM and cytoskeleton modifications. In addition, this diagram presents the biological entities associated with the transcripts isolated using the VGID process, hence demonstrating the advantages of the integrativeanalysis. Many of these entities, undetected as over or under-expressed by VGID, were validated as significantly differentially expressed by microarray analyses, thus demonstrating the validity of the model embodied in this diagram.

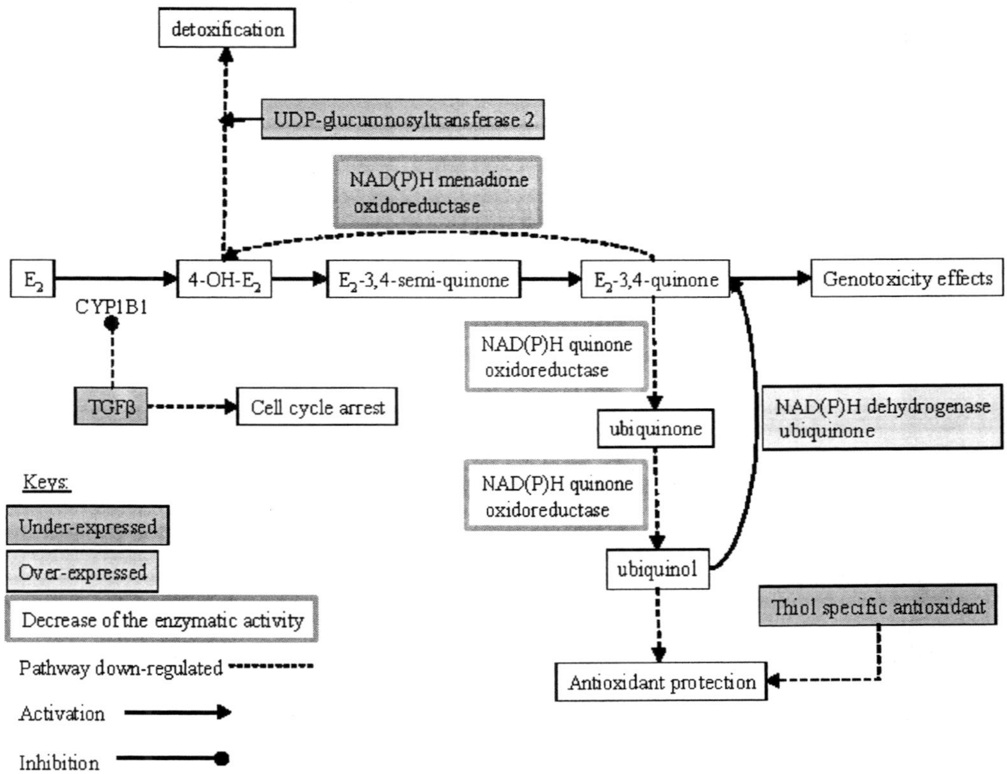

Figure 10. Evidence of E_2 dependent genotoxic effects in MCF7 cells. The diagram was derived from the integration of published information associated with the genes under- and over-expressed in MCF7 cells in response to E_2. Boxes with plain color represent genes found to be differentially expressed using the VGID process and confirmed by cDNA microarrays analysis.

Discussion

The VGID process allows the isolation of cDNA clones representing genes differentially expressed within two RNA populations while microarray analysis allowed to independently test the expression patterns of selected genes. In the present study, the originality of our analytical approach resides in the combination of subtractive hybridization, cDNA microarray and data integration. We combined subtractive hybridization and cDNA microarray to identify genes associated with the expression of the Ha-ras oncogene and by E_2 and/or TAM treatment in the MCF7 cell-line (for entire data, see web page at http:// perso.club-internet.fr/fgadal). This technology is rapid (hybridization takes place within 20 h), sensitive (detection of rare cDNA species with low differential expression level) and economical (small amounts of mRNA are needed for cDNA library synthesis). In this context, microarrays only allow assessment of the expression patterns of selected genes. In the present case, we decided not to introduce an analytical bias through the a priori selection of genes to be investigated. We thought it more appropriate to let the cells `tell us' what to investigate. This precluded the use of probes and therefore the utilization of microarrays. We therefore had to devise an efficient and effective means to access unidentified differentially expressed sequences, hence the use of VGID followed by microarray based verification. We then carried out computer-assisted data integration to achieve an understanding of the physiological mechanisms potentially affected by the genes confirmed to be differentially expressed. Microarray analysis confirmed both the patterns and levels of differential expression of the majority (90% of the entire data) of the genes identified as differentially expressed through the utilization of VGID.

Extensive data have been gathered over the years concerning the cellular mechanisms associated with tumors and tumor progression. However, this previous and widely dispersed work encompasses numerous genes, gene products as well as metabolic and physiological processes analyzed in a wide variety of contexts. While a substantial proportion of this work has been reduced to discrete pathways, most of the data remain functionally unconnected and expression data from higher eukaryotes have so far resisted integration into biologically coherent models. We have reported the first successful large scale integration of mammalian experimental gene expression data together with extensive physiological information extracted from public literature databases, and describe a theoretical biological model, validated *in vitro* (8), which, by exposing regulatory and cross-talk interactions associated with Ha-ras-dependent transformation, attempts to explain the mechanisms implemented in this complex pathological process.

In the work presented here, activity modulations of the enzymes involved in the mechanisms uncovered and their regulations were not directly analyzed. In spite of this imitation, the integrative analytical methods reported here appear particularly powerful for generating directly testable physiological models suggesting detailed interactive networks functionally associated with complex biological phenomena. A global understanding of internal cellular mechanisms alterations is extremely important in predicting complex cellular behavior and suggesting new hypotheses for the determination of therapeutic targets and modes of therapeutic intervention. We expect that, as the maturation of proteomics technologies proceeds, there will be a significant increase in he availability of pertinent and unambiguous protein data. Integrative approaches, such as that described here, will then gain in accuracy and breadth of utilization.

References

[1] Ozer,E., Sis,B., Ozen,E., Sakizli,M., Canda,T. and Sarioglu,S. (2000) BRCA1, C-erbB-2 and H-ras gene expressions in young women with breast cancer. An immunohistochemical study. *Appl. Immunohistochem. Mol. Morphol.*, 8, 12-18.

[2] Soule HD, McGrath CM 1980 Estrogen responsive proliferation of clonal human breast carcinoma cells in athymic mice. *Cancer Letters* 10:177-189

[3] Lippman ME, Bolan G, Huff K 1975 Human breast cancer responsive to androgen in long term tissue culture. *Nature* 258:339-341.

[4] Colditz GA 1998 Relationship between estrogen levels, use of hormone replacement therapy, and breast cancer. *Journal of the National Cancer Institute* 90:814-823

[5] Soule HD, Vazguez J, Long A, Albert S, Brennan M 1973 A human cell line from a pleural effusion derived from a breast carcinoma. *Journal of the National Cancer Institute* 51:1409-1416

[6] Sommers CL, Papageorge A, Wilding G, Gelmann EP 1990 Growth properties and tumorigenesis of MCF-7 cells transfected with isogenic mutants of rasH. *Cancer Research* 50: 67-71

[7] Kasid,A., Lippman,M.E., Papageorge,A.G., Lowy,D.R. and Gelmann,E.P. (1985) Transfection of v-rasH DNA into MCF-7 human breast cancer cells bypasses dependence on estrogen for tumorigenicity. Science, 228, 725-728.

[8] Gadal F, Bozic C, Pillot-Brochet C, Malinge S, Wagner S, Le Cam A, Buffat L, Crépin M, Iris F 2003 Integrated transcriptome analysis of the cellular mechanisms associated with Ha-ras-dependent malignant transformation of the human breast epithelial MCF7 cell line. *Nucleic Acids Research* 31:5789-5804

[9] Ermolaeva,O., Rastogi,M., Pruitt,K.D., Schuler,G.D., Bittner,M.L., Chen,Y., Simon,R., Meltzer,P., Trent,J.M. and Boguski,M.S. (1998) Data management and analysis for gene expression arrays. *Nature Genet.*, 20, 19-23.

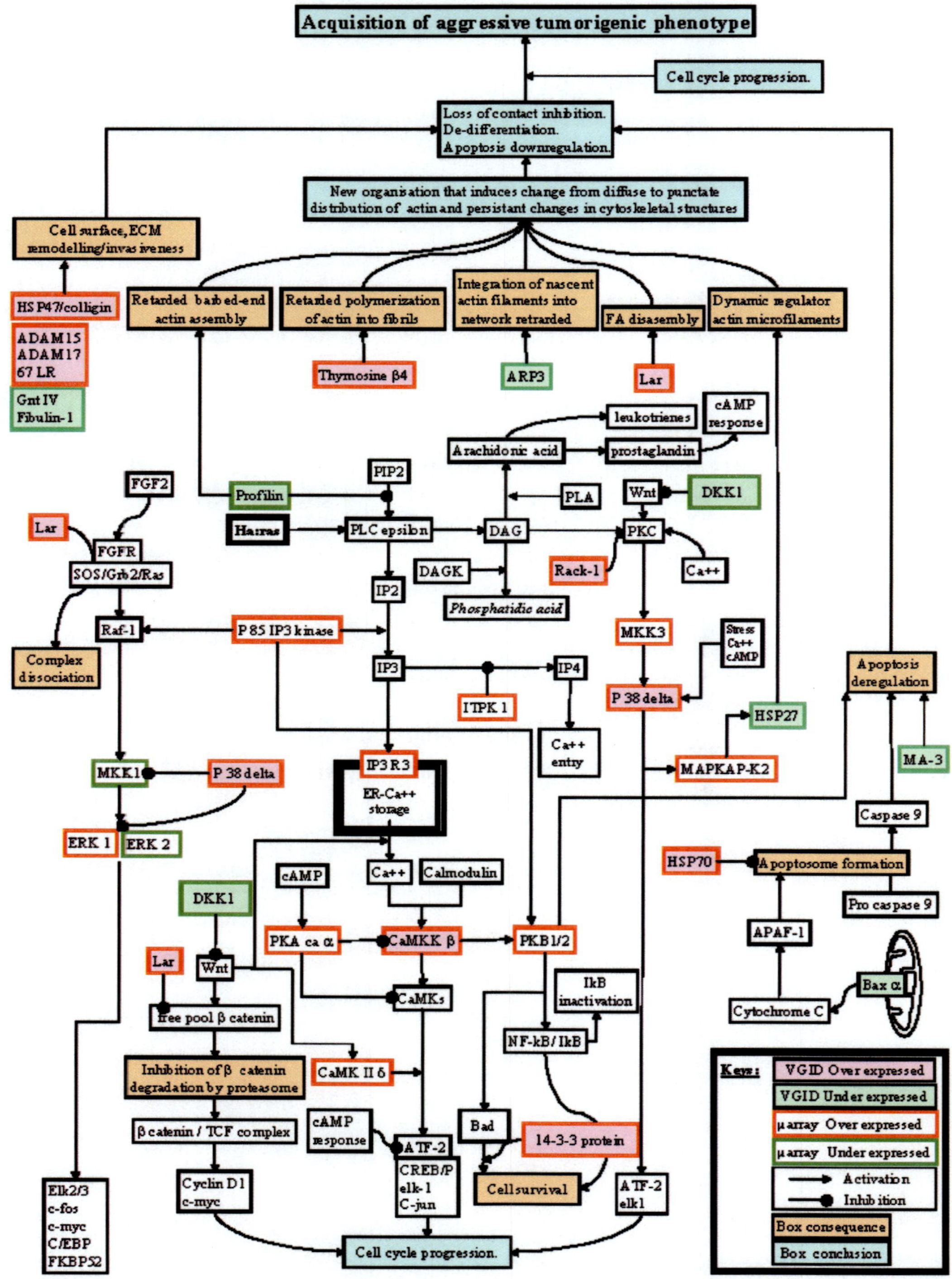

Figure 11. Experimentally testable biological model derived from the integration of published information associated with the genes under- and over-expressed in MCF7-ras cells.

In: Bioinformatics: New Research
Editor: Peter V. Yan, pp. 101-126
ISBN 1-59454-242-2

Chapter V

Computed Energetics of Macromolecules. Part I: Identification of the Functional Residues in Spatial Structures of Proteins and RNA

Ivan Y. Torshin[*1, 2]
[1]Federal Science Center (VEI), Moscow, Russia
[2]Bioinformatics Consulting, LLC, Moscow, Russia

Abstract

Unified models for analysis of structure-function relationship are essential for post-genomic biology, biochemistry and biophysics. Very often, in biological macromolecules only some region of the native molecule is functionally important. Molecular mechanics study presented here shows that many of the important functional residues in proteins and ribozymes are characterized by unusual energy values. The results show that functional regions in macromolecules can be accurately predicted using spatial structure as the only input and with no additional biochemical or sequence information. These predictions appear to be in good agreement with the available biochemical data.

Color graphics are presented at the end of the chapter.

Introduction

The principal aim of a "post-genomic" biology is elucidation of the structures, functions and biochemical properties of the gene products in a genome. In order to interpret and analyze such an enormous array of information, some kind of unified models of the proteins and DNA/RNA function are essential. A unified model is essential as the current descriptions of

[*] E-mail: tiy135@yahoo.com.

protein/RNA structure and function were crafted for individual proteins/RNA. Structural genomics initiatives [1] are doing their important part in the uniform characterization of the protein structures and, to some extent, of the protein function. However, structural genomics initiatives *per se* cannot be an ultimate solution to the problem of establishing gene functions because of, primarily, the two main reasons: 1. various levels of defining what a "function" is and 2. variety of the functional macromolecules.

First of all, it is important to recognize that functional characterization can and ought to be done on several levels. A particular gene product can be characterized by its genetic functions, physiological functions, cellular functions, biochemical functions and biophysical functions [2]. Spatial structure- which is the main output of a structural genomics project rarely can unequivocally refer to genetic, physiological or cellular function. These types of function are addressed by the high-throughput experimental and theoretical methods of the functional genomics [3]. Nevertheless, solving a structure of a protein can provide a clue for elucidating biochemical and biophysical functions: there are examples in structural genomics when having a structure suggested a function for previously uncharacterized protein like major cold shock protein, ZK6523 and other examples [2].

Secondly, proteins are not the only functional molecules produced from genes. For example, ribozymes are functionally diverse RNA molecules with intrinsic catalytic activity [4]. Although known natural ribozymes catalyze phosphodiester-transfer chemistry, there are RNA molecules that catalyze formation of nucleotide from sugar and base [5], synthesize amide bonds [6-7] and even synthesize acyl-coenzyme A [8]. The naturally occurring ribozymes are studied and a number of structures of the ribozymes have been solved (summarized in [9]).

An idea of a unifying approach to defining functions of the gene products was described as "function grid" [2]. In this grid-like data structure "function" (for example, of a protein) is defined through molecular interactions: each protein (it could be RNA as well) is associated with a vector consisting of probabilities to binding to various ligands. Functional similarity between any pair of proteins can be then defined as the cosine of the angle between the two vectors. It is quite clear that probabilities in each vector can be either determined experimentally or computed. In particular, if binding site(s) in a protein or other macromolecule is known or can be reliably predicted, then possibilities of interaction with the known cellular metabolites and other biological molecules can be analyzed.

The present work presents a new physico-chemical model of bio-macromolecular function which can to a great degree assist functional annotation of otherwise completely uncharacterized proteins. This model attempts to bring together the biophysical, biochemical and, to some extent, cellular definitions of "function". The method is based on the molecular mechanics calculations and it has been successfully applied to proteins [10, 11] as well as ribozymes and other RNAs [9, 11, 12]. The idea of this method has been borrowed from general physical chemistry. Transition state theory is an elaborated physico-chemical concept that provides a number of valuable explanations for homogenous, heterogeneous and enzymatic catalysis. In particular, application of the theory to enzymes (that is, proteins with catalytic sites) suggests that the energetic barrier is likely to be reduced by the ground state destabilization. Electrostatic effects would provide an important contribution to enzyme catalysis [13]. These general considerations are confirmed by a number of theoretical and biochemical studies of individual enzymes [14-20] and can be summarized as follows: relative physico-chemical properties of the functional residues of the enzymes are very distinct from the other residues in a molecule. These "relative properties" can be energetical contributions [19] or geometries of the theoretical titration curves [20].

Now, the above postulate forms the central idea of the method under discussion: if some relative physico-chemical property can be calculated from a spatial structure (which can be often modelled from sequence: as in [21], for example), then the residues involved in catalytic site can be identified. As the research shows, the postulate of the unique physical chemistry of the functional residues can be applied not only to enzymes but also to other functional types of proteins ([19] and the present study). In the present study, the physical chemistry of the individual residues was characterized using relative energy values. The relative energy values of the individual residues were analyzed in the known spatial structures of proteins and ribozymes. The results suggest that functional residues can often be accurately predicted if a structure of a protein or a ribozyme (or a model thereof) is available. Such predictions will be useful during functional genomic annotation.

Concerning the computational techniques and the design of the present study: although electrostatic interactions are important for enzyme function and protein stability [13, 18, 19], Van der Waals interactions should not be neglected in calculating the contribution of individual amino acids or nucleotides to the stability of the whole molecule. Therefore, the molecular mechanics and not so-called "continuum electrostatics" calculations were used. The full molecular mechanics potential that included bonding, angular, torsional and non-bonding (electrostatic and Van der Waals) energy terms has been applied for analysis of the energetic properties of the residues in the known spatial structures of proteins and ribozymes. Molecular mechanics calculations were performed using ECMMS library of computational routines specifically developed by the author for the research purposes. The calculations were performed using "multiple trajectories" technique [22, 23] that is more likely to produce models closer to experimental structures than simply an energy minimization or a singular long trajectory of molecular dynamics. The residues with the most unusual relative energies (either "most stabilizing" or "most destabilizing") were compared with the published biochemical data on the known functional residues of the analyzed proteins ([24-54]) and ribozymes ([55-62]) (summarized in the Tables 1 and 2).

Materials and Methods

Protein and RNA Structures

The structures of the ribozymes and proteins of various structure and sizes were taken from PDB [63]. The data on the known functional residues in proteins are summarized in the Table 1, on the functional nucleotides in ribozymes in the Table 2. Although the protein structures were selected in accordance with the availability of the biochemical characterization of the functional residues, the set in the Table 1 is, essentially, a random set of proteins. At the same time, as only few of the ribozyme structures were solved, almost all of them are listed in the Table 2.

Table 1. Proteins in this study. Functional residues are those essential for the primary function of the protein (for enzymes, catalytic and substrate-binding residues; ligand-binding residues or those of the protein-protein interfaces for the rest of the proteins). In some proteins, there are several important functional sites (like residues of the AB interface in phosphoglycerate mutase 1 or Ca-binding site in elastase); these sites are indicated in bold font. Fold classes (general protein architectures) were assigned using SCOP into three-main categories: aa, all-alpha, bb, all-beta and ab: mixed alpha/ beta folds. The proteins are ordered alphabetically

Protein	PDB, chain	Fold class	size	biochemistry	known functional residues (from biochemical and structural studies)	
					residues	reference(s)
ABP	1abf	ab	306	arabinose binding	K10 Q11 E14 W16 F17 E20 D89 D90 R151 N205 N232	[26]
APase	1alkA	ab	449	enzyme alkaline phosphatase	D51 D101 S102 D153 R166 E322 E327 K328 H331 D369 H370 H372 H412; AB: 10 16-39 55-63 76 81-89 94-99 112-114 124 129 381-384 392-398 404-407 411-418 425-440	[27]
Barnase	1b27A	ab	110	enzyme nuclease	K27 K49 D54 R59 E60 K66 R69 E73 R83 R87 H102	[28]
barstar	1b27d	ab	91	PP	D33 D36 D40 E77 E81	[28]
calbindin	3icb	aa	75	Ca-binding	E17 D19 E26 E27 D54 N56 D58 E60 E65	[81]
Cellulase E2	1tml	ab	286	enzyme cellulase	R78 D79 D117 H159 N190 R221 R237 K259 D263 D265	[30][24]
CROprotein	3croL	aa	65	DNA-binding	R10 Q17 K27 Q28 Q29 Q32 K40 R41 P42 R43	[31]
Cu SOD	1spdA	bb	159	enzyme superoxide dismutase	H47 H49 H64 H72 R80 H81 D84 R116 H121	[32][24]
Cytochrome P450	1akd	aa	414	hem-binding	F87 Y96 P100 T101 Q108 R112 V119 L244-L250 D251 T252-F256 L294-R299 Q322 T349-G351 H355-G359 A363 I395 V396; K:E84,E91,E94,Y96;	[33] [34]
Dhfr	1rf7	ab	159	enzyme dihydrofolate reductase	E17 D27 L28 F31 K32 T35 R44 R52 P55 R57 Y111 T113 H114	[35][24]
Elastase	1elf	bb	240	enzyme elastase	H43 H60 C61 L149 N155 C199 Q200 G201 D202; Ca: R24 E74-N81 E84 Y86	[36]
Fe SOD	1isbA	ab	192	enzyme superoxide dismutase	H26 H73 D156 H160	[37]
i-fabp	2ifb	bb	131	fatty-acid binding	Y14-M18 I23 F55 V60-F62 Y70-D74 W82 F93 R106 Y117	[38]
LDH	1ldnA	ab	330	enzyme lactate dehydro-genase	I26-V31 D52 C95-N99 R106 I120 A136 N138 S161 R169 H193 A237 T247 I251	[39]
l-fabp	1lfo	bb	128	fatty-acid binding	F15 L28-I35 E40 I41 L50 I52-K57 F63 T73 M74 T93-F95 T102 I109 M113 R122	[40]
m-fabp	1hmt	bb	132	fatty-acid binding	F16 M20-L23 T29 A33 P38 T53 F57-T60 A75-D76 L115 R126-Y128	[41]
Myoglobin	1a6g	aa	151	hem-binding	L32 K42 F43 R45 H64 V68 L72 L89 S92 H93 H97 I99 Y103 L104 I107 F138	[42]
parvalbumin	1rtp1	aa	109	Ca-binding	D51 D53 S55 E59 E62 D90 D92 D94 E101	[43]
Pgm	4pgmA	ab	246	enzyme phosphoglycerate mutase 1	R7-N14 T20 R59 E86 K97 R113 H181; AB: D50 K56 E69 K70 D72 R80 E135 R136 K174	[44][25]

Protein	PDB, chain	Fold class	size	biochemistry	known functional residues (from biochemical and structural studies)	
					residues	reference(s)
Pla2	1pir	aa	124	enzyme phospholipase A2	Y28 G30 G32 R43 E46 H48 D49 N50 Y52 R53 D54 K56 N79 E92Q N97 R100 N101 C105	[45-47]
Pmi	1pmi	bb	440	enzyme phosphomannose isomerase	E48 K100 H113 K136 E138 H285 E294 R304	[48]
Ras protein	2q21	ab	171	PP	Q25 E31 D33 P34 I36 E37 D38 Y40 R41 D54 Q61 E62 E63 Y64 M67 K88; ATP: 13-18 28 117-119 145-147	[49]
Snase	1sta	bb	151	enzyme staphylococcal nuclease	D19 D21 R35 L36 L38 V39 D40 E43 K49 D83 K84 R87 Y113 Y115 N118	[50-53]
TPI	5timA	ab	250	enzyme triosephosphate isomerase	N11 K13 H95 E167 G211 S213; AB: 11-18, 44-48, 65-86, 95-102	[24][25] [54]

Table 2. The known functional nucleotides in the ribozymes. The entries are ordered according to the ribozyme size. nr, number of residues in the PDB file; clv: cleavage site. Residue numeration of the original papers was preserved

PDB	Data	RNA type	nr	active site	substrate-binding	Mg-binding	Ref
1e4pA	NMR	hairpin	24	A7,G8,C18,G19, clv:G5,A6	-	-	[55]
1ldz_	NMR	leadzyme	30	C6,G7,G9,C10,G23, G24,A25	-	-	[56]
1hmhA	Xray	Hammerhead	34	G10.1,G5,G8,A14	-	A9,A13,A14	[57]
300dA	Xray	Hammerhead	41	G5,A6,U16.1,C3	-	G10.1,A9,U7,C1.2	[58]
1m5kB	Xray	Hairpin	92	G8,A9,A10,A24,A38 G21,A22,A23,C25	-	-	[59]
1cx0B	Xray	HDVribozyme	94	U120,C122,G125,G138,G139, G140	-	-	[60]
1grzA	Xray	Group I intron	246	A207,C208,A261,A306	-	-	[61]
1fg0A	Xray	23S ribosomal subunit	496	G2102,G2482,A2485,A2486, G2588,U2619, U2620	C2542, U2589, U2590, C2608, G2618	-	[62]

Molecular Modeling

A description of the ECMMS library and the particular procedure used for energy calculations are given below. The calculations used "swarm" or "multiple trajectories" technique [22, 23]. Calculations were made with or without hetero-atoms. Either explicit or implicit solvent modelling was used. Minimization (100 steps, conjugate gradients) was intermingled by short (1ps) trajectories of molecular dynamics (MD) to achieve a stable energy minimum [23]. Using different sets of initial velocities, 10 parallel trajectories of this minimization procedure were made, then the 10 resulting structures were averaged and the average structure was minimized.

ECMMS ("Energy Calculator for Macro-Molecular Structures") is a computational library of routines for molecular mechanics calculations. The entire library is written in

Borland/FreePascal. The main idea behind ECMMS is the possibility to make computationally efficient executables for highly specialized types of molecular mechanics calculations (an example of source code for such an executable is given below). Composing computationally efficient and specialized executables (that is, standalone applications) for a particular research project is distinct from more generic scripting approach as implemented in ICM [64] or TINKER [65] and in many other widely known commercial programs. Another distinctive feature of ECMMS strategy is extreme simplicity of the interface of the final executable which also improves computational efficiency of the calculations.

Currently, ECMMS uses UFF+AMBER calculation scheme [66-70]. The reason for combining UFF and AMBER was largely due to extraordinary high accuracy of UFF field in calculations on bond and angle terms. The UFF (Universal Force Field) is capable of reproducing most structural features across the Mendeleev's periodic table with errors less than 0.1 angstrom in bond distances and 5-10 degrees in angle bend [70]. At the same time, AMBER (Assisted Model Building with Energy Refinement) [66] is a force field specifically developed for proteins and nucleic acids. AMBER contains values of partial atomic charges obtained from quantum mechanics calculations. These charge values are more physically plausible than the use of partial charges in UFF scheme [68, 69, 71].

ECCMS allows construction of computationally efficient executables. For example, calculations for alkaline phosphatase, a large 450-residue protein, took less than 10 minutes on a 3Ghz PC computer (using implicit solvent modeling). The procedural "script", designed for the purposes of the present study is shown below. The script as presented takes into account (though implicitly) both configurational and solvation entropy.

```
program ComputedEnergeticsOfMacromolecules;
uses ecmms;
begin
   setnucleic(RNA); //ribozymes;
   load_pdb(paramstr(1));
   chn:=1;
   if chaintype[chn]=nucleic then linknucleicchainn(_chn[chn], _resls[chn].i1,_resls[chn].i2);
   if chaintype[chn]=protein then linkproteinchain(_chn[chn], _resls[chn].i1,_resls[chn].i2);

//initial modeling
   buildhydrogens(_chn[chn]);
   setactive(1,numberofatoms);
   seteterms("bonding bending torsional non-bonding");
   cjmin(100);
//multiple trajectories and averaging
   setsolvation(ImplicitScheme);
   storexyz(0); //stores current coordinates in cash(0)
   for j:=1 to 10 do
     begin
       restorexyz(0);
       moldy("time=1ps; T=300K"); //molecular dynamics on cash(0)
       cjmin(100);
       storexyz(j); // store coordinates in cash(j)
```

```
    end;
  avrgmol(1,10,11); //averaging models 1-10 to cash(11)
  restorexyz(11); //copy from cash(11) to "current" (i.e., cash(0))
  cjmin(20);
//Calculating energy per-residue
  for i:=_resls[chn].i1+1 to _resls[chn].i2-1 do E_residue(i);
  WriteEnergyProfile(paramstr(2)+'.pro');
  WriteEnergyHistogram(paramstr(2));
end.
```

Identification of the Most Stabilizing and Most Destabilizing Residues

The contributions of individual residues to stability were calculated using the full molecular mechanics potential UFF+AMBER [66, 70] as already mentioned. The energy values for each individual base were obtained using the "E_residue" procedure of ECMMS, then the energy histograms (such as in Figures 1&2) were drawn. The configurational component of the entropy was taken into account by using the parallel trajectories of molecular dynamics simulations with the subsequent averaging of the structures (as shown above). The solvation component was taken into account either implicitly or explicitly. Implicit treatment has included using electrostatic screening potential [72-74] and dielectric constant of 4.0 for both proteins and RNA. For RNA, the screening potential was supplemented by reduced net charges on phosphate groups [73] to imitate the effects of the counter-ion screening. In proteins, an empirical energy cut-offs of $0.4E_{max}$ or $0.4E_{min}$ (0.4 of the maximal/minimal per-residue energy for the molecule) were used for selecting the residues with unusual (highest or lowest) calculated energies. In RNA, the empirical cut-off for selecting the "least stabilizing" nucleotides was $0.9E_{max.}$

Results

Results of the energy calculations were analyzed and present here as "energy profiles" and "energy histograms" (such as shown in Figure 1). It can be seen that "energy profile" represent the per-residue energy values along the sequence (Figure 1a) while in an "energy histogram" the residues were sorted according to the energy values (Figure 1b). A histogram is considerably more convenient for selection of the most stabilizing and the most destabilizing residues both in proteins and RNA. There are two important differences between protein and RNA histograms. The first: in proteins there are most stabilizing as well as most destabilizing residues. In RNA calculations show only the stabilizing residues (using explicit solvent modeling). The second: using implicit solvent modeling in proteins leads to remarkable differentiation of the per-residue energies (Figure 1b). In RNA the energy differences were less pronounced when using implicit solvent (Figure 2c). However, both in proteins and RNA using the implicit solvent modeling allowed rather accurate identification of the known functional sites. In proteins of very different biochemistry and structure (enzymes, proteins involved in protein-protein interactions, metal, DNA-, hem- and fatty-acid binding proteins), 72% of the topmost destabilizing residues (Table 3, on average) and 64% of the topmost stabilizing residues (Table 4, on average) were either known functional residues or were spatially close to the known functional site regions. Calculations also suggest that ligand binding stabilizes the protein structure by reducing destabilization of the most destabilizing residues (Table 5). The results of calculations on RNA structures show that on average for the set of ribozymes, 70% of the least stabilizing nucleotides were either known to be functional or were less than 4.0 angstrom from the known functional residues (Table 6).

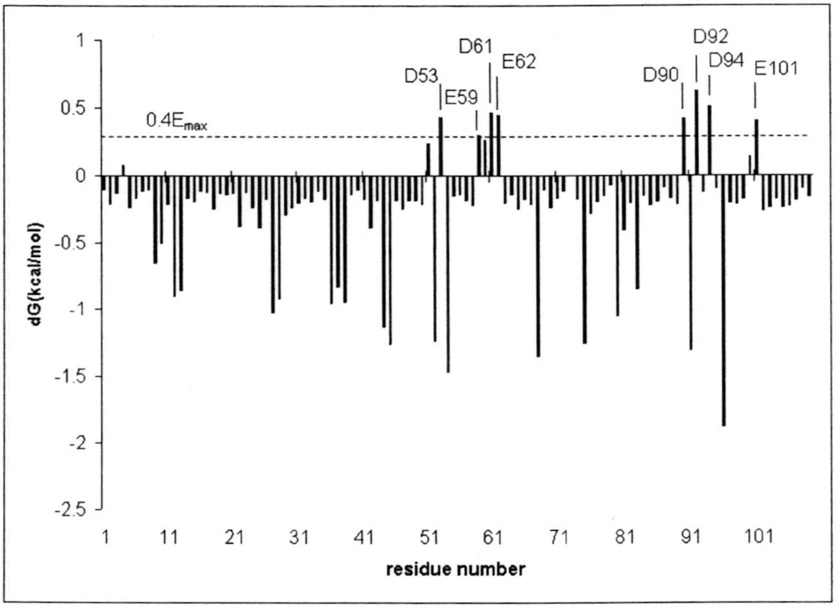

Figure 1a

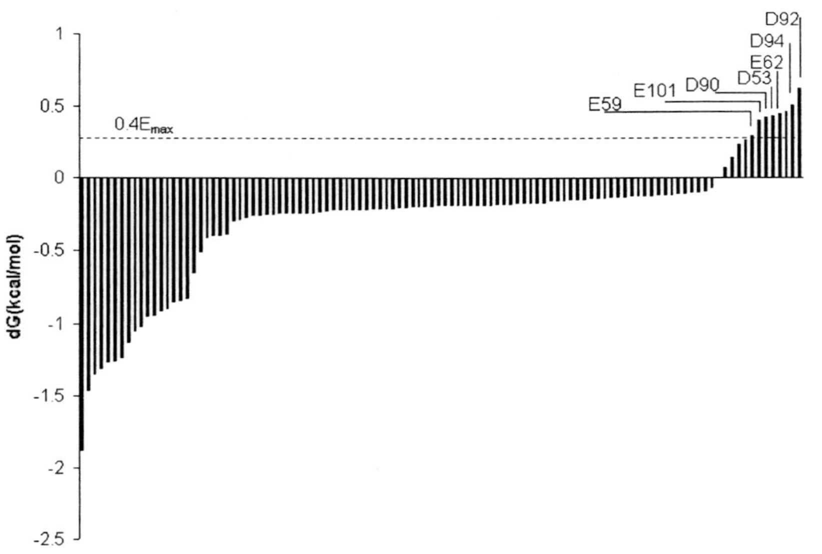

Figure 1b

Figure 1. Most destabilizing residues in proteins, on the example of parvalbumin. The most stabilizing residues were analyzed in the same way as described in the 1st part. a) Energy profile (energy-per-residue vs. residue sequence number). PDB numbering is preserved. An approximate location of the 0.4Emax level is shown (dotted line). b) Energy histogram (energies are ordered from the highest on the right to the lowest on the left). Energy histogram allows to select the 8 residues that were defined as "the most destabilizing". In the protein there are 108 residues totally, 22 negatively charged and 19 positively charged. Locations of the known functional residues in the energy histogram are indicated. c) Spatial structure of PDB 1rtp (parvalbumin). C-alpha trace, the known functional residues (wireframe), Ca-ions (spheres) are shown. Most destabilizing residues are marked with yellow. It can be seen that all of the most destabilizing residues in this protein were located in the Ca-binding regions and all of the most destabilizing residues (Asp53, Glu59, Glu62, Asp90, Asp92, Asp94 and Glu101) with the exception of Asp61 are known to be functionally important. Out of the known functional residues, only Ser55 was not the most destabilizing. The known functional Asp51 slightly missed the 0.4Emax cutoff (see Figure 1b). None of the most destabilizing residues was a false positive. This slide of the figure was prepared with WebLab viewer (http://www.msi.com).

Table 3. Most destabilizing residues in the three-dimensional structures of the proteins. The order of the proteins is the same as in the Table 1

Protein	Residues with known function	residues adjacent to the functional site	False positives (no known function)	% efficiency 1	% efficiency 2
ABP	E14 E20 D89	E13 D178 D235	P165 D184 P277	67	33
APase	R166 H331 H370 H372 H412; AB: H86 K92 H129	K127 K167	-	100	80
barnase	R59 K66 R69 H102	A46 P47	S38 K39	75	50
barstar	D33 D36 D40 E77 E81	E47	E58 E65	75	63
calbindin	E17 D19 E27 D54 D58 E60	-	E11 E51	75	75
Cellulase E2	D79 D117 D263	D156 E230 D233	D99 E132 E135	67	33
CRO protein	R10 K27 K40 R41 R43	R9 K8	K14	90	63
Cu SOD	H47 H49 H64 H72 D84 H121	E78 E122 D125	D77	90	60
Cytochrome P450	K: E84 E91	E152 D153 E156	D188 E195 E198 D202	57	11
Dhfr	P55	P25	P66 D87 P89 P105 E120	35	14
Elastase	R24 H75	R226	H95 R131 R151 H208	43	35
Fe SOD	H26 H73 H160	H30 H31	-	100	60
i-fabp	-	G22 G44 G65 A69 G75	K29 G110	67	0
Ldh	N138	E55 D82 D84 E104 E122	E221	85	14
l-fabp	G32 G55 S56	G23 G76 T94	P25 G87	75	38
m-fabp	P38 N59	K37 H54 T56 G99 Q100 T121	G88 G111	80	20
myoglobin	K42 R45 H64 H97	K63 K87 K96 K98	K16 H119	80	50
Parvalbumin	D53 E59 E62 D90 D92 D94 E101	D61	-	100	90
Pgm	R7 H8 K97 R113 H181 AB:K56 R80	R114 R186	-	100	78
Pla2	G30 G32	G33	P14 H17 L64 N67	43	35
Pmi	H113 E138 H285 E294	D132 D283 D300	D133 D352 E357	70	40
Ras protein	E31 D33 P34 D38 E63	D30 D57	D105 V109	78	56
Snase	K84	K16 H46 K48 K78 K116	K70 K127 K134	67	11
TPI	K13 H47 H95 K197	-	H35,H57,K152	57	57
Total percentages (average for the set)				72%	42%

Table 4. The most stabilizing residues in the three-dimensional structures of the proteins. The order of the proteins is the same as in the Table 1

Protein	Residues with known function	residues adjacent to the functional site	False positives (no known function)	% efficiency 1	% efficiency 2
ABP	K10 R151	-	K37 K45 R128 K197 R214	29	29
APase	D51 D101 D153 E322 E327 D369; AB: R10	D123 E126 D128	D434	91	55
Barnase	D54 E73	D75 D93 D101	D12 D22 D86	63	25
Barstar	-	K22 R76 K79	R12 R55 K61	50	0
Calbindin	-	K16 K25 K29 K55	K12 K41	67	0
Cellulase E2	R78 R221R237 K259	R192	R25 K66 R95 K142 K202	50	40
CRO protein	-	M15 I31 E35	E19 E47 L52 D55	42	0
Cu SOD	R80 R116	R70 K71 K123 K137	K31 K37 K129	67	22
Cytochrome P450	R299	R90 K178 R186 197	R57 R67 K239 R330	56	11
Dhfr	R44 P55 R57 Y111 H114	W30 K109	R12 W74 F103 W133	64	46
Elastase	E74 E84 D202	D63 E65 D108	E21 D102 D169 D193	60	30
Fe SOD	D156	E21 E24 E159 D165	K50 K127 K132	63	13
i-fabp	Y14 F47 F62 W82 F93 R106 Y119	-	-	100	100
Ldh	R106 R169	R87 R234	R22 R157 R212 Y286	50	25
l-fabp	V48 Y54 F63 M113 Y120	F18 V48	-	100	71
m-fabp	K58 R78 R106 R126 Y128	K52	F64 F70 K81	67	56
myoglobin	Y103 F138	F33 F46 R139	L115 F123 M131	63	25
parvalbumin	-	K52 K54 K68 K91 K96	K45 R75 K80	63	0
Pgm	E12 E86	E15 D24 E34 D96 D134	D91 E149 E214	70	20
Pla2	R43 H48 Y52 E92 R100	D99 F106	Y73	88	63
Pmi	K100 K136 R304	K20	R199 R227 K236 R340	50	38
Ras protein	R41 K88 ATP: K16	R68	R97 K101	67	50
Snase	D19 D21 D40 E43 D83	D77	E73 E75 E122 E129	55	45
TPI	E97 E104 E167	E129	D111,E133,D158,D227	50	37
Total percentages (average for the set)				64%	35%

Table 5. Calculations on the free and ligand-bound forms. ddG values were defined as dG(bound)-dG(free) (kkal/mol). It can be seen that for each of the residues the ddG<0. In other words, binding of the ligand reduces destabilization provided by the binding residue and, therefore, stabilizes the protein

Protein	dG values for the functional residues that were the most destabilizing					
calbindin	E17	D19	E27	D54	D58	E60	E65
dG(free)	1.6	1.9	1.5	1.8	2.1	2.1	1.4
dG(bound)	-0.2	-0.1	-1.3	-0.4	-0.4	0.02	-1.2
ddG	-1.8	-2.0	-2.8	-2.2	-2.5	-2.1	-2.6
barstar	D32	D35	D39	E76	E80	-	-
dG(free)	0.4	0.9	0.8	0.7	0.9	-	-
dG(bound)	0.3	-0.2	-0.3	-0.1	0.4	-	-
ddG	-0.1	-1.1	-1.1	-0.8	-0.5	-	-
barnase	R59	K66	R69	H102	-	-	-
dG(free)	0.3	0.2	0.1	0.3	-	-	-
dG(bound)	-2.7	-0.9	-1.5	-0.3	-	-	-
ddG	-3.0	-1.1	-1.6	-0.6	-	-	-
CRO	R10	K27	K40	R41	R43	-	-
dG(free)	0.3	0.5	0.8	1.0	0.7	-	-
dG(bound)	-2.5	-3.2	-2.5	-2.5	-3.5	-	-
ddG	-2.8	-3.7	-3.3	-3.5	-4.2	-	-

Table 6. The least stabilizing nucleotides in ribozymes. Residue numeration of the original papers was preserved. Atoms of the "adjacent to active site" nucleotides were less than 4 angstrom from the known residues of an active site; these residues were typically in the active site cleft. Due to much larger number of nucleotides in 1fg0A (catalytic fragment of 23S ribosome subunit) the presented here data are for 0.95 Emax cut-off instead of the "standard" 0.9 Emax

PDB	RNA	Known functional nucleotides	adjacent to the active site	Other, "false positives"
1e4pA	Hairpin	G8, C18, G19, G5	A9	A20
1ldz_	leadzyme	G7, G23, G24	A8, G26	G3
1hmhA	Hammerhead	G5, G8, A9, G10.1	A6, U7	G11.4, G11.3
300dA	Hammerhead	G5, A6, U7, A9	G16.2, G8	G12-A14
1m5kB	Hairpin	A23,A24,C25,A38	A40,U41,U42	C13,A14,A15,U39
1cx0B	HDVribozyme	U120, C122, G138	G101, C121, C163, A165	G129, G131, G164, A166
1grzA	Group I intron	A207, A261, A306	G112, U305	A183, U185, G212, G215, G254, A256, G257, G272, G329
1fg0A	23S ribosomal subunit	G2102,G2482,A2485, A2486, U2620; mg: U2542, C2608	C2105, U2107, G2284, U2484, C2487, A2488, A2532, U2535; U2527, U2529, U2541, G2543, A2637	G2073, G2279, G2280, G2281, G2285, G2293, G2462, A2463, G2471, U2545, G2605, G2606, G2609

The Most Destabilizing Residues in Proteins

In the Tables 3 and 4, the predictive value of the results is characterized by "efficiencies". An "efficiency" is defined as ratio of the number of topmost destabilizing residues with known function (2-5 residues, on average) to the total number of the most destabilizing residues (8-10 residues). An efficiency is complementary to the false positive percentages: to an efficiency of 100% correspond 0% of the false positives. "Efficiencies" in the Tables 3&4 were calculated either 1. using both known functional and "adjacent" residues (effciciency1) or 2. using only known functional residues (efficiency2). The "adjacent" residues were typically within 6-8 angstrom from the known functional site. It is quite remarkable that in 80% of the proteins (19 out of 24) at least 1/3rd of the destabilizing residues were known functional residues. Only in 4 proteins "efficiency2" values were rather low, these proteins were i-fabp, cytochrome P450, dhfr and ldh (Table 3).

Although most of the topmost destabilizing residues were charged (histidines, arginines, lysines, aspartates and glutamates) by no means charged residues were the only destabilizing residues identified. As data in the Table 3 show, there were also a number of phenylalanines, prolines, tyrosines and residues of other amino acid types. Identification of the residues types other than the charged distinguishes the present methodology from the continuum electrostatics calculations in which exclusively charged residues are identified as the most destabilizing [19].

There were no preferences for some residue type to be most destabilizing and all of the negatively (D,E) charged and positively charged (R,K or H) residue types were equally found among the most destabilizing (Table 3) as well as most stabilizing (residues). However, if in a protein most destabilizing residues were positively charged, many of the most stabilizing residues were negatively charged as a rule. Vice versa, if the most destabilizing residues of a protein were negative, then the most stabilizing were positive residues.

The Most Stabilizing Residues in Proteins

Unexpectedly, a large proportion (64%, on average) of the most stabilizing residues in this set of proteins happened to be functional or to be located within 6.0 angstrom from the functional sites (Table 4). The result is different from those reported in previous studies [10, 11] of smaller sets of proteins. Only in several proteins none of the most stabilizing residues was known to be functional (CRO protein, calbindin, barstar, parvalbumin, cytochrome P450 and Fe SOD). It should be noticed that among these 6 proteins only one is an enzyme (Fe SOD) while the enzymes are prevailing in the proteins considered in the present study. The 3 of these proteins bind positively charged metal ions (calbindin, parvalbumin and Fe SOD) and the CRO protein binds negatively charged DNA.

An interesting general tendency was the pair-wise arrangement of the most destabilizing and destabilizing residues in a sequence. This feature was observed in at least 20% of the proteins in the set. For example, Ca-binding residues in calbindin (E17, D19, E27, D54, D58 and E60) were the most destabilizing while the adjacent residues K16, K25, K29 and K55 were the most stabilizing with no known function. Therefore, in calbindin there are at least four sequence clusters of the most-stabilizing + most-destabilizing residue pairs: K16-E17, K25-E27, E27-K29 and D54-K55. Although it is not clear what could be the significance of such an arrangement, an apparent guess is that the pair-wise arrangement may be a feature of protein design that could increase overall protein stability (if spots of the higher and lower energies are brought together, they will, sort of, neutralize each other). Both residues of such a sequence pair might be functional: for example, in TPI (triose phosphate isomerase) there are most destabilizing H95 and most stabilizing E97 (Tables 3, 4), both known to be functional from previous studies.

Substrate Binding Tends to Increase Stabilization of the Protein Structure

Let's approach closer to the physical sense of the destabilizing residues being often involved in ligand binding (Table 3) and ask a thermodynamic question: how the per-residues energies of the destabilizing residues would change upon binding the ligand by a ligand-free form of a protein? The methods of the present paper allow calculation of the energies with and without ligands and such calculations were done for several proteins (Table 5). Proteins in the Table 5 were selected to represent biochemically various types of the bound ligands: calbindin (Ca-binding), barstar, barnase (protein-protein interface) and CRO protein (protein-DNA interface). The results for all of the four proteins unanimously suggest that substrate binding significantly stabilizes the protein structure by increasing stabilization of the binding residues. In other words, ligand reduces the energies of the most destabilizing residues. In fact, after a ligand is bound, the destabilizing residues become stabilizing (sign of the dG changes), as a rule. There were only a few exclusions to this trend: E60 in calbindin and E80 in barstar (Table 5). In most of the cases a strongly destabilizing residue becomes not less strongly stabilizing after binding the ligand.

The Least Stabilizing Nucleotides in Ribozymes

When applied to protein structures, the calculations show "stabilizing" ($dG<0$) as well as "destabilizing" residues ($dG>0$). In RNA and DNA, however, all of the bases have $dG<0$ (when using explicit solvent modeling), thus all of the residues are "stabilizing". Taking into account both configurational and solvation components of entropy is important for calculating physico-chemically plausible values of the free energy (dG). Configurational entropy is better taken into account by using averaging of shorter trajectories rather than a long molecular dynamics trajectory [22, 23], this matter is considered elsewhere [9]. Comparisons of the results of energy calculations using implicit solvent/counterions and explicit solvent/counterions (considered in detail also in [9] and an example is given in the Figure 2bc) show that the relative energetical differences between individual bases are seen much clearer when using explicit solvent model. Nevertheless, using explicit and implicit solvent models produces the results that are similar in terms of the number of catalytic nucleotides identified. For example, in the hammerhead ribozyme (PDB 1hmh), while using explicit solvent, the nucleotides over the cutoff were G8, U7, A6, G11.4, A1.2.4, G5, U4, G10.1 (Figure 2b); for implicit solvent the nucleotides were G8, U7, A6, G11.4, G11.3, A9, G5, G10.1 (Figure 2c). In both cases G5, G8 and G10.1, known to be functional [57], were identified. In short, calculations using implicit solvent or those performed using an explicit solvent model have quite similar relative ranking of per-base energy values. However, calculations with implicit solvent are considerably simpler and much faster. The results of calculations using the implicit solvent/counterions modeling were used to compile the Table 6 for all ribozymes in this study.

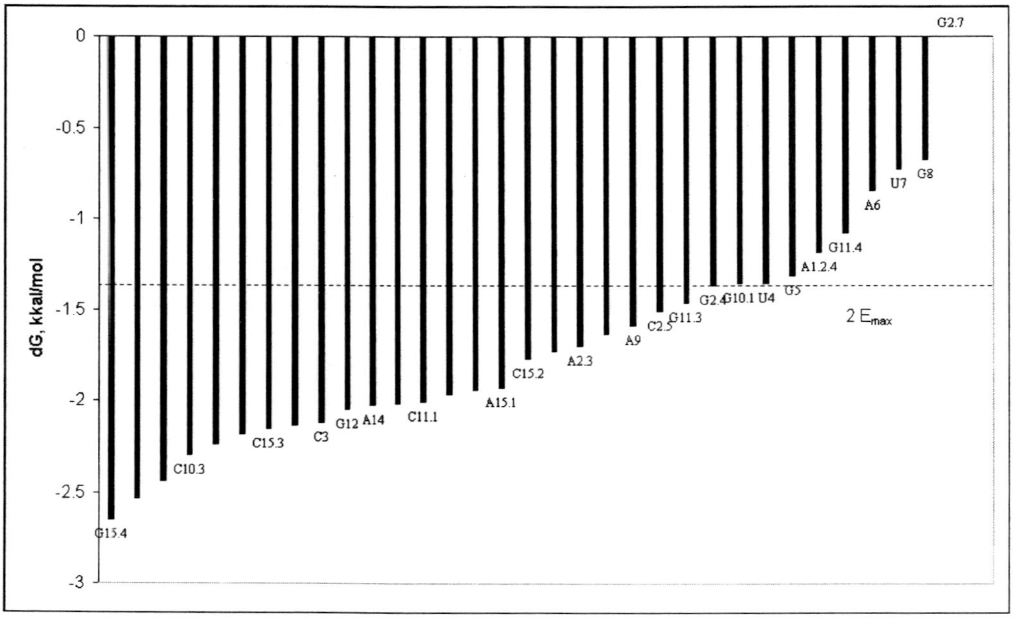

Figure 2b

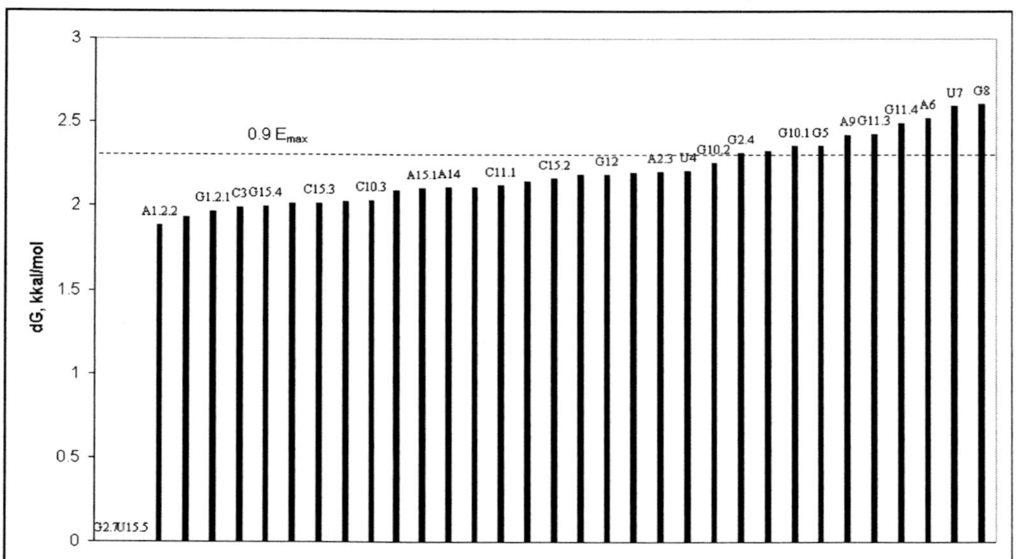

Figure 2c

Figure 2. The least stabilizing nucleotides in the structures of ribozymes. a) The known functional nucleotides in hammerhead ribozyme (PDB 1hmh). The catalytic nucleotides are in red, the cleavage site is in orange. b) Energy histogram for the hammerhead structure, explicit solvent + counterions modeling. There are only stabilizing nucleotides (dG<0), in distinction from proteins (Figure 1). Note the sharp differences in energy for the least stabilizing nucleotides (on the right). c) Energy histogram of the hammerhead, explicit solvent modeling. For all the residues calculated dG>0. However, the nucleotides above the energy cut-off of 0.9Emax are mostly the same as using the explicit solvent + counterions model. d) Spatial clustering of the least stabilizing nucleotides in the structure of the largest ribozyme in this study- catalytic fragment of the ribosomal subunit (PDB 1fg0). The known active site nucleotides are in red, the adjacent nucleotides (Table 6) are in yellow. It can be seen that most of the least destabilizing nucleotides are clustered around the active site region.

In all of the structures the least stabilizing residues (including "known", "adjacent" and "false positives" in the Table 6) were typically placed less than 10 angstrom from the active sites. On average for the set, majority (~70%) of the least stabilizing residues were either known to be functional or were less than 4.0 angstrom from the known functional residues (Table 6). The percentage of "other" or "false positive" was relatively small (5% of all the residues in a molecule on average for the set and no more than 10% for an individual structure). For example, the following nucleotides within catalytic core of a hairpin (PDB 1m5k) were identified biochemically as essential: G8, A9, A10, G21, A22, A23, A24 and C25 [59, 75]. Half of them were among the least stabilizing (Table 6). The “adjacent” nucleotides A40, U42, A43 (also calculated to be the least stabilizing) seem to form base pairs with the catalytically important A23, A22 and G21. Mutations of the A40, U41, U42 and A43 are, actually, known to affect catalysis (at least 10 fold drop in activity was observed [75]). Thus, among the 12 residues identified by the methods as the ”least stabilizing”, 8 nucleotides are known to be important for catalysis and only 4 are “false positives” (no known function).

The calculations identify as the least stabilizing not only the known functional nucleotides but also other nucleotides. These other nucleotides are separated in the Table 6 into two groups: “adjacent to active site" (less than 4 angstrom from the known functional residues) and "other" ("false positive"). Although marked as "false positives", in all of the structures these "false positives" were typically placed less than 10 angstrom from the active sites. Many of the “adjacent” residues were located in the active site regions and were involved in base pair interactions with the functional residues or at least had hydrogen bonds with them. For example, in 1cx0B (HDV ribozyme) the adjacent residue C121 forms a base pair with the catalytic G139, while G162 forms a hydrogen bond with catalytic G140. The adjacent G161 has hydrophobic (Van der Waals) interaction with the catalytic G140 (Figure 3c). Another example: metal-binding site in P4 fragment of RnaseP is known to be important for catalysis by RnaseP [76]. The bases G5, G9, C20, and G21 of the metal-binding site were among the least stabilizing, as well as C19 that forms base pair with C7 of the metal binding site. Only two false positives were identified: A4 and A18. Non-catalytic but still functionally important residues were also identified in other ribozyme structures. In 1fg0 (the catalytic core of 20S ribosome subunit entirely comprised of RNA [62, 77], Figure 2d) at least some of the "false positive" residues are known to be functional though they are far from the catalytic site. C2280, G2281 interact with K48 of ribosomal protein L15P, G2279 interacts with D49 and S53 of ribosomal protein L44E; U2462 and U2463 interact with R69, G70 and G71 of the ribosomal protein L15 [78].

The least successfully the method was applied to the catalytic core of the group I intron (P4-P6 fragment, PDB: 1gidA). This structure is not listed in the Tables 2, 6 as it is a fragment of a catalytic core and also because the biochemical data on the functional nucleotides are more complex, so the data are rather discussed below in some detail. About

15% of the nucleotides in the structure were found to be the least stabilizing (using the $0.9E_{max}$ cut-off). Although the known catalytic residues A114 and A207 were not identified among those, a least stabilizing A113 had hydrogen bonds with both catalytic A114 and A207. Another interesting feature was that the other (non-catalytic) functional residues were calculated to be the least stabilizing. For example, among known Mg-binding residues (A173, A171, G163, U249, G250, A184, G188, G112, G119, U202, U120 [79]) the nucleotides G112, A171, A184, G188 were the least stabilizing. Among the residues essential for core packing of this ribozyme (A183, A186, C137, G181, G164, C217 [79]), the G181, G164, A186, A183 were the least stabilizing. The remainder (about 15) of least stabilizing bases were clustered in the central region of the RNA molecule around the known magnesium-binding and core-packing bases. Only five bases were far outside the active site region: G129, U253, G254, C255 and U155 (which binds a cobalt hexamine ion). Thus, although the method did not identify the two known catalytic residues, the results show that residues important for other functional aspects of the ribozyme were the least stabilizing.

An important point to be considered is the measures of stabilization provided by some or other base in a RNA molecule. Unlike proteins, the experimental data on the effects of mutations on the RNA stability are rather scarce. No extensive mutagenesis has been done even of a single ribozyme. Moreover, in proteins substitutions like Arg->Ala or Asp->Ala are substitutions of a "wild-type residue" (referred to further as a "native residue") for a smaller residue with distinctly different physico-chemical properties. Such substitutions are of "side-chain deletion" type and thus can unequivocally ascertain contribution of a native Arg or Asp etc to the stability of the native structure (some of such valuable biochemical data for proteins are summarized in [19]). In RNA, however, there are mainly four nucleotides of similar size and similar physico-chemical properties. Therefore, results of RNA mutagenesis employed for the study of the contribution of individual bases to RNA stability would be more equivocal. Consequently, as *in vitro* (biochemical) mutational data on ribozyme stability are scarce, an attempt to do an exhaustive single-nucleotide mutagenesis *in silico* (that is, computationally) was made [9]. The results clearly show that more than 80% of the mutations destabilize the RNA and not stabilize it. This result (at least 80% of mutations destabilizing the RNA) correlates well with the general notion that most of the mutations of individual bases would disrupt the native packing and thus these mutations are bound to be destabilizing. These results suggest that measurements of the *mutant* stabilities cannot always be adequately compared with the calculations of the *relative* energetical contribution of each native base to stability of the native RNA. In other words, not only mutation of a catalytic base but also any mutation of almost any base proves to be destabilizing for the native structure. Therefore, it is necessary to distinguish between the "*mutationally* destabilizing bases" (which are identified by altering the native structure through engineered mutations) and the "*relatively* destabilizing bases" (those having the highest energies in the intact, native structure). It is the analysis of the *relatively* stability of the bases that identifies half of the known catalytic bases, as show the results of the present and other studies. It should also be noted that changes in overall ribozyme stability after a mutation couldn't be used to distinguish between catalytic and any other bases [9].

Thus, at least a half of the known catalytic residues can be identified using the spatial structure alone without any additional data such as sequence comparison or biochemistry. Results of prediction for structural models of ribozymes are in agreement with the biochemical data on the potential catalytic regions of those ribozymes [9, 11]. In distinction from proteins (functional residues tend to destabilize the proteins [19, 20]), the catalytic and other functional bases in ribozymes do not destabilize the RNAs but provide the least stabilization possible. Yet these energetical differences allow to distinguish between functional and non-functional nucleotides. It also should be remarked that this method can (potentially) be applied to other types of RNA and not only to ribozymes [9].

Discussion

Spatial structure of a protein or RNA rarely can unequivocally refer to genetic, physiological or cellular function although analysis of the structure suggests biochemical and biophysical functions. In the context of a unifying approach to defining function(s) of the gene products [2], each protein is characterized by a vector consisting of probabilities of binding to various ligands. Functional similarity between any two proteins can be then defined as cosine of the angle between these two vectors. If these probabilities can be computed from the spatial structure of the protein then a unified descriptor of a protein function can also be compiled. However, before calculating probabilities by any method (by using some kind of docking simulations, for example), it will be important to know definitely the functional site(s) of the protein or other macromolecule.

There is a number of methods for identification of the potential functional residues from structure of a protein: using net charge center model [24], regions of untypical conformations ([80] and references therein), continuum electrostatics calculations [19] and theoretical titration curves [20]. Each of these methods has peculiar restrictions. First of all, these methods were practically applied only to proteins. Further, net charge center model [24] has definite restriction on the shape and compactness of the protein molecule, continuum electrostatics calculations can identify only charged residues [19] because of the neglect of Van der Waals interactions. Analysis of the regions of unusual conformation is limited only to structures solved by protein crystallography and the analysis of the titration curves seems to be applicable exclusively to enzymes [20].

The present work presents a new physico-chemical model of the structure-function relationship that applies not only to proteins but also to RNA. The postulate of the relative physico-chemical properties of the functional residues of the proteins (that is, functional residues being very distinct from the other residues in the molecule) comprises the basis of the present approach. Using full molecular mechanics potential instead of continuum electrostatics lifts up the restriction on the amino acid types. At the same time, using such universal physical notion as "energy" allows to overcome the restrictions on the biochemical types of the proteins and even to extend the method to system with entirely different chemistry: nucleic acids. In the present study, calculations applied to proteins of different biochemistry were shown to conform (at least to some extent) with the above postulate of the relative physico-chemical properties of the functional residues. It does, however, important to consider not only the majority of the successful results but also the minority of the proteins that does not seem to be entirely covered by the above postulate. This analysis is presented in the following sections of the Discussion.

Definitions of the Term "Functional Residues"

The assessment of the results apparently depends on the definitions of what is referred to as a "functional residue" as well as "false positive". As the data on functional residues in proteins (collected in the Table 1) show, even in enzymes can by at least two types of essentially different functional residues. Many enzymes (for example, alkaline phosphatase, triose phosphate isomerase, phosphoglucomutase and others in this study) are oligomeric. Oligomeric state is often is essential for the catalytic function of the enzyme as the residues of the active site, this fact was mostly shown for glycolytic enzymes (see [25] and references therein). Therefore, residues forming the protein-protein interface cannot be dismissed as "non-functional" since their mutation often abolishes the catalytic activity of the enzyme. Moreover, even not all of the residues of the catalytic site may be known for any particular enzyme. In various dynamic states of an enzyme structure, different residues can interact with the substrate/product. Therefore, in order to establish all of the residues that can be important for ligand binding and catalysis either an extensive mutagenesis or, at least, a molecular dynamics with a model of the substrate will be necessary.

Apart from the protein-protein interfaces in enzymes, there are other examples of "non-conventional" but still essential functional amino acids. For example, there are so-called substrate steering residues [24]. These residues are important for directing the substrates towards the active sites of the enzymes and their mutation inevitably affects catalysis, especially in enzymes with the catalytic efficiency limited by the diffusion stage. For example, there is indirect evidence that K197 in the DTT cavity of triose phosphate isomerase may be important for steering [24], as well as H114 in DHFR [24]. Analysis of the structure of the lactate dehydrogenase suggests that E104, identical in many lactate dehydrogenases and non-identical E122, D84, D88 could be important for steering of the positively charged NAD into the NAD binding site of the enzyme (data not shown). One can also mention as an example the i-fabp (fatty acid binding protein). In i-fabp the highly identical glycines 44 and 65 are located at the border of the ligand-binding cavity. Mutation of these most destabilizing glycines could influence i-fabp binding properties by obstructing entrance to the cavity. Another example is K-binding residues in the P450 cytochrome. It was established that the anionic side chain at the 84 position (which was the topmost destabilizing residue in this protein, Table 3) is crucial for the cooperativity of camphor and metal binding. Physiological role for potassium binding by cytochrome P450cam is the promotion of the camphor binding even at the expense of turnover rate. This allows the organism to utilize low environmental concentrations of this substrate for growth [34]. In short, application of the postulate of the relative physical chemistry of the functional residues does not yet allow distinguishing between various functional types of the residues (although it does allow to identify a number of the functional residues).

Proteins vary in respect of the correctly identified residues and the number of "false positives". On average, 72% of the most destabilizing and 64% of the most stabilizing residues tend to be related to the known functional sites. In some proteins, however, the known functional residues were either exclusively most destabilizing (CRO protein, calbindin, barstar, parvalbumin and Fe SOD, compare the entries in Tables 3, 4) or exclusively most stabilizing (Snase, dhfr and i-fabp, Tables 3, 4). In only two proteins (that is, in 8% of all the proteins in the set): P450-cytochrome and lactate dehydrogenase, most of the known functional residues were neither most destabilizing nor the most stabilizing. However, some interesting observations were made for these two proteins. In cytochrome P450 hem-biding residues were neither the most destabilizing nor the most stabilizing (in distinction from the hem-binding site in myoglobin where a number of hem-binding residues were among the most destabilizing). Several hem-binding residues in P450 were indeed destabilizing (dG>0) though not the most destabilizing (dG>0.4E_{max}). However, lowering the cutoff of 0.4E_{max} to, say, 0.1E_{max} leads to a very large percentage of the "false positives" which does not make application of the method entirely practical. It can be noticed (Tables 1,3,4) that among the hem-binding residues of the P450 were F87, L244 while the most destabilizing E91 as well as the most stabilizing R90 and K239 were close in sequence to theses known residues of the hem-binding site. Such a sequence proximity to the known functional residues can be observed even clearer in LDH: the residues of the active site of the enzyme D52, R106, I120, A237, I26 and S161 (Table 1) while the most destabilizing E55, E104, E122 (Table 3) and the most stabilizing R234, R22 and R157 (Table 4) were less than 3-4 residues away from the known functional residues. The same sequence proximity to the known functional residues was also observed in a number of other proteins (in particular, in fatty-acid binding proteins). The above analysis of the exceptions to the postulate of the relative physical chemistry of the functional residues raises a serious question: what factors do determine the prevalence of the most stabilizing or the most destabilizing residues in the functional sites? The answer to these and other questions are definitely to be found in the future research.

"False Positives" and Possible Approaches to Reduce their Number

Assessment of the results depends not only on the definition of what the term "functional residue" refers to but also on what is called by the term "false positive". In this study, a "false positive" was any residue that was further than 6-8 angstrom from any of the functional sites known to be most important. This does not mean that the residues called as "false positive" in this study would not have some other important function, yet unknown to biochemists. It also should be noted the principal difference between a "false positive" identified in the present study and a false positive identified by a method of prediction based on some kind of statistical (for example, a method of predicting secondary structure from sequence, prediction of solvent accessibilities from sequence etc). The false positives found in this study are far from being random and do represent certain structural features of the proteins studied. For example, almost all of the "false positives" in P450 cytochrome were charged residues that were closely clustered in the amino acid sequence (cluster 1:E152, D153 and E156; cluster 2: D188 E195 E198 D202; Tables 3, 4). Such sequence clusters of the charged residues are considered in more detail in the 2nd part of this article (published in this same volume). Here it suffices to notice that these "false positives" in the two sequence clusters in P450 are rather an exception: sequence clusters of charged residues often tend to be functional (Part 2 of this study). The sequence clustering of the false positives was also observed in a number of other proteins (Tables 3 and 4). In other words, the false positives identified in this study show some kind of determinism (in distinction from any statistical method of prediction where false positives are likely to be entirely random). Due to this apparent determinism, various ways of sieving out the false positives can be considered (for example, improvement of the force field and/or of the current computational procedures).

A more immediately apparent solution to the problem of false positives may be spatial clustering of the identified residues. Rather often, the functional residues tend to be collected in one part of a molecule [9, 24]. Therefore, clustering spatially proximal residues (those less than 6-8 from each other, for example) will definitely eliminate vast majority of the false positives in the Tables 3 and 4. As a variation of the method of spatial clustering, one can consider whether the identified most destabilizing or the most stabilizing residues are located in the cavities of the protein structure. The method of spatial clustering can also be applied to the ribozyme structures.

Another possible approach to lessen the number of false positives is to use data on sequence similarity of the individual residues. This cannot be applied to a novel protein and there are at least 40% of the novel proteins in the human genome. However, even if a sequence alignment could be made, using this kind of information can eliminate a number of the actual functional residues which are not, nevertheless, identical in the sequences of proteins from various source organisms. For example, substrate steering residues, already mentioned above can be extremely important for enzyme catalysis. However, no more than 50% of such residues are characterized by a high degree of sequence identity (reviewed in [24]). In other words, lack of sequence similarity does not necessarily suggest lack of function. At the same time, analysis of sequence similarity is a statistical method and the results greatly depend on the selected sequences not less than on the software and the procedure used to prepare the alignment.

Other potential approaches of eliminating (rather, understanding the physical nature of) the false positives can be more intricate analyses of the results like those presented in the Tables 3 and 4. Firstly, an interesting observation was already made above: the most stabilizing and the most destabilizing residues sometimes tend to cluster in the amino acid sequence. Such an apparent feature of design can be a way to increase the overall stability of the protein: destabilizing effect of a “higher energy spot” (most destabilizing residue) can, at least in part, be neutralized by the adjacent “lower energy spot” (most stabilizing residue). This observation, along with others can be used to distinguish between actually functional residues and the residues less likely to be functional. Another possible approach could be using statistics on the amino acid types of the residues identified and the frequencies of these types of residues in the sequence of the whole protein. For example, if most of the residues identified were of one type, such an observation may be the result of the statistical prevalence of the residues of this type in the sequence of the protein.

Thus, the results presented in this article definitely show that many of the residues with extremal energetical properties in the protein and RNA structures (in other words, the most destabilizing and the most stabilizing residues) tend to be known functional residues. The rate of identification of the functional residues can be increased by lowering the only empirical parameter in this study: the energy cut-off (which was $0.4E_{max}$ for proteins and $0.9E_{max}$ for ribozymes in this study). However, lowering the cutoff also leads to larger percentage of the "false positives" which does not make application of the method entirely practical. Therefore, application of the method should be determined by the purposes of the research. That is, if it is necessary to predict functional residues in a novel protein, one can use both predictions of the most destabilizing as well as the most stabilizing residues. The value of the energy cutoff can also be adjusted as necessary. This strategy is most applicable to biochemical studies of novel proteins. If, however, a lower rate of the false positives is required (which is the case of genomic annotation, when a theoretical method should give reasonably accurate predictions with the least false positives as possible), then, perhaps, only the data on the most destabilizing residues should be used (as the most destabilizing residues are more likely to be the functional, as it was already discussed).

Conclusion

This paper proposes a unifying model of the structure-function relationship. As the results show, this model brings together the results of biochemical, biophysical and structural studies in the framework of the molecular mechanics calculations- the part of the classical physical chemistry. Practically, the method can allow identification of 70%-80% (on average) of the known functional residues in proteins and 50%-60% functional nucleotides in ribozymes. Some questions are to be answered in the further research. What factors could determine prevalence of most destabilizing vs. most stabilizing residues in the functional sites? How can the various functional types of residues (that is, catalytic, substrate binding, protein-protein interactions etc) be distinguished using the calculations or some additional analyses? Can this method, in some way, be applied to a protein or a ribozyme with no known spatial structure? A potential solution for clearer distinguishing between the functional residues and false positives may be an improvement of the protein and RNA force fields. "False positives" can also be excluded by analysis of the spatial clustering of the identified residues. Also, at least in case of ribozymes, comparison of the calculations using implicit and explicit solvents can also contribute to removing the "false positives" [9]. Identification of the potentially functional residues without information on the spatial structure is considered in the second part of the present article.

References

[1] (http://targetdb.pdb.org/)

[2] Lan N Montelione GT and Gerstein M. Ontologies for proteomics: towards a systematic definition of structure and function that scales to genomic level . *Curr Opin Chem Biol* 2003,7:44-54

[3] http://www.functionalgenomics.org.uk/sections/programme/index.htm

[4] Doudna, J. A. and Cech, T. R. (2002) *Nature*. 418(6894), 222-228

[5] Woese, C.R. (1980) In: Ribosomes. *Structure, function, and genetics*. pp. 357- 373 (eds. G. Chambliss, G.R. Craven, J. Davies, K. Davis, L. Kahan and M. Nomura). University Park Press, Baltimore.

[6] Cech, T. R., Zaug, A. J. and Grabowski, P. J. (1981) *Cell*. 27(3 Pt 2), 487-496

[7] Guerrier-Takada, C., Gardiner, K., Marsh, T., Pace, N. and Altman, S. (1983) *Cell*. 35(3 Pt 2), 849-857

[8] Moore, P. B. (1993) RNA: *Versatility in form and function*. In: The RNA World, pp. 119-136, eds. RF Gesteland and JF Atkins (Cold Spring Harbor, NY: Cold Spring Harbor Laboratory Press).

[9] Torshin, I.Y. Computed energetics of nucleotides in spatial ribozyme structures: an accurate identification of functional regions from structure. *TheScientificWorldJOURNAL* **4,** 228–247 (2004).

[10] Torshin IY. Functional residues- from amino acid sequence. *SERMACS* 2003:55th Southeast Regional Meeting of the American Chemical Society, 2003, Atlanta, GA, USA A164.

[11] Torshin IY. *Computed energetics of macromolecules: identification of the functional residues in proteins and functional nucleotides in RNA*. 227th meeting of American Chemical Society, Division of physical chemistry, March 28 2004, Anaheim, CA, USA, A345.

[12] Torshin IY. Energy histograms of ribozymes allow identification of functional nucleotides. *SERMACS* 2003:55th Southeast Regional Meeting of the American Chemical Society, 2003, Atlanta, GA,USA A162.

[13] Warshel, A. (1998) *J. Biol. Chem.* 273(42), 27035-27038

[14] Meiering, E. M., Serrano, L., and Fersht, A. R. (1992) *J. Mol. Biol.* 225(3), 585-589

[15] Shoichet, B. K., Baase, W. A., Kuroki, R., and Matthews, B. W. (1995) *Proc. Natl. Acad. Sci. U. S. A.* 92(2), 452-456

[16] Kanaya, S., Oobatake, M., and Liu, Y. (1996) *J. Biol. Chem.* 271(51), 32729-32736

[17] Schreiber, G., Buckle, A. M., and Fersht, A. R. (1994) *Structure.* 2(10), 945-951

[18] Sanchez-Ruiz, J. M., and Makhatadze, G. I. (2001) *Trends Biotechnol.* 19(4), 132-135

[19] Elcock, A. H. (2001) *J. Mol. Biol.* 312(4), 885-896

[20] Ondrechen, M. J., Clifton, J. G., and Ringe, D. (2001) *Proc. Natl. Acad. Sci. U. S. A.* 98(22), 12473-12478

[21] Torshin IY (2002). Net charge center for protein fold recognition, Proc 5th C.A.S.P. Intl. meeting, Azilomar, CA, Dec 2002, p. A-163. An extended abstract of the method is available at http://predictioncenter.llnl.gov/casp5/doc/Abstr.doc

[22] Caves, L. S., Evanseck, J. D., and Karplus, M. (1998) *Protein Sci.* 7(3), 649-666

[23] Huber, T. and van Gunsteren, W. F. (1998) *J. Phys. Chem.* 102(29), 5937-5943

[24] Torshin I, Harrison RW. *Med Sci Monit.* 2003 Aug;9(8):BR289-301.

[25] Torshin IY. Functional maps of the junctions between interglobular contacts and active sites in glycolytic enzymes -- a comparative analysis of the biochemical and structural data. *Med Sci Monit.* 2002 Apr;8(4):BR123-35.

[26] Quiocho FA, Wilson DK, Vyas NK. *Nature.* 1989 Aug 3;340(6232):404-7.

[27] Kim EE, Wyckoff HW. *J Mol Biol.* 1991 Mar 20;218(2):449-64.

[28] Buckle AM, Schreiber G, Fersht AR. *Biochemistry.* 1994 Aug 2;33(30):8878-89.

[30] Spezio M, Wilson DB, Karplus PA. *Biochemistry.* 1993 Sep 28;32(38):9906-16.

[31] Mondragon A, Harrison SC. *J Mol Biol.* 1991 May 20;219(2):321-34.

[32] Deng HX, Hentati A, Tainer JA, Iqbal Z, Cayabyab A, Hung WY, Getzoff ED, Hu P, Herzfeldt B, Roos RP, et al. *Science.* 1993 Aug 20;261(5124):1047-51.

[33] Poulos TL, Finzel BC, Howard AJ. *J Mol Biol.* 1987 Jun 5;195(3):687-700.

[34] Westlake AC, Harford-Cross CF, Donovan J, Wong LL. *Eur J Biochem.* 1999 Nov;265(3):929-35.

[35] Sawaya MR, Kraut J. *Biochemistry.* 1997 Jan 21;36(3):586-603.

[36] Ding X, Rasmussen BF, Petsko GA, Ringe D. *Biochemistry.* 1994 Aug 9;33(31):9285-93.

[37] Carlioz A, Ludwig ML, Stallings WC, Fee JA, Steinman HM, Touati D. *J Biol Chem.* 1988 Jan 25;263(3):1555-62.

[38] Sacchettini JC, Gordon JI, Banaszak LJ. *J Mol Biol.* 1989 Jul 20;208(2):327-39.

[39] Wigley DB, Gamblin SJ, Turkenburg JP, Dodson EJ, Piontek K, Muirhead H, Holbrook JJ. *J Mol Biol.* 1992 Jan 5;223(1):317-35.

[40] Thompson J, Winter N, Terwey D, Bratt J, Banaszak L. *J Biol Chem.* 1997 Mar 14;272(11):7140-50.

[41] Zanotti G, Scapin G, Spadon P, Veerkamp JH, Sacchettini JC. *J Biol Chem.* 1992 Sep 15;267(26):18541-50.

[42] Vojtechovsky J, Chu K, Berendzen J, Sweet RM, Schlichting I. *Biophys J.* 1999 Oct;77(4):2153-74.

[43] McPhalen CA, Sielecki AR, Santarsiero BD, James MN. *J Mol Biol.* 1994 Jan 14;235(2):718-32.

[44] Rigden DJ, Alexeev D, Phillips SE, Fothergill-Gilmore LA. *J Mol Biol.* 1998 Feb 20;276(2):449-59.

[45] van den Berg B, Tessari M, de Haas GH, Verheij HM, Boelens R, Kaptein R. *EMBO J.* 1995 Sep 1;14(17):4123-31.

[46] Sheffield PJ, Bhat KM, Owen AJ, Perry B, Sumner IG, Warwicker J. *Biochem Biophys Res Commun.* 1995 Nov 22;216(3):778-84.

[47] Goodenough PW, Bhat KM, Collins ME, Perry BN, Pickersgill RW, Sumner IG, Warwicker J, de Haas GH, Verheij HM. *Protein Eng.* 1991 Dec;4(8):929-34.

[48] Cleasby A, Wonacott A, Skarzynski T, Hubbard RE, Davies GJ, Proudfoot AE, Bernard AR, Payton MA, Wells TN. *Nat Struct Biol.* 1996 May;3(5):470-9.

[49] Tong LA, de Vos AM, Milburn MV, Kim SH. *J Mol Biol.* 1991 Feb 5;217(3):503-16.

[50] Keefe LJ, Quirk S, Gittis A, Sondek J, Lattman EE. *Protein Sci.* 1994 Mar;3(3):391-401.

[51] Libson AM, Gittis AG, Lattman EE. *Biochemistry.* 1994 Jul 5;33(26):8007-16.

[52] Keefe LJ, Quirk S, Gittis A, Sondek J, Lattman EE. *Protein Sci.* 1994 Mar;3(3):391-401.

[53] Judice JK, Gamble TR, Murphy EC, de Vos AM, Schultz PG. *Science.* 1993 Sep 17;261(5128):1578-81.

[54] Wierenga RK, Noble ME, Vriend G, Nauche S, Hol WG. *J Mol Biol.* 1991 Aug 20;220(4):995-1015.

[55] Michiels, P. J., Schouten, C. H., Hilbers, C. W., and Heus, H. A. (2000) *RNA.* 6(12), 1821-1832

[56] Hoogstraten, C. G., Legault, P., and Pardi, A. (1998) *J. Mol. Biol.* 284(2), 337-350

[57] Pley, H. W., Flaherty, K. M., and McKay, D. B. (1994) *Nature.* 372(6501), 68-74

[58] Scott, W. G., Murray, J. B., Arnold, J. R., Stoddard, B. L., and Klug, A. (1996) *Science.* 274(5295), 2065-2069

[59] Rupert, P. B. and Ferre-D'Amare, A. R. (2001) *Nature* 410, 780-786.

[60] Ferre-D'Amare, A. R., Zhou, K., and Doudna, J. A. (1998) *Nature.* 395(6702), 567-574

[61] Golden, B. L., Gooding, A. R., Podell, E. R., and Cech, T. R. (1998) *Science.* 282(5387), 259-264

[62] Nissen, P., Hansen, J., Ban, N., Moore, P. B., and Steitz, T. A. (2000) *Science.* 289(5481), 920-930

[63] Berman, H. M., Westbrook, J., Feng, Z., Gilliland, G., Bhat, T. N., Weissig, H., Shindyalov, I. N., and Bourne, P. E. (2000) *Nucleic Acids Res*. 28(1), 235-242

[64] Abagyan, R.A., Totrov, M.M. and Kuznetsov, D.N. (1994). *J.Comp.Chem*. 15, 488-506.

[65] P. Ren and J. W. Ponder (2003), *J. Phys. Chem. B*, 107, 5933-5947

[66] Weiner, SJ, Kollman, PA, Nguyen, DT, Case, DA. (1986) *J. Comp. Chem*., 7, 230-241.

[67] Ponder, J.W. and Case, D.A. (2003). *Adv. Prot. Chem*. 66, 27-85.

[68] Rappe, A, Goddard III, W (1991) *J. Phys. Chem*., 95, 3358-3365

[69] Gundertofte K, Liljeforsfors, T, Norby, P and Peterson, I (1996) *J. Comp Chem*., 17, 429

[70] Rappe, AK, Casewit, CJ, Colwell, KS, Goddard III WA and Skiff, WM. (1992) *J. Am. Chem. Soc*., 114, 10024-10035

[71] Harrison, R. W., Reed, C. C., and Weber, I. T. (1997) *Proteins. Suppl* 1, 68-73

[72] Mehler, E.L. and Solmajer, T. (1991) *Protein Eng*. 4(8),903-10.

[73] Manning, G.S. (1978) *Q. Rev. Biophys*. 11(2), 179-246.

[74] Lavery R., "Nucleic acids conformation and flexibility: modeling using molecular mechanics" (1998) in *Encycopedia of Computational Chemistry*, J Wiley&Sons, NY (www.mrw.interscience.wiley.com/ecc)

[75] Berzal-Herranz A, Joseph S, Chowrira BM, Butcher SE, Burke JM. *EMBO J* 1993 Jun;12(6):2567-73

[76] Schmitz, M. and Tinoco I, Jr. (2000) *RNA*. 6(9), 1212-1225

[78] Ban, N., Nissen, P., Hansen, J., Moore, P. B., and Steitz, T. A. (2000) *Science*. 289(5481), 905-920

[79] Cate, J. H., Gooding, A. R., Podell, E., Zhou, K., Golden, B. L., Kundrot, C. E., Cech, T. R., and Doudna, J. A. (1996) *Science*. 273(5282), 1678-1685

[80] Petock JM, Torshin IY, Weber IT, Harrison RW. *Proteins*. 2003 Dec 1;53(4):872-9.

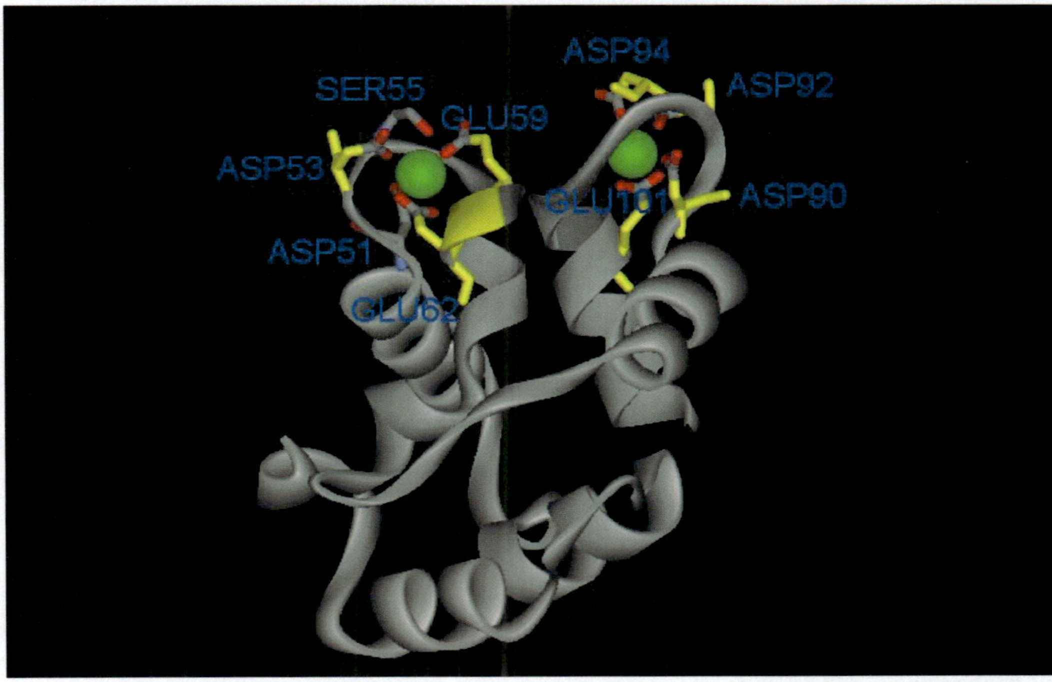

Figure 1c

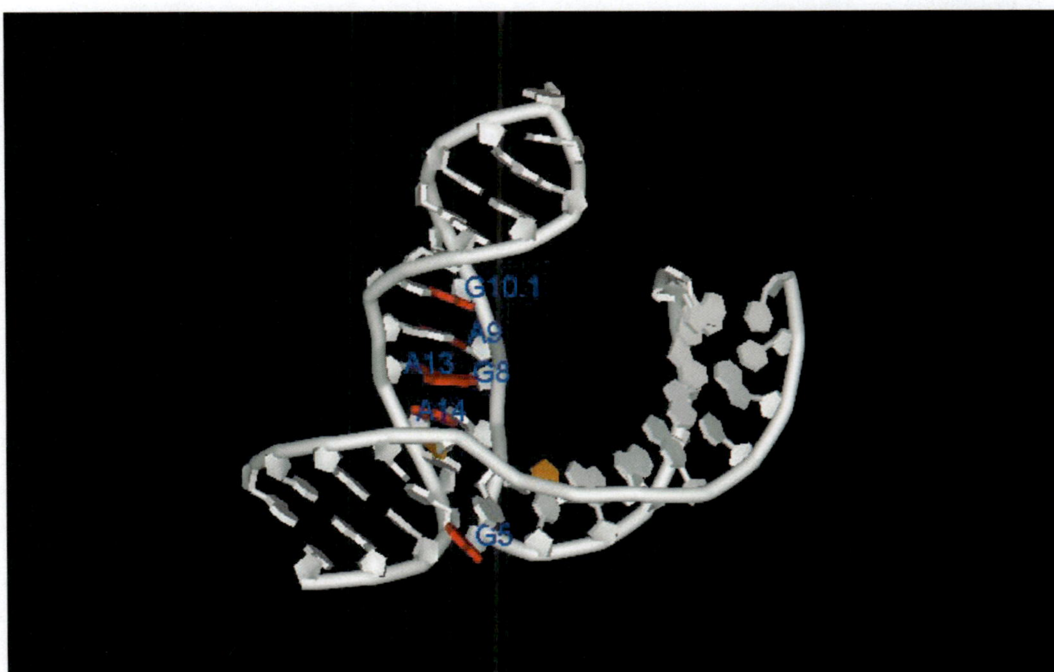

Figure 2a

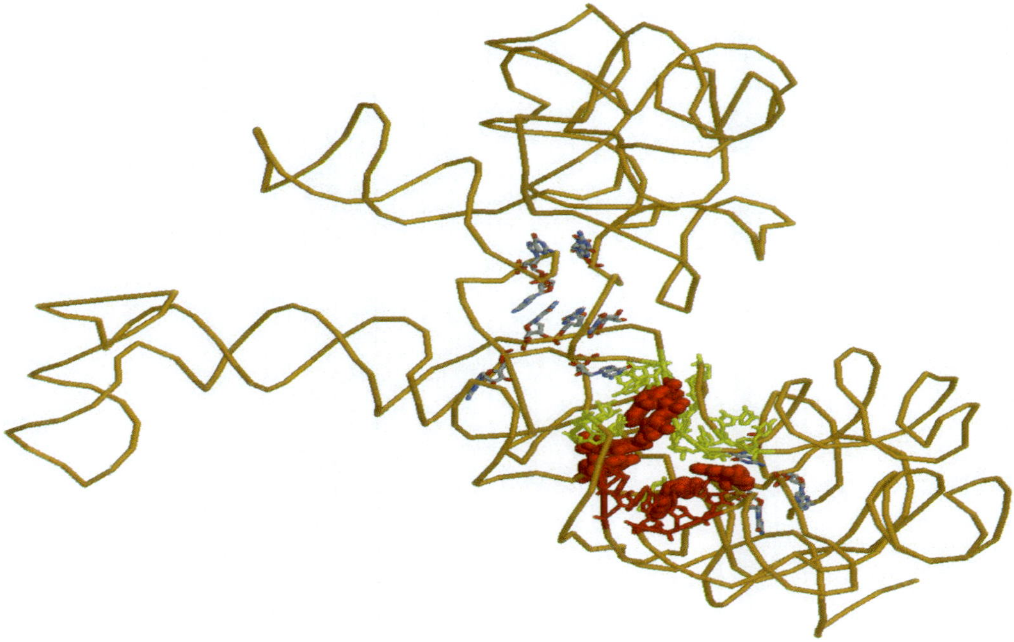

Figure 2d

In: Bioinformatics: New Research
Editor: Peter V. Yan, pp. 127-167
ISBN 1-59454-242-2

Chapter VI

Structural Alphabet: From a Local Point of View to a Global Description of Protein 3D Structures

Alexandre G. de Brevern**#, *Cristina Benros*# *and Serge Hazout
Equipe de Bioinformatique Génomique et Moléculaire (EBGM),
INSERM E03-46, Université Denis DIDEROT-Paris 7, case 7113,
2, place Jussieu, 75251 Paris, France

Abstract

The study of protein structures' local conformations has a long history principally based on the analysis of the classical repetitive structures (i.e. α-helix and β-sheet), and also on the characterization of some particular structures in the coil state (e.g. turns). The secondary structures are interesting for describing the global protein fold, but miss all the orientations of the connecting regions and so neglect many particularities of the coil state.
In order to take these structural features into account we have identified a local structural alphabet composed of 16 folding patterns of five consecutive residues called Protein Blocks (PBs). Conversely to the secondary structures, the PBs are able to approximate every part of the protein structures. These PBs have been used both to describe precisely the 3D protein backbones with an average *rmsd* of 0.42 Å, and to perform a local structure prediction with a rate of correct prediction of 48.7%.
In this chapter, we present the interest of the Protein Blocks by comparing the secondary structure assignment with the assignment in terms of PBs. We highlight the discrepancies between different secondary structure assignment methods and show some interesting correspondence between particular local folds and the Protein Blocks. Then, we use the Protein Block prediction to classify proteins into the classical structural classes, namely all α, all β and mixed. The prediction rate of theses different classes are good, i.e. 71.5%, with no confusion between all α and all β classes. Finally, we present a new approach named TopKAPi that stands for "Triangular Kohonen Map for Analyzing Proteins". It enables us to

---

* Corresponding author: mailing address: Dr. de Brevern A.G., Equipe de Bioinformatique Génomique et Moléculaire (EBGM), INSERM E 03-46, Université Denis DIDEROT-Paris 7, case 7113, 2, place Jussieu, 75251 Paris, France. E-mail : debrevern@urbb.jussieu.fr. Tel: (33) 1 44 27 77 31. Fax: (33) 1 43 26 38 30.
# Both authors have contributed equally to this work.

classify and analyze proteins according to their Protein Block frequencies using for this purpose a novel unsupervised clustering method: a triangular self-organizing Kohonen map. This method enables us to determine new relationships between local structures and amino acid distributions. This new methodology could be of great interest in proteomics and sequence alignment.

Color graphics are presented at the end of the chapter.

Key words: secondary structure, local folds, Bayesian prediction approach, structure-sequence relationship, protein structural classes, *ab initio*.

Introduction

The first protein structure obtained by X-ray diffraction [1] had marked the beginning of the description and analysis of protein structures. Two ways have since been followed with the theoretical methods and the descriptive methods. In the early years, due to the limited number of available structures, the first kind of approaches was used for proposing potential local structures based on physico-chemical properties (e.g. the γ-helix [2]). Their presence and interest in experimentally determined structures were confirmed or not only in a second step [3]. In this chapter, we focus on the second kind of approaches based on the description and characterization of particular local fold structures observed in experimentally determined protein structures. Figure 1 summarizes different levels of description of the protein folds that we are going to follow in this introduction: (i) the 3-states secondary structures, (ii) the secondary structures with more distinct states, (iii) the structural alphabets and (iv) the description of the complete protein topology.

(i) the 3-states secondary structures. One of the major events in protein history is the series of seven consecutive papers of Pauling and Corey in 1951. They described an impressive number of potential local folds including the α-helix and the β-sheet [2, 4]. The average characteristics of these local structures are described in Table 1. The α-helix (or 3.6_{13} helix) is characterized by intramolecular hydrogen bonds between amino acid residues *i* and *i* +4 [5]. Its extremities show specific physicochemical stabilizations [6]. The β-sheet is defined by hydrogen bonds between neighboring parallel (or antiparallel) chains [4]. As for the α-helix, its edges have been widely analyzed [7 - 9]. Many studies have also analyzed the packing of these two repetitive structures [10 - 13] and the sequence - structure relationship between sequence and structure [14 - 17].

The high propensity of these helicoidal and extented local structures in experimentally determined structures has since achieved a kind of dogma, the 'secondary structures' composed of the α-helix, the β-strand and a state corresponding to everything else, the coil. The structures are often limited to this simple description.

(ii) the secondary structures with more distinct states. Different studies have examined and extended these definitions both in creating new states and in refining the assignment criteria. They have improved our knowledge of the repetitive helicoidal and extended structures and have also highlighted the interest of the coil state which has been poorly described too many times as 'random' coil.

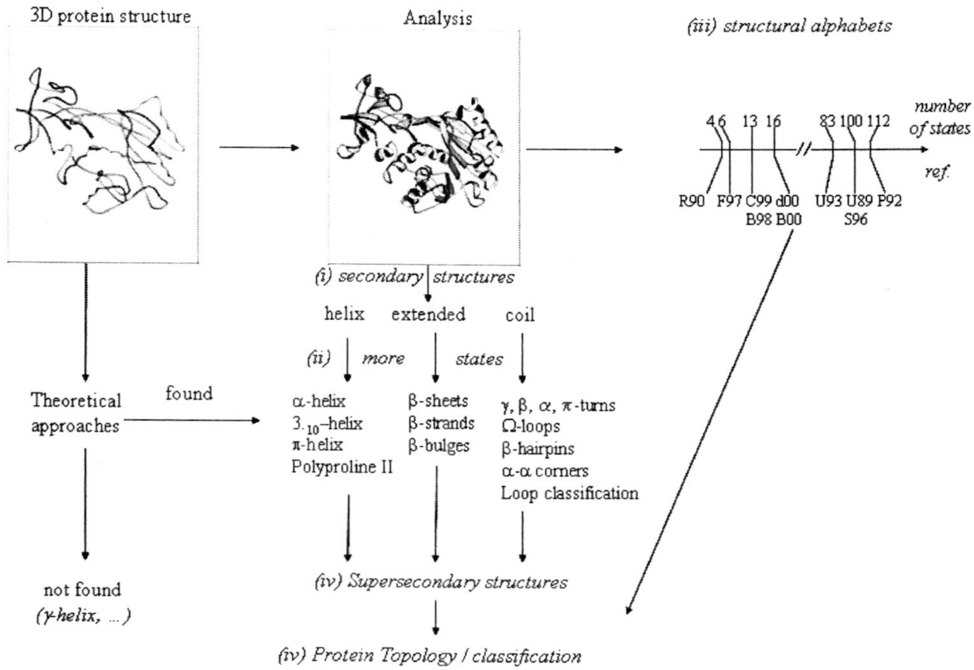

Figure 1. *Protein structure analysis.* From the 3D atom coordinates of a protein structure different analyses are possible. Theoretical approaches consist in predicting potential interesting local structures based on physicochemical criteria. Descriptive approaches are based on the analysis of known local structures at different levels of organization: (i) *the secondary structures* defined by three states (helicoidal, extended and non-helicoidal /non-extended). (ii) a more detailed description (see Text). Another way to describe the protein structures is by (iii) *the use of structural alphabets* that are characterized by different states (references : R90 [125], F97 [126], C99 [129], B98 [127], d00 [128], B00 [161], U93 [120], U89 [118], S96 [121], P92 [119]). The local folds combinations create local topologies referred to as (iv) *super-secondary structures* which describe the *complete protein topology.*

The new local folds pointed out exhibit interesting energetic and / or geometrical properties. Thus, less common helices, like 3_{10} – helices are characterized by intramolecular hydrogen bonds between amino acid residues *i* and *i* +3 [18 - 20] and π-helices (i.e. 4.4_6-helices) with hydrogen bonds between amino acid residues *i* and *i* +5 [21 - 25]. These two types of helicoidal structures are often encountered at the extremities of longer α-helices and seem to play an important role in the stabilization of longer helicoidal structures [26]. The π-bulges constitute a particular kind of discontinuity in helicoidal structures. Like the π-helices, they are not frequent but seem directly associated to protein functions [23, 27]. The Polyproline II helices correspond to a specific local fold initially found in fibrous proteins [28, 29]. They contribute to the creation of coiled coil supersecondary structures characteristic of these proteins. They are also found in globular proteins and are not composed only of Proline [30 - 33]. Among the predicted helicoidal local folds never observed in proteins we can quote the γ-helix (or 5.11_{17}-helix) [2, 3], the 2.2_7-helix and the 4.3_{14}-helix [18]. As for the Polyproline I, it is only found in apolar solvents.

In the same way, accurate analyses have been carried out for the β-sheet category. An interesting point is that since the description of the β-strands, several analyses have shown that a strand can be found independently of a β-sheet and named the E-strand [34]. Moreover, orthogonal ββ motifs, i.e. consecutive strands, have been identified, forming an 'L' structure with an angle of 90° [13, 35]. Globally, the irregularities within the β-strands have been classified into 4 distinct classes of β-bulges [36, 37] and can be related to the proteins' function and stability [38].

The regions between the repetitive helicoidal and extended structures have been intensively studied too. Thus, Venkatachalam, using a theoretical approach close to Ramachandran method [39], determined small local folds characterized by the reversing of the polypeptide chain maintained by a hydrogen bond between two close residues, i.e. the turns [40]. After this description, a classification was done and has greatly evolved. The tight turns are characterized by precise dihedral angle values and a short distance between their ends [41]. The two most studied turns are the γ- (3 residues) and the β-turns (4 residues). The γ- turns are composed of two categories, *classic* and *inverse* [42 - 45]. The β-turns have a more complex history. At the beginning, the four main categories were the types I, I', II and II' [46, 47]. The extension of the β-turn classification created new categories: the turns III, III', V and V', the turn VI characterized by a Proline, the turn VII associated with a kink and the turn IV corresponding to all the non classified turns [48]. The first analyses of turns in protein structures used this classification [49 - 52]. However, at the beginning of the 80's, different turns have been excluded, the turns III and III' which were too close to the 3.10 helix, the turns V, V' and VII which were too rare and their definitions inaccurate [53]. Wilmot and Thornton defined the turn VIII which is associated with an important number of observations [54]. It is the first turn not directly associated with a stabilizing bond between its ends. The definitions used by Thornton's group [37, 55] are considered as the standard. Nevertheless, some analyses have been done using the excluded turns V, V' and VII [56, 57]. Shorter turns (e.g. 2 residues δ-turns) [58] and longer ones (e.g. 5 residues α-turns [59, 60] and 6 residues π-turns [61, 62]) have been studied less. The different classes of turns can be overlapping, e.g. two β-turns can have 3 positions in common. The turns can also be multiple at the same position, e.g. a β-turn can encompass a γ-turn [63 - 65]. The turns account for some 25% of the structures.

Other interesting local structures, less frequent than the turns have also been identified in the coil state. For instance, the Ω-loops constitute a particular category characterized by a small distance at their extremities and an important number of contacts in their structure [66, 67]. They correspond to compact globular loops mainly located at the surface of the proteins [68]. They may be directly associated with the protein functions [69, 70] and folding [70].

However, even if the coil state is better characterized, some local folds still remained unassigned. Hence, another approach is developed and consists in classifying the protein fragments between α-helices and / or β-sheets. Different kinds of classifications have been carried out. The first type consists in analyzing only specific successions from one state to another. For instance, the study of the connections between two successive β-strands has been studied and has resulted in the classification of the β-hairpins [71 - 74]. Interestingly, the short length hairpins are often characterized by a specific turn [13] and the longer ones by a β-bulge in one of the strands [75]. Sometimes stabilization by disulfide bonds can be observed [76]. The β-hairpins are well studied in molecular dynamics [77, 78]. The same approach was performed for the short loops connecting two α-helices and resulted in the characterization of the α-α corners which are similar to the 'L' structure of orthogonal ββ [79]. Other studies have focused on one precise loop category like α-helix-turn-β-strand [80], or on particular combinations of β-strands like the Ψ-loop [55, 81]. The second type of classification consists in more systematic analyses of the short and medium loops. Many studies have been carried out for short loops connecting α-helices and β-sheets [82 - 84]. Others have also been done systematically for the short [85, 86] and medium loops [87, 88], whatever the flanking regions.

All theses methods can only be used for short length loops [89] or for a combination of small loops [90] since longer loops are less frequent and considered as too variables. Nevertheless, the different loop classifications have shown their interest in local structure prediction to construct loops in non-complete structures [91 - 95]. Databases of loops useful for molecular modeling have been created [88, 96 - 98].

Even if the repetitive secondary structures have been intensively analyzed [17, 99], the characterization of the α-helices and the β-strands has led to different assignment methods based upon energetic, geometrical and/or angular criteria, which do not always agree particularly at the edges. The first software was developed by Levitt and Greer and used only the C_α positions, as these atoms are the most precisely defined by X-ray crystallography [100]. Table 2 summarizes the different methods analyzed in this study with the number and type of states they focus on. DSSP [101] is the most popular method. Moreover, it is the basis of the secondary structure assignment given by the Protein DataBank [102, 103]. It is based on the hydrogen bonding patterns. STRIDE [104] uses the same criteria with parameters slightly different and the computation of backbone dihedral angles. SECSTR focuses on the correct assignment of $3_{.10}$ – and π-helices [24]. Recently, DSSPcont tries to optimize the parameters of DSSP by taking into account multiple NMR models assignment and tries to compensate at best the fluctuations of the assignment between the different model observations [105 - 107]. However, the results are not really improved. DEFINE, [108] like the Levitt and Greer method, uses only the C_α positions. It computes inter-C_α distance matrices and compares the results to ideal repetitive secondary structures. PCURVE [109] is based on the helicoidal parameters of each peptide unit and generates a global peptide axis. PSEA [110] assigns the repetitive secondary structures from the sole C_α position using distance and angles criteria. XTLSSTR uses all the backbone atoms to compute two angles and three distances [111]. It is especially dedicated to the spectroscopists. PROMOTIF uses an implementation similar to DSSP, but focuses on the characterization of γ- and β-turns, β-hairpins and β-bulges [55].

The assignment methods may generate particular problems. Hence, DSSP may assign very long helices which do not correspond to reality [112]. Bansal and co-workers have analyzed and classified the helices and showed that important parts of them are in fact curved or composed of distinct helices [113]. In the same way, Woodcock and co-workers [114] noted that these methods do not assign the same state to certain residues, especially those located at the beginnings and ends of repetitive structures, *i. e.* the secondary structure assignments differ according to the chosen method. This observation has led to the development of a consensus approach [115] which represents an average measure of DSSP, DEFINE and PCURVE. This study has shown that less than 2/3 of the residues are associated to the same state by these three algorithms. The use of one or another method does not reflect the same type of reality. For instance, the α-helix defined by DSSP, with its eight states grouped in only three states, does not correspond only to the α-helix (3.16_{13} helix), but incorporates the $3._{10}$ helix and the π-helix (4.4_6-helix). In the same way, β-sheets (DSSP 'E' state) correspond to β-strands implicated in parallel or anti-parallel characteristic patterns but not β-strands without a hydrogen bond partner (DSSP 'B' state). These features may induce difficulties in analyzing the protein structures or dynamic trajectories. So, it is important to note that the repetitive structures definitions only reflect a given classification.

(iii) the structural alphabet. Various teams have tried to proceed without using classic secondary structure descriptions. Instead, they categorize the 3D structures without any *a priori*. Thus, every local fold is associated to one specific small prototype. The complete set of prototypes defines "a structural alphabet" [116, 117]. Numerous structural alphabets have been defined and differed by the description parameters of the protein backbone (C_α coordinates, C_α distances, α or dihedral angles) and by the method used for defining them (hierarchical clustering, empirical function, Kohonen Maps, neural network or Hidden Markov Model) [116]. Each structural alphabet or fragment library is defined as a series of N prototypes of l residues length. N is highly variable (between 4 and 123), l only varies between 4 and 7.

Two main types of research must be distinguished. The first one consists in describing an important number of prototypes to reconstruct precisely a protein structure. The second one aims at predicting the 3D structures from the sole knowledge of the sequence and so is limited to few prototypes.

Hence, the earliest works used hundreds of prototypes (N = 83 to 120) to reconstruct protein structures [118 - 121]. Levitt's group [122, 123] and Micheletti and co-workers [124] tried to optimize the construction of such libraries from a geometrical point of view. This structural description allows new insight into protein 3D structures and reveals peculiar sequence specificity [116].

However, to perform a prediction from the sequence, the number of prototypes, N, must be smaller, i.e. a correct prediction implies the selection of a more limited number of local conformations as shown by Rooman's and Fetrow's works [125, 126]. Indeed to capture most of the local folds, it is advisable to have a balance between a number of states sufficient for approximating correctly the local folds and limited for ensuring a correct prediction level. An alphabet composed of N = 10 to 20 states corresponds to this goal [127, 128]. These methods have proved their efficiency both in the description and the prediction of small loops [129, 130] or long fragments [131 - 137]. Bystroff and Baker's I-Sites must be pointed out as one of the most interesting structural alphabet. It has been used with a high efficiency for improving *new fold* methods [138, 139].

The different alphabets have in common to describe more precisely the repetitive structures (helicoidal and extended) and their edges, and to focus on a better description of the coil state.

In this work, we use the structural alphabet we have defined in a previous study. It is composed of 16 mean protein fragments of 5 residue lengths called Protein Blocks. These PBs have been used both to describe the 3D protein backbones and to perform a local structure prediction [128, 133]. A comparison between different structural alphabets has shown its informativity [140].

(iv) the local structures describe the protein topology. The succession of secondary structures defines the supersecondary structures, i.e. αβ, βα, ββ and αα. Their combinations generate some particular motifs like the greek key (ββββ) or the Rosmann fold (βαβαβ) [141]. They can be used to define the complete topology of the proteins like in the TOPS family database [142]. Thus, they are used to classify proteins into different structural families like that of SCOP [143] or CATH [144], even if a recent study has shown the difficulties of finding a good consensus between all these classifications [145]. Most of these classifications give few major families and then an important number of sub-families. Nevertheless, these descriptions have proved their efficiency to find distant structural homologues [146] or to work with genomic data [147]. They are the classic benchmark of fold recognition [140].

Here, we examine the relationship between the structural alphabet and the 3D structure topology.

The results of our study are divided into three consecutive parts. (i) As proteins are classically described by their content in secondary structures, we looked at the correspondence between the different secondary structure states and our Protein Blocks. We highlighted the differences between many secondary structure assignment methods. (ii) We have previously described a Bayesian approach to predict the Protein Blocks from the sequence [128]. It has been improved and gives now a prediction rate of 48.7%. In the second part of this chapter, we analyzed the results of the prediction and their use to protein classification according to their structural classes. These classes are defined as all-α, all-β and mixed (α+β and α/β) following the definitions of Michie and co-workers [148]. (iii) Finally, we described a new method called TopKAPi, for Triangular Kohonen map for Analyzing Proteins. Firstly, it allows classifying and analyzing protein structures based only on the Protein Blocks frequencies. Then, it permits to analyze the amino acid distributions associated with this new classification. We show new insights into the sequence and structure relationships.

Materials and Methods

Figure 2 gives the main steps of the research carried out in this chapter and described here.

Data sets: Different sets of proteins were used in this work. The four first ones have already been used in a recent work [133]: *PAPIA* from PDB-REPRDB database [149], *PDBselect* databank [150, 151], *culled-Pdb* (now *PSICES*) [152], *SCOP - ASTRAL* [143, 153]. We have preferentially used the *PAPIA* set which is composed of 717 protein chains and 180,854 residues. The set contained proteins with no more than 30% pairwise sequence identity. The selected chains had X-ray crystallographic resolutions less than 2.0 Å and an R-factor less than 0.2. Each selected structure had an *RMSD* value more than 10 Å with every representative chain. A new updated data set (noted *PAPIA03*) has been composed from PDB-REPRDB database [149] with the same criteria as *PAPIA* and is composed of 1,407 protein chains and 293,507 residues. We have verified that the amino acid compositions were not significantly modified between the two protein sets. Each chain was carefully examined with geometric criteria to avoid bias from zones with missing density.

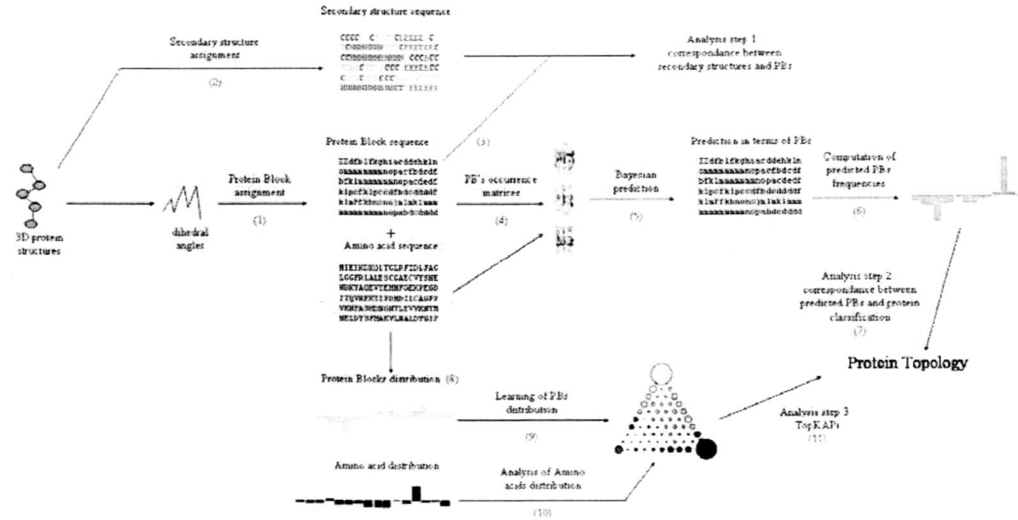

Figure 2. *Main principles of this study.* The first step consisted to extract from a non redundant databank the dihedral angles of the protein structures. (1) These last allowed to encode the 3D structures in terms of Protein Blocks. (2) Using different assignment algorithms the 3D structures were encoded also in terms of secondary structures. (3) We first analyzed the agreement between secondary structures and PBs. (4) Then, using the amino acid sequences, we computed amino acid occurrence matrices associated to each PB. (5) We used this information to perform Bayesian prediction and from the prediction in terms of PBs, (6) we computed the predicted frequencies of PBs per protein. (7) We analyzed the correspondence between the predicted frequencies of PBs and the class of the proteins (all α, all β or mixed). (8) In parallel, from the true PBs and the amino acids of the proteins, we computed the frequencies of PBs and amino acids per protein. (9) We learnt these frequencies of PBs per protein using an adapted triangular Self-Organizing Maps, named TopKaPi. Then, we analyzed (10) the amino acid distributions in TopKaPi and (11) the different clusters of PBs.

Protein Blocks (PBs): The structural alphabet we defined in a previous study [128] is composed of 16 local prototypes called "Protein Blocks" (PBs). They are overlapping fragments of 5 residues in length, encoded as sequence windows of 8 consecutive (ψ, ϕ) pairs. They were obtained by an unsupervised classifier similar to Kohonen Maps [154, 155] and Hidden Markov Models [156]. Figure 3 gives a representation of the 16 Protein Blocks. The PBs *m* and *d* correspond to the prototypes for the central α-helix and the central β-strand, respectively. PBs *a* through *c* primarily represents β-strand N-caps and *e* and *f*, C-caps. PBs *g* through *j* are specific to coils, PBs *k* and *l* to α-helix N-caps, and *n* through *p* to their C-caps. This structural alphabet allows a reasonable approximation of the protein 3D-structures with a *RMSD* now evaluated at 0.42 Å. This value has been assessed again in this study with the new databanks.

Protein coding: Protein structures are encoded as sequences of ϕ - ψ dihedral angles, so that a protein of *M* amino acids long is defined by a signal of 2(*M*-1) dihedral angular values. Each fragment of *M* residues (*M*=5) centered at the α-carbon $C\alpha_n$ is represented by a vector of 8 dihedral angles (Ψ_{n-2}, Φ_{n-1}, Ψ_{n-1}, Φ_n, Ψ_n, Φ_{n+1}, Ψ_{n+1}, and Φ_{n+2}). The fragment is compared to each PB with the *RMSDa* measure [121], i.e. Euclidean distance using angle values. The lowest *RMSDa* value for the 2(*M*-1) angles determines the assignment of the PB (Fig2, arrow 1).

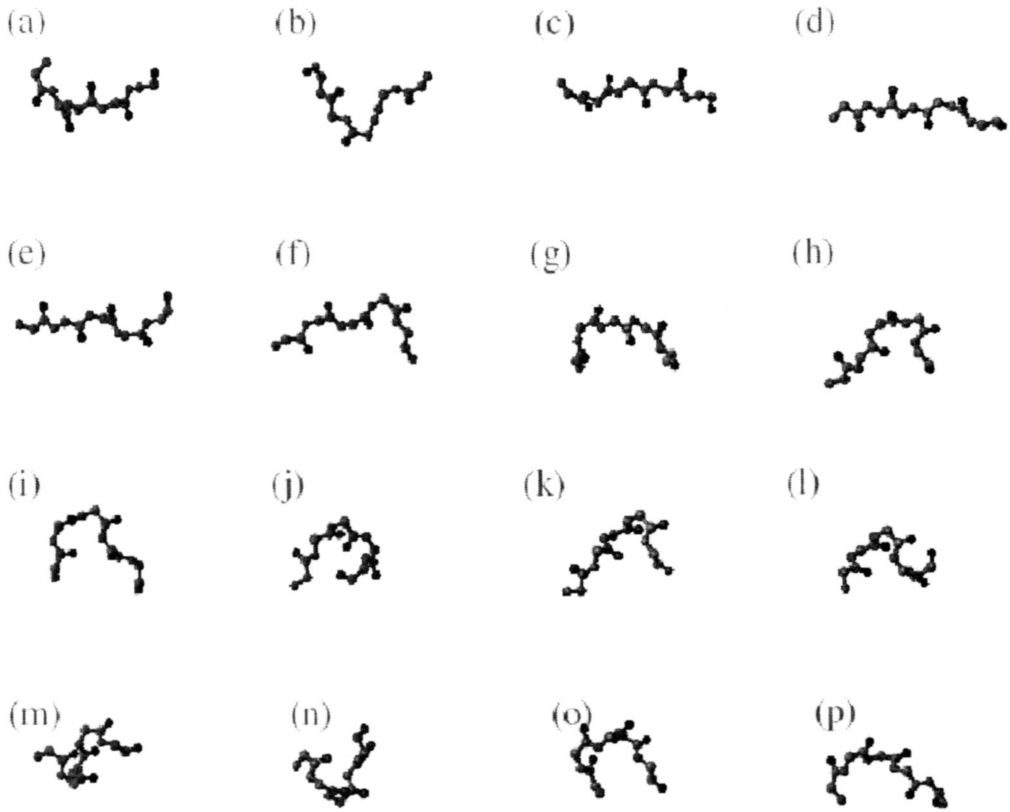

Figure 3. Backbone representation of the 16 Protein Blocks with MOLMOL software [162]. PB *a* to PB *p* are displayed from left to right and from top to bottom.

Secondary structure assignments: They have been done with ten distinct softwares. The first seven correspond to DSSP [101] (CMBI version 2000), DEFINE [108] (version 2.0), PCURVE [109] (version 3.1), STRIDE [104], PSEA [110] (version 2.0), XTLSSTR [111], SECSTR [24] (Table 2). Default parameters were used for each softwares. Three more programs have been used: HELANAL [113] to analyze the α-helices, EXTENDED-BETA, which corresponds to an alphabet developed in Kevin Karplus' laboratory to study more precisely the β-strands [140] and PROMOTIF [55]. DSSP was used to define the α-helices analyzed by HELANAL. Hence, we encoded the 3D protein structures in terms of secondary structures using these different algorithms (Fig. 2, arrow 2), and analyzed the correspondence between the secondary structure and the PB assignments (Fig. 2, arrow 3).

Z-score : Amino acid occurrence matrices were computed for each PB and normalized into Z-scores as follows : Z-score= $(n_{obs}\ (i,x)\ -\ n_{th}\ (i,x))/\ \sqrt{\ n_{th}\ (i,x)}$, with n_{obs} (i,x) the occurrence number of observing amino acid i in PB x, and n_{th} (i,x) the occurrence number expected. $n_{th}\ (i,x) = N_x\ .\ f_i$, where N_x and f_i denote the occurrence number of PB x and the frequency of amino acid i in the entire databank respectively (Fig. 2, arrow 4). Positive Z-scores, more than a user-fixed threshold ε (respectively negative, less than -ε) correspond to overrepresented amino acids (respectively underrepresented).

Prediction of PBs by a Bayesian probabilistic approach: The goal is to predict the optimal PB for each position along a sequence of length L (Fig. 2, arrow 5). To this end, we used a Bayesian probabilistic approach similar to that proposed in a previous work [128]. We focused on the conditional probability of observing the PB_k given an amino acid chain X, (a_1, a_2,..., a_p), noted P(PB_k / X). Bayes' theorem accomplishes the inversion between the sequence X and the structure PB_k. This leads to:

$$P(X \mid PB_k) = P(a_1 \mid PB_k) \times P(a_2 \mid PB_k) \times \ldots \times P(a_p \mid PB_k)$$

A window of length p (p =15 here) is slid along the sequence and centered on a position s. To define the optimal Protein Block, PB* for a given amino acid fragment X at a site in a protein, we used the prediction score R_k:

$$R_k = P(X \mid PB_k) / P(X) = P(PB_k \mid X) / P(PB_k)$$

The ratio R_k measures the information provided by the knowledge of the amino acid chain X in the prediction of the Protein Block PB_k. This criterion is equivalent to a ratio of likelihood's. The optimal structural block PB_k among the 16 possible blocks is defined as PB* = argmax{R_k}. Then PB* is assigned to the central residue of the chain X. The final prediction rate, noted Q_{16}, is the ratio between the number of PBs correctly predicted and all the PBs of the protein.

To assess the prediction, the databank was divided into two sets. The first one was used to define the PBs sequence-structure relationship and hence to compute : P(PB_k / X). The second set was used to perform the prediction.

To improve the prediction rate, we used the concept of the sequence families which lies on the fact that a local fold can be associated to different clusters of sequences. The initial prediction rate was of 34.2% and was improved to 40.7% [128]. Now, with a new approach (*manuscript in preparation*), the prediction rate reaches 48.7%.

Protein classes assignment: To define for a protein its class, we have used the definition of Michie and co-workers: an all-α protein is characterized by a frequency of α-helix of more than 60% and of β-strand less than 15%, and, an all-β protein by a frequency of α-helix of less than 15% and of β-strand of more than 35% [148].

Analysis of the protein structural classes from the prediction in terms of PBs: the predicted PBs frequencies per proteins were computed from the results of the Bayesian prediction. They were analyzed using a Principal Component Analysis (PCA) [157] in regards to their structural classes [148] (all α, all β or mixed) (Fig. 2, arrows 6 and 7).

Prediction of the structural classes from the prediction in terms of PBs: For the 3 structural classes, mean values of each predicted PB frequencies were computed. The prediction step is a comparison between each target protein predicted PB frequencies and the mean values for the 3 structural classes using an Euclidean distance. The smallest distance defines the assignment to the predicted class.

TopKAPi. In parallel, we computed the true PB frequencies per protein (Fig. 2, arrow 8) and found them using a Self-Organizing Map, named TopKaPi for Triangular Kohonen map for Analyzing Proteins (Fig. 2, arrow 9). Kohonen Map or SOM (Self – Organizing Map) is an efficient way to classify data [155]. The analysis of the results is highly facilitated by the nearness of related clusters. The main specificity of our SOM, is to be a triangle. It is composed of $w = G \times (G\text{-}1)/2$ neurons (triangle side of G neurons). A neuron w' is similar to the vector v (dimension 16). The learning is iterative and consists in 5 consecutive steps:

(i) random choice of an observation vector v .
(ii) v is compared to every w neurons using a Euclidean distance.
(iii) the winning neuron w^*, the closest to v, is identified, i.e. the Euclidean distance is minimal.
(iv) each neuron w' of the SOM is modified :

$$w' +1 \leftarrow w' + (v - w')\ \alpha(n)\ \pi(n)$$

with $\alpha(n)$ the learning factor and $\pi(n)$ the neighbourhood factor $\alpha(n)$ is defined as $\alpha_0 / (1 + (n / N))$, with $\alpha_0 = 5 /1000$, n the number of observation vectors learnt and N the total number of observation vectors. $\pi(n)$ controls the diffusion process and is defined by $\exp(-2(r-r^*)2/ \rho(n)2)$, r is the coordinates of the neurons w', r^* the coordinates of the winning neuron w^*, $\rho(n) = \rho0 / (1 + (n / N))$ with $\rho_0 = 2.4$.

(v) the process is reiterated from (i) to (iv) with another vector.
(vi) To learn all the observation vectors of the databanks, the whole databank is used C times ($C = 50$).

Then, we analyzed the correspondence between the different clusters obtained and the relationship between local structure in terms of PB distribution and frequencies of amino acids (Fig. 2, arrows 10 and 11).

Part I: Secondary Structures and PBs

Correspondence between the Different Secondary Structure Assignment Methods

The secondary structure definitions are often considered as fixed and the assignment unique [4, 5]. However, as we have noted in the introduction, the reality is more complicated. Table 3 gives the agreement ratios between the different *S*econdary *S*tructure *A*ssignment *M*ethods (SSAMs). These values are computed as the proportion of identical assignment between two SSAMs. To compute these ratios, we have carried out for the SSAMs with more than 3 states a reduction of their N states to a classical 3-state alphabet (helix, extended and coil). We have done the classical associations for the helicoidal states (i.e. α-helix, $3._{10}$ –helix and π-helix), the extended states (i.e. extended strand and β-sheet) and the coil state (the other states: turn, bend, polyproline II and coil), even if these associations are not always pertinent. Table 3 shows that two SSAMs can strongly disagree.

A first cluster of SSAMs can be distinguished with DSSP [101], STRIDE [104] and SECSTR [24], which have agreement rates within the range [91.4%; 95.3%]. These 3 SSAMs will be noted DSS (*D*SSP – *S*TRIDE – *S*ECSTR). They have in common a similar assignment criterion, i.e. the hydrogen bonds computation. Interestingly, between these three methods, the extended structures are not the ones that have the most disruptive assignment. When a divergence in the assignment occurs, in 80% of the case it is between the helicoidal state and the coil state. This fact is particularly clear for SECSTR which was designed to better assign the less frequent helicoidal states ($3._{10}$ and π-helices).

When different assignment criteria are compared (e.g. distances or angles), the agreement rates are within the range [75.9%; 83.2%] for DSS, PSEA [110], PCURVE [109] and XTLSSTR [111]. DEFINE [108] is clearly an outlier SSAM. It creates long successions of identical states, and its helix frequency is only equal to 27%. This value is largely inferior to all the other SSAMs since the helix frequency is always greater than 31%. Moreover, it is the only one to create high assignment confusion between helix and strand. This awkward confusion is within the range [2% - 5%] between DEFINE and all the other methods. For the others, this confusion α / β is always less than 0.05%. Thus, we show that the definition of new rules and methods since the beginning of the 90's has not changed the heterogeneity of the secondary structure assignments, and that the remarks of Woodcock and co-workers [114] about the difficulties of comparing different assignment methods still remain true.

Example of a Protein Coding Using Different Secondary Structure Assignment Methods

Figure 4 gives the example of the secondary structure assignments obtained for the Hhai Methyltransferase protein (PDB code: 10MH) using the different SSAMs. As Table 3, this figure highlights the difficulties of comparing these methods.

Firstly, the secondary structures of the Hhai Methyltransferase are assigned with a 3-state alphabet by DSSP, STRIDE, PSEA, DEFINE and PCURVE, and the difficulties of finding a consensus (cons.) between all these methods appear clearly since there are very few stars corresponding to a perfect match between the 5 SSAMs. The main disagreements are observed for the α-helices and β-strands edges and length. With the consensus method (noted C93) described by Colloc'h, Etchebest and co-workers [115] which involves the three oldest methods among these five ones, i.e. DSSP, DEFINE and PCURVE, we observe a rate of complete non agreement (i.e. one method assigns a α-helix, the second one a β-strand and the third one a coil) of 1%.

Secondly, the secondary structure assignments are represented for the methods that give more than three states and the results are even more difficult to analyze. For instance, at the N-terminus of the protein (box 1), when XTLSSTR assigns two positions as PolyProline II followed by a strand and a series of turns, DSSP shows a small bend followed by a turn, STRIDE a longer series of turns, and SECSTR assigns a 3_{10} helix instead of the turns. The box 2 is another interesting example, because it reflects classical confusing problems. The 3-state descriptions give a region mainly in coil or with a short helix (except for DEFINE). The consensus C93 also gives a short helix. SECSTR and DSSP assign a 3_{10} helix which stays coherent with C93. Nevertheless, XTLSSTR and STRIDE assign those positions as turns. This classical confusion between 3_{10} helix and turns is the main reason for the exclusion of type III β-turn from the β-turn classification. In the following positions, we observe the same feature but inversed. XTLSSTR assigns a 3_{10} helix when STRIDE and DSSP give a turn.

```
      AA      MIEIKDKQLTGLRFIDLFAGLGGFRLALESCGAECVYSNE
      DSSP3   CCCCCCCCCCCCEEEEECCCCCHHHHHHHCCCCEEEEEEC
      STRID3  CCCCCCCCCCCCEEEEECCCCCHHHHHHHHCCCEEEEEEC
      PSEA    CCCCCCCCCCCCEEEEECCCCCHHHHHHHHHHEEEEEEEE
      DEFINE  CCCCCCCCCCCCCCCEEEEEECHHHHHHHHHHEEEEEEEE
      PCURVE  EEECCCCCCCCCEEEEECCCCCCHHHHHHCCCCCCCEEEC
      cons.   ...********....*.....*.******.......***.
      PB      ZZdfblfkghiacddehklnommmmmmmmnopacfbdcdf
      [C93]   CCCCCCCCCCCCEEEEECCCCCHHHHHHHHCCCEEEEEEC
      XTLSS.  CPPCEEE    EEEEEEC   HHHHHHH   CPPPCEEEC
      SECSTR  CCCCCCC    CEEEEECCCCCHHHHHHHCCCCEECCEEC
      DSSP    CCCC  C    CEEEEE C  CHHHHHHH   CEEEEEEC
      STRIDE  CCC         EEEEE     HHHHHHHHCCCEEEEEEC
      HELAN.  ----------------------sssssss-----------
Box 1 BETAEX  ------------qpqpp----------------qqeeqp-

      AA      WDKYAQEVYEMNFGEKPEGDITQVNEKTIPDHDILCAGFP
      DSSP3   CCHHHHHHHHHHHCCCCCCCHHHCCCCCCCCCCEEEEECC
      STRID3  CCHHHHHHHHHHHCCCCCCCCCCCCCCCCCCCCEEEEECC
      PSEA    EEHHHHHHHHHHCCEEEEECCCCCCCCCCCCCCEEEECCC
      DEFINE  EEHHHHHHHHHHHHEEEEEEHHHHHHHHEEEEEEEEEEEE
      PCURVE  CCHHHHHHHHHHCCEEEECCCCCCCCCCCCCCEEEEEEEE
      cons.   ..**********.....................****...
      PB      bfklmmmmmmmnopacdedfklpcfklpccdfbdcddddf
      [C93]   CCHHHHHHHHHHHCEEEECCHHHCCCCCCCCCCEEEEEEE
      XTLSS.  CHHHHHHHHHHHHEEEPPC    C    PPPCEEEECCPP
      SECSTR  CCHHHHHHHHHHHCCCCECC   CCCCCCCCCCEEEEECC
      DSSP    CCHHHHHHHHHHH CCCBCC    C    CCC EEEEECC
      STRIDE  CCHHHHHHHHHHHCCCCBC          CCCCEEEEECC
      HELAN.  --vvvvvvvvvvv---------------------------
      BETAEX  -----------------b---------------ppppq--
Box 1
      AA      CQAFSISGKQKGFEDSRGTLFFDIARIVREKKPKVVFMEN
      DSSP3   CCCCCCCCCCCHHHCCCCCCHHHHHHHHHHHCCCEEEEEE
      STRID3  CCCCCCCCCCCHHHCCCCCHHHHHHHHHHHHCCCEEEEEE
      PSEA    CCCCCCCCCCCCCCCCCCCCHHHHHHHHHHCCCCEEEEEE
      DEFINE  EHHHHHHHEEEHHHHHHHHHHHHHHHHHHHHHHHEEEEEE
      PCURVE  CCCCCCCCCCCCCCCCHHHHHHHHHHHHHHHCCEEEEEEE
      cons.   ....................**********....******
      PB      klmPfkbnonojmlmklmmmmmmmmmmmmnopabdcdddd
      [C93]   CCCCCCCCCCCHHHCCHHHHHHHHHHHHHHHCC-EEEEEE
      XTLSS.     C   CCC           HHHHHHHHHCCEEEEEEEE
      SECSTR  CCCCCCCCCCC           HHHHHHHHCCCEEEEEEE
      DSSP    C   C   CCC         HHHHHHHHHHHCC EEEEEE
      STRIDE          CCC        HHHHHHHHHHHHCCCEEEEEE
      HELAN.  --------------------vvvvvvvvvvv---------
      BETAEX  ----------------------------------mmmmmz
```

Figure 4. Example of multiple secondary structure assignments for the N-terminal extremity of the protein 1OMH with DSSP3 and STRID3 (DSSP and STRIDE reduced to 3 states), PSEA, DEFINE, PCURVE, a consensus method (cons. with a star when the 5 methods agree), the consensus defined by Colloc'h and co-workers ([C93]), XTLSSTR, SECSTR, DSSP, STRIDE, HELANAL and the extended BETA alphabet (BETAEX). For the labels see Table 2.

The interest of the Protein Blocks appears through this example. When most of the SSAMs agree, the assigned PBs are coherent with the regular secondary structure states. For instance, the core of the α-helices are described by PB *m* and the core of the β-strands by PBs *c* and *d*. In addition, the PBs give a more detailed description in the confused positions. For example, in box 2, the Polyproline II helix assigned by XTLSSTR has its N-cap characterized by the PBs *fklpc*, a well characterized series of 5 PBs identified in a previous work as a Structural Word (SW). A SW is a series of PBs which is found with an important occurrence in the databank. The SWs identified have shown a particularly high structural stability [133]. This SW *fklpc* is characterized by a strong kink which induces a significant change in the backbone orientation. Its last dihedral angles are mainly associated to β-strand values. Thus, it is coherent with a transition between a tight turn and a Polyproline II helix, this last having dihedral angle values in the β-strand upper left region of the Ramachandran Map.

Figure 5 shows the global 3D structure of the Hhai Methyltransferase according to the seven assignment methods. This picture highlights again the heterogeneity of the secondary structure assignments. For instance, we can note the helices in the upper right of each picture. With DSSP and STRIDE, two helices are found creating an α-α corner, i.e. two helices which are orthogonal [79]. With PSEA, only one helix remains, the shorter one is not considered. DEFINE assigns all in a helicoidal state in a surprising way, i.e. even the residues which are in the kink (deviation of 90°). XTLSSTR gives the same result as PSEA, but shorten the remaining helix. SECSTR, as already noted, does a treatment very similar to DSSP and STRIDE with slight differences at the extremities. With the exception of some particularly well characterized structures like the Schellman box, the precise determination of repetitive structure capping limits is highly difficult [16]. Moreover, some algorithms are highly sensitive to the quality of the protein structures, i.e. resolution and temperature factors. For instance, a limited change in resolution or temperature factors can modify the DSSP secondary structure assignments.

The Protein Blocks and the Classical Secondary Structure 3-State Description

Table 4 (parts a and b) gives the complete distribution of the 3-state secondary structures for the seven studied methods in the Protein Blocks. As seen in the last paragraphs, DEFINE has a distinct behaviour in regards to the other methods, so we will not take it into account in the following sections.

For all the methods, we observe that the PB *m* is associated to the α-helix with a mean frequency of 90%. The 10% left correspond to coil. The α-helix is also described by the PBs *n* (67%) and *l* (54%). The PB *d* is associated at 72% to the β-strand and at 28% to the coil. These values underline one more time the β-strand definition problem. The main interest of our structural alphabet is a better description of the coil state by PBs *i* (90%), *b* (87%), *j* (82%), *p* (82%), *h* (80%), *f* (71%), *o* (66%), *k* (56%), *c* (54%) and *e* (51%).

Tables 4a and 4b enable us to further analyze the differences between the secondary structure assignment methods. For seven PBs (i.e. PBs *a*, *b*, *g*, *i*, *j*, *o* and *p*), we observe some significant differences in their secondary structure assignments. For instance, the PB *o* has an α-helix frequency of 29.3 % and a coil frequency of 70.2% with DSSP whereas these frequencies are equal to 49.7% and 49.9%, respectively with STRIDE, although these two methods are very close. The PBs *g*, *i* and *p* also present high variations in their α-helix and coil frequencies according to the different methods. The PB *a* shows high differences with β-strand and coil frequencies of 20.0 % and 79.8% with DSSP versus 26.3% and 73.6% with STRIDE. Furthermore, its β-strand frequency is only equal to 16.3% with SECSTR. A low value of SECSTR compared to DSSP and STRIDE is also observed for PBs *b* and *i*: the β-strand frequencies of PB *i* and *b* are equal to 6.1% and 14.1% for DSSP, to 6.6% and 15.1% for STRIDE and only 0.5% and 0.4% for SECSTR. This last point is intriguing as SECSTR was specifically dedicated to perform a better assignment of the helicoidal states than DSSP and STRIDE while giving a similar assignment for the extended state.

We compare all the SSAMs according to their 3-state secondary structure frequencies in the different PBs. For the helicoidal state, we observe a hierarchy XTLSSTR > DSS > PCURVE > PSEA in the frequencies associated to PB *m*. For the extended state, it is the inverse for the frequencies characterizing the PB *d*, with XTLSSTR < DSS < PCURVE < PSEA. Finally, for the coil state, we can roughly note the hierarchy PSEA > PCURVE > DSS > XTLSSTR.

The Protein Blocks and the Secondary Structure N-State Description

Table 5 focuses on three SSAMs that describe the secondary structures with more than three states, i.e. DSSP, STRIDE and SECSTR, and shows the correspondence with the PBs. The helicoidal state is characterized by α-helices, 3_{10} –helices and π-helices. For the α-helix state, the frequencies in the different PBs are close except as previously noted for the PB *o* which has an α-helix frequency equal to 22.2% for DSSP, 41.4% for STRIDE and only 14.5% for SECSTR. All the α-helix frequencies are lower for SECSTR. However, it is the opposite for the 3_{10} –helices and in a lesser extent for the π-helices, since for the PBs from *g* to *p* the 3_{10} –helix frequencies are 2 to 10% greater than DSSP and STRIDE. This last fact is consistent with the main purpose of SECSTR. The PB *l* has a 3_{10} –helix frequency of 19.2%. The PB *g* and *p* are also especially well furnished with 3_{10} –helix frequencies of about 17%. The π-helix frequencies are low, but far superior with SECSTR.

The coil state defined in Table 4 is decomposed in four categories, namely the coil ('C'), the turn ('T'), the bend ('N') and the isolated β-bridge ('B'). As observed in Table 4, the non-repetitive structures present equivalent frequencies in the different PBs according to the three SSAMs. However, Table 5 shows that between the different types of classification, the results are clearly distinct. The turns of DSSP (states 'T' and 'N') are not equivalent to the turns of STRIDE ('T'). Their average frequencies per PBs differ by more than 10%. The turns of DSSP are more frequent in PBs *o* (+25%), *p* (+25%), *b* (+19%) and *j* (+17%) and the turns of STRIDE ('T') are more frequent in PBs *f* (+21%), *e* (+21%), *a* (+11%) and *g* (+7%). This point is particularly important as the turns are commonly used to describe more precisely the protein structures. For the isolated β-bridge ('B'), the frequencies are really similar between DSSP and STRIDE, the difference between the two assignment methods are always less than 0.9%. For the extended strand, the results are the same as previously found. These results highlight the complexity of describing only particular regions. The differences in the number of analyzed local folds can bias the analysis of the results.

The Protein Blocks and the Precise Description of the Repetitive Secondary Structures

Table 6 summarizes the distribution of the α-helices and extended strands using more detailed descriptions.

The helices of the Protein DataBank [102, 103] are known not to be ideal helices according to the thermodynamical properties. The use of the SSAMs often creates helices that are too long. The longest helices in the Protein DataBank contain about 60 residues. Barlow and Thornton [112] have shown that 3/4 of the helices are not linear, i.e. they are curved or kinked. HELANAL [113] allows to redefine helices into 5 categories: short (less than 9 residues), linear, curved, kinked or unassigned. We have used DSSP definitions of the helices to compute the assignment. As expected, the most frequent PB associated with the different categories is PB *m* with 48.6% associated to curved helices, 17.5% to short helices, 10.3% to kinked helices and only 8.5% to linear helices. PB *m* represents 70.1% of the PBs associated to short helices, 82.6% to linear helices, 84.2% to curved helices and 84.4% to kinked helices. We observe that the short helices are described by several other PBs including PB *n* (18.6%), *l* (16.8%) and *k* (13.5%), with PB *n* frequency greater than that of PB *m*. For the other types of helix, PB *m* remains the most important although for the curved helices for instance many other PBs are involved in their description.

In the same way than for HELANAL, the extended beta alphabet used the DSSP outputs to define different new labels : isolated β-bridge ('b'), extended strand in parallel sheet ('p') or parallel edge ('q'), antiparallel sheet ('a'), antiparallel edge ('z'), parallel and antiparallel mixed ('m') and strand only ('e'). As expected, the PBs *d*, *c* and also *e* are the most frequent ones. In addition, two interesting facts must be pointed out. The first one is the isolated β-bridge ('b') which is characterized by the PB *g* with a frequency of 3.6% even though it is not a PB particularly associated to extended structures. The second one is the distribution of the extended strand alone ('e') which is mainly associated to the PB *b*, a PB associated with long loops and Ccap of β-strand, and to PB *i*, which is more associated to the coil state than to the extended state.

These results show that even for the repetitive not-so ideal structures, the Protein Blocks constitute an interesting analyzing tool.

The Protein Blocks and XTLSSTR 9-State Description

Table 7 summarizes the correspondence between the 16 Protein Blocks and the 9 states defined by XTLSSTR. This method has some interesting particularities like the assignment of turns not with the classical dihedral angle criteria but defined as hydrogen- or non hydrogen bonding-turns, and of polyproline II helices. Moreover, it identifies the Ccaps of the $3._{10}$ –helices and of the polyproline II helices. This SSAM gives different results in regards to the precedent methods. The PB *f* is now associated with a non negligible proportion of α-helix (12.7%) and of $3._{10}$ –helix (5.7%). This last fact is related to the PB *g* $3._{10}$ –Ccap frequency (7.4%) since the main transition of PB *f* is PB *g*. This value is coherent with the DSS frequency of $3._{10}$ –helix associated to PB *g* (DSSP, STRIDE and SECSTR frequencies are equal to 8.5%, 7.4% and 17.3%, respectively; cf. Table 5a). The PBs *o* and *p* are associated to the 3_{10} –Ccap (frequencies of 11.2% and 12.5%, respectively). In addition, we observe that globally more hydrogen bond turns are found than unhydrogen bond turns. Several PBs are involved in their description with no particular specificity related to the hydrogen bond stabilization. As for the polyproline II helices, they appear more frequent in globular proteins than expected [23]. Their dihedral angle distribution is often confused with β-strands in the upper left of Ramachandran Map and therfore is confused with the β-sheet assignment. This feature is observed again in these results where PBs *a*, *c*, *d*, *e* and *g* have polyproline II frequencies equal to 22.1%, 23.1%, 17.1%, 20.0% and 14.7%, respectively. Some PBs are specific to the C-cap of the polyproline II helix, e.g. PBs *f* and *h*. These observations are in agreement with the main transitions between successive PBs since PB *e* often goes to PB *f* and PB *g* to PB *h*.

Thus, the goal of this detailed analysis was to emphasize the fact that the "classic" secondary structures can be described with different criteria which results in ambiguous assignments. Moreover, we have highlighted the interest of using more than three states for better describing protein structures through a structural alphabet. The 16 PBs enable to analyze specifically every part of the protein structures.

In the next section of this chapter, we propose a prediction scheme of the protein structural classes from the PB prediction.

Part II: PBs and Protein Structural Classes

Goal

The question tackled in this section is the potentiality of classifying one protein into its true protein class from the sole knowledge of its prediction in terms of Protein Blocks. The process used is in three steps : (i) Protein Blocks are predicted from the sequence, (ii) the relative frequencies of the 16 PBs are computed and the three mean frequencies vectors, called prototypes, representing the three protein classes, are computed from the learning protein set, (iii) the comparisons between the three mean prototypes representing the protein classes and the relative frequencies of the 16 PBs are done for target proteins to predict their classes.

Having a good idea of the protein classes can be an efficient way for refining the prediction research. For instance, it can enable to direct the prediction of a protein, i.e. if a protein is all-α, the information derived from all-β proteins would not be used for this protein. The interest of this study is not to use the *true* PBs, but the *predicted* PBs. The prediction rate is, as previously said, equal to 40.7% [128]. Hence, the difficulty here is to predict accurately protein classes from this partial information.

Protein Classes

As noted by Thornton and co-workers, the secondary structures form particular motifs that define the global protein topology, e.g. the TIM barrel fold [141]. This information is used to classify the protein structures. Different algorithms have been developed and the classification is done either automatically like in the CATH database [144] or mainly manually like in the SCOP database [143]. Different classes are defined and give information about the relationships between the proteins. Interestingly, the different methods give the same types of hierarchical relationships with few superfamilies and many subfamilies. On the basis of their secondary structures, the folds are grouped into four main classes: all-α (essentially α-helices), all-β (essentially β-strands), $\alpha + \beta$ (α–helices and β-strands are largely segregated) and α / β (α–helices and β-strands are largely interspersed). The assignment of a structure to a particular class is in some cases a difficult task. In fact, even with an automatic classification, a manual inspection is needed. From the sole knowledge of the amino acid sequence, the task is even more complicated when no homologous sequence is found.

Bayesian Prediction of the Protein Blocks

In a previous study [128], we have tackled the Protein Blocks prediction from the amino acid sequence. To this end, we extracted the amino acid preferences for each local pattern and used this information in a Bayesian process to predict the structural motifs able to be adopted by a given protein chain. With this strategy, for each amino acid sequence, the potential series of Protein Blocks is predicted [128, 133]. To evaluate the prediction, we computed a Q_{16} ratio which corresponds to the number of well predicted PBs. This value is similar to the Q_3 of secondary structures with more states to predict, i.e. N=16 possibilities against N=3 for the secondary structures. With the new databank used in this study, we have an initial Q_{16} ratio equal to 35.4%, which is very similar to the result of our previous work, i.e. 34.4% [128]. Table 8 (col 3) gives the prediction rates for each of the 16 PBs. The high differences of the PB frequencies in the databank need to be taken into account (Table 8, col 2) since some of the PBs are overrepresented like PBs *m* and *d* (30.2% and 18.8% respectively). Consequently, we made sure that the Q_{16} ratio was not biased by over-predictions of PBs *m* and *d*.

However, associating one PB with one class of sequences is a restrictive point of view. A same fold pattern (or PB) may be associated with different types of sequences (1 Protein Block -> *n* sequences). Thus, we have defined a new process to split the set of fragment sequences associated with one PB into different clusters. These clusters allow a better description of the sequence specificities associated with each PB. They are called sequence families (see [128] for more details). In our previous work, this process allowed an increase the Q_{16} ratio from 34.4% to 40.7% (see Table 8, col. 4). Since, we have improved the splitting process (*unpublished results*) which gives a better Q_{16} ratio now equal to 48.7% (see Table 8, col. 5). A clear improvement was observed for the PBs *m* and *d* (+28.6 and +19.0%, respectively), but also for the other PBs (with a mean improvement rate of +2.1%).

From this improved prediction, we have analyzed the association between the predicted PB frequencies and the protein structural classes. To carry out this analysis, we have focused on three protein classes, i.e. all-α, all-β and mixed. In this last class, we have merged the $\alpha + \beta$ and α / β proteins as our approach does not take account of the secondary structures sequentiality. The categorization of the proteins has been done using the criteria of Michie and co-workers [148] and DSSP secondary structure assignment.

Analysis of the Prediction Informativity

In a first step, we have analyzed the informativity of the prediction, i.e. the information contained in the relative predicted frequencies of Protein Blocks. For this purpose, we have performed a Principal Component Analysis (PCA) on the relative frequencies of the predicted PBs obtained for each protein. Such a descriptive approach allows quantifying this informativity by coding all the data in their original dimension, i.e. without information loss. The first component explains 92% of the information; the others represent less than 1.0%. This shows that the information of the predicted Protein Block frequencies has an important determinism.

Figure 6 shows for each structural class the distribution of the first component values. We observe that the all-α proteins are the only one to have a first component value that can be less than -0.2. At the opposite, none of the all-β proteins is found at a value less than 0.0. The mixed group is between the two first ones and overlaps more the all-β proteins than the all-α proteins. Figure 7 shows the projection of the two first components. The all-α (red crosses) and the all-β proteins (blue crosses) seem to be distinguishable using the PCA and form two distinct clusters. The first component is the most discriminative. However, the all-β proteins used more of the second component than the all-α proteins. This analysis shows that we are able to discriminate the three structural classes according to the protein PB predicted frequencies.

Prediction of the Structural Classes

In this part, we have identified the PBs principally involved in the different classes and we have used the predicted PB frequencies for prediction purpose. Figure 8 shows the relative frequencies of the predicted Protein Blocks for each structural class. These frequencies are normalized in regards to the frequencies of the predicted Protein Blocks in the databank and centred on 0, *i.e.* 0 represents the background frequency of the PB. The α - β proteins have average frequencies close to the background random Protein Block frequencies. The all - β proteins have over - representations of the Protein Blocks from PB *a* to PB *j* and under – representations for the others. The all - α proteins have under – representations of the Protein Blocks from PB *a* to PB *j* and an important over – representation of PB *m*. These results are highly coherent with the definition of the different classes.

From these 3 mean representations of the protein classes, we have developed a simple prediction strategy of the protein class from the PB predicted frequencies. Each target protein's predicted PB frequencies vector is compared with the three vectors of the protein classes using an Euclidean distance. The minimal distance gives the predicted class, i.e. the minimal difference between the protein and the prototype. Table 9 summarizes the results of the prediction by giving the confusion matrix between true and predicted protein classes. The prediction rate is equal to 71.5%. The prediction rates for the two extreme classes, i.e. all - α and all - β are high, i.e. 84% and 74%, respectively. The rate of correct prediction is lower for the mixed class, i.e. 69%. These results show that our simple prediction scheme is efficient. No confusion between all - α and all-β proteins is observed.

This work shows that from the prediction step, we can tackle the protein class with a good accuracy. It is interesting since the prediction is actually done indiscriminately for all types of globular proteins. By focusing on one particular class, we can supervise more efficiently the prediction. Hence, it can be useful to learn separately (all - α and α - β) proteins and (all - β and α - β) proteins.

Part III: Triangular Kohonen Map for Analyzing Proteins (TopKAPi)

In the continuity of our previous work, we have attempted to assess the contribution of our structural alphabet for discriminating protein structures. A first step consisted in encoding the protein structures of our non-redundant databank in terms of Protein Blocks, and, in translating this information into PB frequencies, then into Z-scores. This work is related to the representation of relationships into a set of related proteins [159, 160].

A Sammon Map [158] was computed with this data and defined in a 2D space. Interestingly, it showed a triangular pattern (figure not shown). It must be noted that the Sammon Map is only an approximated projection of the protein set. To carry out an unsupervised clustering of the proteins, the approach SOM (Self – Organizing Map) is a good choice [154, 155]. We computed a specific SOM that takes into account the triangular projection, “a triangular SOM”. This particular SOM is called TopKAPi, for *T*riangular *K*ohonen map for *A*nalyzing *P*roteins. After having performed different trials with TopKAPi, we have selected a triangular network with a side of $G = 11$, i.e. a total of 66 neurons.

The interest of such an approach is to control the training to avoid a possible redundancy in the clustering. In fact, we have defined the initial PBs Z-score distributions in the network. From the previous analysis, we have selected the three proteins forming the largest triangle in the space, i.e. the sum of the distances between the three selected proteins is maximal. After locating these normalized PBs distributions at the vertices of the triangular network, we have defined the PBs distribution in each neuron by linear interpolation. The PBs distribution neurons evolve thanks to the concept of information diffusion around the winner neuron.

This choice states on a protein location evenness over the network allowing a number of proteins per neuron adequate for estimating the Z-scores. After training, we observed a median number equals 13 proteins per neuron. The two maximums are equal to 95 and 89.

Learning Step

Figure 9 shows the distribution of the proteins in the network neurons. The size of the circles is proportional to the numbers. Every neuron is characterized by an average distribution normalized in Z-scores. The 66 PB distributions are shared into five classes (labelled from G1 to G5; see the colors of Figure 9) by a hierarchical clustering. The average distributions associated with the clusters are displayed. Two subsets of proteins are easily pointed out: the structures “all-α helix” (characterized by a high positive Z-score for PB *m*) and the structures “all-β sheet” (characterized by a high positive Z-score for PB *c*, *d*, *e*, *h* and *i*). The other clusters are intermediate groups since the Z-scores distributions are reduced in magnitude.

Figure 10 gives the Sammon map [158] obtained using inter-neuron distance matrix. We observe a coherent repartition of the five clusters more linear than expected. Nevertheless, it shows the complete antagonism between all-α proteins and all-β proteins. It highlights too the interest of the triangular representation of TopKAPi which allows the emergence of the cluster colored in blue characterized by an underpresentation of PBs *d* and *m*.

Protein Blocks Distributions

Figure 11 gives the overrepresentation (in pink and red) and the underepresentation (in yellow and blue) observed in every neuron (the grey corresponds to values close to 0). Before interpreting these figures, we have carried out a hierarchical clustering of these Z-score distributions per block. Figure 12 gives the dendogram showing the PB associations in the protein description. Two specific protein blocks are clearly distinguishable, as expected PBs *m* and *d* which correspond to α-helix and β-strand cores, respectively. Another class of PBs are defined: {*k*, *o*, *p*, *l*, *n*} associated to the N- and C-caps of the α-helix. The last class is heterogeneous; it groups the N- and C-caps of the β-strand and the coils. The PB subset {*e*, *h*, *i*} is more frequently associated to β-β transition. The PB subset {*g*, *a*, *j*} is more specific to coil or flexible regions. The last subset {*f*, *b*, *c*} is more ambiguous containing N- and C-caps of β-strand and coils.

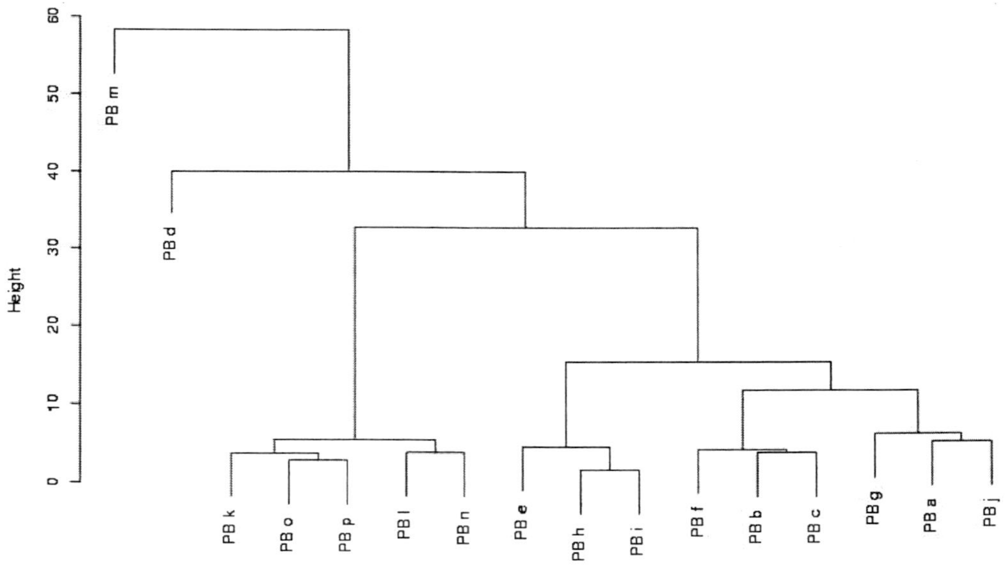

Figure 12. Hierarchical clustering of the PBs Z-score distributions in TopKAPi.

From the protein classification into five clusters (G_1-G_5), previously defined, and this PB classification, we point out:

1. class G_1: an overrepresentation of PB *m* and an underrepresentation of a large subset of PBs {*a*, *b*, *c*, *d*, *e*, *f*, *h*, *i*}. The graph of PB *m* shows large contrast in the Z-scores. This group is specific to all-α proteins.
2. class G_2: an overrepresentation of PBs located in helices and their extremities i.e. {*l*, *m*, *n*, *o*} and an underrepresentation of PBs located in β-strands. The Z-scores are less high than in G_1.
3. class G_3: an overrepresentation of certain PBs {*a*, *e*, *g*, *h*, *i*, *j*, *k*, *l*, *p*} related to protein showing little regular secondary structures, i.e. mainly composed of coils.
4. class G_4: an overrepresentation of PBs *b*, *c*, *d* and *f* associated to protein showing high frequency of β-strands.
5. class G_5: an overrepresentation of PBs *a* to *f*, *h* to *i* and an underrepresentation of PBs *l*, *m* and *n*. This group is specific to "all β" proteins associated to high Z-scores for PBs *c* and *d*.

Amino Acid Distribution

Figure 13 shows the Z-score distributions per amino acid. We observe a higher heterogeneity in the locations of over- and under-representations. This can be explained by the fact that the training is only based on the structure, i.e. the PB distribution.

In each protein cluster, we highlight some amino acid propensities to be located in certain protein classes such as:

1. class G_1: overrepresentations of L, Q, E, K with underrepresentation of C, P and G. The presence of these amino acid frequencies is a specificity of all-α proteins.
2. class G_2: presence of I, A, E and K. Few differences are observed between clusters G_1 and G_2. It seems that the amino acids specific to α-helices, i.e. A and L, are not found in the same protein types.
3. class G_3: this group containing low proportion of regular secondary structures shows high affinities for amino acids such as A, C, G and S.
4. class G_4: this intermediate group close to the "all-β" does not show significant relationship with the amino acids. We observe a large heterogeneity of the Z-score values.
5. class G_5: The graph reveals high contrast on positive Z-scores for certain amino acids, e.g. C, V, G, S and T.

This study has allowed the definition of five protein classes characterized by PB distributions and associated with under or overrepresentations of certain amino acids. This classification is not only based on the proportions of the PBs located in α-helix or β-strand, but also on the proportions of PBs located in the extremities of the regular secondary structures or in the coils. A further work associating the PB distributions and the amino acid distributions in the training should improve the definition of the protein classes.

Conclusion

Through this chapter, our aim was primarily to highlight the interest of a structural alphabet composed of local structural prototypes, i.e. the 16 Protein Blocks, to describe every part of protein 3D structures. Also, we accurately compared the 3-state secondary structure assignment with the assignment in terms of PBs. The analysis of the correspondence between the different secondary structure assignment methods showed high discrepancies: 20% of the residues are assigned to different states. The agreement ratio between two Secondary Structure Assignment Methods (SSAMs) is highly dependent on the metrics used and the difficulties of comparing different assignment methods have been pointed out several times.

The Protein Blocks encompass most of the features of the secondary structure description with 3 or more states. They describe more precisely the repetitive structures (helicoidal and extended), their edges and the coil state which is composed of really distinct local folds. We highlighted interesting correspondences between particular local folds and the PBs.

Use Protein Blocks prediction to classify proteins into the classical structural classes, namely all-α, all-β and mixed gave a good prediction rate, i.e. 71.5%, with no confusion between all α and all β classes. Predicting protein structural classes can be useful for directing the prediction in terms of PBs from sequence and for understanding the protein folding of particular protein classes.

Finally, our novel clustering approach, TopKAPi enables us to classify and analyze proteins according to their Protein Block frequencies. Moreover, we have characterized some propensities of amino acids to be located in the five protein clusters previously defined.

In conclusion, the structural alphabet is a tool for analyzing local protein structures, that allows one to work with a chain of characters rather than with carbon α coordinates. Moreover, a structural alphabet facilitates the definition of 'Structural Words', PB series of high frequencies, specific to a folding pattern. Hence, it constitutes a new way for characterizing local folds. Also, it represents an intermediate step for protein modelling in terms of the 16 PBs. The present study reveals the interest of a structural alphabet for defining the protein classes. Other multiple perspectives appear in this way of representing 3D protein structures and particularly in molecular modelling.

References

[1] Kendrew, J.C., Bodo, G., Dintzis, H.M., Parrish, R.G., Wyckoff, H. and Philips, D.C. (1958) A three-dimensional model of the myoglobin molecule obtained by x-ray analysis. *Nature* 181, 662-666.

[2] Pauling, L. and Corey, R.B. (1951) Atomic Coordinates and Structure Factors for Two Helical Configurations of Polypeptide Chains *Proc Natl Acad Sci, USA* 37, 235-240.

[3] Eisenberg, D. (2003) The discovery of the alpha-helix and beta-sheet, the principal structural features of proteins. *Proc Natl Acad Sci, USA* 100, 11207-11210.

[4] Pauling, L. and Corey, R.B. (1951) The Pleated Sheet, A New Layer Configuration of Polypeptide Chains. *Proc Natl Acad Sci, USA* 37, 251-256.

[5] Pauling, L. and Corey, R.B. (1950) Two Hydrogen-Bonded Spiral Configurations of the Polypeptide Chain. *J. Am. Chem. Soc* 72, 53.

[6] Ho, B.K., Thomas, A. and Brasseur, R. (2003) Revisiting the Ramachandran plot: hard-sphere repulsion, electrostatics, and H-bonding in the alpha-helix. *Prot Sci.* 12, 2508-2522.

[7] Colloc'h, N. and Cohen, F.E. (1991) Beta-breakers: an aperiodic secondary structure. *J Mol Biol.* 221, 603-613.

[8] Regan, L. (1994) Protein structure. Born to be beta. *Curr Biol.* 4, 656-658.

[9] Richardson, J.S. and Richardson, D.C. (2002) Natural beta-sheet proteins use negative design to avoid edge-to-edge aggregation. *Proc Natl Acad Sci, USA* 99, 2754-2759.

[10] Richardson, J.S. (1976) Handedness of Crossover Connections in Beta Sheets. *Proc Natl Acad Sci, USA* 73, 2619-2623.

[11] Chotia, C., Levitt, M. and Richardson, D. (1977) Structure of Proteins: Packing of Alpha-Helices and Pleated Sheets. *Proc Natl Acad Sci, USA* 74, 4130-4134.

[12] Chotia, C., Levitt, M. and Richardson, D. (1981) Helix to helix packing in proteins. *J Mol Biol* 145, 215-250.

[13] Efimov, A.V. (1991) Structure of coiled beta-beta-hairpins and beta-beta-corners. *FEBS Lett.* 284, 288-292.

[14] Aurora, R., Srinivasan, R. and Rose, G.D. (1994) Rules for alpha-helix termination by glycine. *Science* 264,1126-1130.

[15] Hutchinson, E and Sessions, RB and Thornton, JM and Woolfson, DN (1998) Determinants of strand register in antiparallel beta-sheets of proteins, Protein Sci, 7, 2287-2300.

[16] Aurora, R. and Rose, G.D. (1998) Helix Capping. *Protein Sci.* 7, 21-38.

[17] Liu, W.M. and Chou, KC. (1998) Singular points of protein beta-sheets. *Protein Sci.* 7, 2324-2330.

[18] Donohue, J. (1953) Hydrogen bonded helical configurations of the polypeptide chain. *Proc Natl Acad Sci USA* 39, 470– 478.

[19] Pal, L. and Basu, G. (1999) Novel protein structural motifs containing two-turn and longer 3(10)-helices. *Protein Eng.* 12, 811-814.

[20] Pal, L., Basu,. G. and Chakrabarti, P. (2002) Variants of 3_{10}-helices in proteins. *Proteins* 48, 571-579.

[21] Low, B.W. and Baybutt, R.B. (1952) The □-helix -A hydrogen bonded configuration of the polypeptide chain. *J Am Chem Soc* 74, 5806.

[22] Low, B.W. and Greenville-Wells, H.J. (1953) Generalized mathematical relationships for polypeptide chain helices. The coordinates of the □-helix. *Proc Natl Acad Sci USA* 39, 785–801.

[23] Weaver, T.M. (2000) The pi-helix translates structure into function. *Protein Sci.* 9, 201-206.

[24] Fodje, M.N. and Al-Karadaghi, S. (2002). Occurrence, conformational features and amino acid propensities for the □-helix. Protein Eng. 15, 353-358.

[25] Sudha, R., Kohtani, M., Breaux, G.A. and Jarrold, M.F. (2004) □-Helix Preference in Unsolvated Peptides. *J. Am. Chem. Soc.* 126, 2777-2784.

[26] Armen, R., Alonso, D.O. and Daggett, V. (2003) The role of alpha-, 3(10)-, and pi-helix in helix-->coil transitions. *Protein Sci.* 12, 1145-1157.

[27] Cartailler, J.P. and Luecke, H. (2004) Structural and functional characterization of pi bulges and other short intrahelical deformations. *Structure* 12, 133-144.

[28] Pauling, L. and Corey, R.B. (1951) The Structure of Fibrous Proteins of the Collagen-Gelatin Group. *Proc Natl Acad Sci, USA*. 37, 272-281.

[29] Cowan, P.M. and McGavin, S. (1955) Structure of poly-L-proline. *Nature* 176, 501-503.

[30] Adzhubei, A.A. and Sternberg M.J. (1993) Left-handed polyproline II helices commonly occur in globular proteins. *J Mol Biol*. 229, 472-493.

[31] Stapley, B.J. and Creamer, T.P. (1999) A survey of left-handed polyproline II helices. *Protein Sci*. 8, 587-595.

[32] Creamer, T.P. (1998) Left-handed Polyproline II helix formation is (very) locally driven. *Proteins* 33, 218-226.

[33] Creamer T.P. and Campbell, M.N. (2002) Determinants of the polyproline II helix from modeling studies. *Adv Protein Chem* 62, 263-282.

[34] Eswar, N., Ramakrishnan C. and Srinivasan, N (2003) Stranded in isolation: structural role of isolated extended strands in proteins. *Protein Eng*. 16, 331-339.

[35] Sowdhamini, R., Srinivasan, N., Ramakrishnan, C. and Balaram P. (1992) Orthogonal beta beta motifs in proteins. *J Mol Biol* 223, 845-851.

[36] Richardson, J.S., Getzoff, E.D. and Richardson, D.C. (1978) The beta bulge: a common small unit of nonrepetitive protein structure. *Proc Natl Acad Sci USA* 75, 2574-2578.

[37] Chan, A.W., Hutchinson, E.G., Harris, D. and Thornton, J.M. (1993). Identification, classification, and analysis of □-bulges in proteins. *Protein Sci*. 2, 1574-1590.

[38] Axe, D.D., Foster, N.W. and Fersht, A.R. (1999) An irregular beta-bulge common to a group of bacterial RNases is an important determinant of stability and function in barnase. *J Mol Biol* 286, 1471-1485.

[39] Ramachandran, G. N. and Sasisekharan, V. (1968) Conformation of polypeptides and proteins *Advan. Protein Chem*. 23, 283.

[40] Venkatachalam, C.M. (1968) Stereochemical criteria for polypeptides and proteins. V. Conformation of a system of three linked peptide units. *Biopolymers* 10, 1425-1436.

[41] Richardson, J.S., Getzoff, E.D. and Richardson, D.C. (1978). The □ bulge: a common small unit of nonrepetitive protein structure. *Proc Natl Acad Sci, USA* 75, 2574-2578.

[42] Némethy, G. and Printz, M.P. (1972) The gamma turn, a possible folded conformation of the polypeptide chain. Comparison with the beta turn. *Macromolecules* 5, 755-758.

[43] Matthews, B.W. (1972) the gamma-turn. Evidence for a new folded conformation in Proteins. *Macromolecules* 5, 818-819.

[44] Milner-White, E.J. (1988) Recurring loop motif in proteins that occurs in right-handed and left-handed forms. Its relationship with □-helices and □-bulge loops. *J Mol Biol*. 199, 503-511.

[45] Rose, G.D., Gierasch, L.M. and Smith, J.A. (1985) Turns in peptides and proteins. *Adv. Prot. Chem*. 37, 1-109.

[46] Lewis, P.N., Momany, F.A. and Scheraga, H.A. (1971) Folding of polypeptide chains in proteins: a proposed mechanism for folding. *Proc Natl Acad Sci USA*. 68, 2293-2297.

[47] Kuntz, I.D. (1972) Protein folding. *J Am Chem Soc*. 94, 4009-4012.

[48] Lewis, P.N., Momany, F.A. and Scheraga, H.A. (1973) Chain reversals in proteins. *Bioch Biophys Acta* 303, 211-229.

[49] Chou, P.Y. and Fasman, G.D. (1977) Beta-turns in proteins. *J Mol Biol* 115, 135-175.

[50] Rose, G.D. and Seltzer, J.P. (1977) A New algorithm for finding the peptide chain turns in a globular protein. *J Mol Biol* 113, 153-164,

[51] Rose, G.D. and Wetlaufer, D.B. (1977) The number of turns in globular proteins, *Nature* 5622, 769-770.

[52] Zimmermann, S.S. and Scheraga, H.A. (1977) Influence of local interactions on protein structure. I. Conformational energy studies of N-acetyl-N'-methylamides of Pro-X and X-Pro dipeptides. *Biopolymers* 16, 811-843.

[53] Richardson, J.S. (1981) The anatomy and taxonomy of protein structure. *Adv Protein Chem* 34, 167-339.

[54] Wilmot, C.M. and Thornton, J.M. (1988) Analysis and prediction of the different types of □-turn in proteins. *J Mol Biol* 5, 221-232.

[55] Hutchinson, E.G. and Thornton, J.M. (1996) PROMOTIF - A program to identify structural motifs in proteins. *Protein Sci.* 5, 212-220.

[56] Ball, S.G. and Hughes, AS (1993) beta-turn topography. *Tetrahedron* 49, 3467-3478.

[57] Ashish, X., Grover, A. and Kishore, R. (2000) Characterization of a novel type VII beta-turn conformation for a bio-active tetrapeptide rigin. *Eur J Biochem* 267,1455-1463.

[58] Chou, K.C. (2000) Prediction of tight turns and their types in proteins. *Anal. Biochem.* 286, 1-16.

[59] Pavone, V., Gaeta, G., Lombardi, A., Nastri, F., Maglio, O., Isernia, C. and Saviano, M. (1996) Discovering protein secondary structures: classification and description of isolated □-turns. *Biopolymers* 38, 705-721.

[60] Kaur, H. and Raghava, G.P.S. (2004) Prediction of □-turns in proteins using PSI-BLAST profiles and secondary structure information. *Proteins* 55, 83-90.

[61] Milner-White, E.J., Ross, B.M., Ismail, R., Belhadj-Mostefa, K. and Poet R. (1988) One type of gamma-turn, rather than the other gives rise to chain-reversal in proteins. *J Mol Biol.* 204, 777-782.

[62] Rajashankar, K.R., and Ramakumar, S. (1996). □-turns in proteins and peptides: classification, conformation, occurrence, hydratation and sequence. *Protein Sci.* 5, 932-946.

[63] Guruprasad, K. and Rajkumar, S. (2000) beta- and gamma-turns in proteins revisited: a new set of amino acid turn-type dependent positional preferences and potentials. *J Biosci* 25, 143-156.

[64] Guruprasad, K., Prasad, M.S. and Kumar, G.R. (2000) Analysis of gammabeta, betagamma, gammagamma, betabeta multiple turns in proteins, *J Pept Res* 56, 250-263.

[65] Guruprasad, K., Rao, M.J., Adindla, S., and Guruprasad L. (2003) Combinations of turns in proteins. *J Pept Res.* 62, 167-174.

[66] Leszczynski, J.F. and Rose, G.D. (1986) Loops in globular proteins: a novel category of secondary structure. *Science* 234, 849-855.

[67] Fetrow, J.S. (1995) Omega loops: nonregular secondary structures significant in protein function and stability. *FASEB J.* 9, 708-717.

[68] Pal, M. and Dasgupta, S. (2003) The nature of the turn in omega loops of proteins, *Proteins* 51, 606-616.

[69] Fetrow, J.S., Cardillo, T.S. and Sherman, F. (1989) Deletions and replacements of omega loops in yeast Iso-1-cytochrome c. *Proteins* 6, 372-381.

[70] Krishna, M.M.G., Lin, Y., Rumbley, J.N. and Englander, S.W. (2003) Cooperative Omega loops in Cytochrome c: Role in folding and function. *J Mol Biol* 331, 29-36.

[71] Sibanda, B.L. and Thornton, J.M. (1985) Beta-hairpin families in globular proteins. *Nature* 316, 170-174.

[72] Milner-White, E.J. and Poet, R. (1986) Four classes of beta-hairpins in proteins. *Biochem J.* 240, 289-292.

[73] Sibanda, B.L., Blundell, T.L. and Thornton, J.M. (1989) Conformation of beta-hairpins in protein structures. A systematic classification with applications to modelling by homology, electron density fitting and protein engineering. *J Mol Biol.* 206, 759-777.

[74] Sibanda, B.L. & Thornton, J.M. (1991). Conformation of □ hairpins in protein structures: classification and diversity in homologous structures. Methods Enzymol. 202, 59-82.

[75] Sibanda, B.L. and Thornton, J.M. (1993) Accommodating sequence changes in beta-hairpins in proteins. *J Mol Biol* 229, 428-447.

[76] Gunasekaran, K., Ramakrishan, C. and Balaram, P. (1997) Beta-hairpins in proteins revisited: lessons for de novo design. *Protein Eng.* 10, 1131-1141.

[77] Blandl, T., Cochran, A.G. and Skelton N.J. (2003) Turn stability in beta-hairpin peptides: Investigation of peptides containing 3:5 type I G1 bulge turns. *Protein Sci.* 12, 237-247.

[78] Kim, J., Brych, S.R., Lee, J., Logan, T.M., Blaber, M. (2003) Identification of a key structural element for protein folding within beta-hairpin turns. *J Mol Biol* 328, 951-961.

[79] Efimov A.V. (1984) A novel super-secondary structure of proteins and the relation between the structure and the amino acid sequence. *FEBS Lett* 166, 33-38.

[80] Rice, P.A., Goldman, A. and Steitz, T.A. (1990) A helix-turn-strand structural motif common in □-□ proteins. *Proteins* 8, 334-340

[81] Tang, J., James, M.N., Hsu, I.N., Jenkins, J.A. and Blundell, T.L. (1978) Structure evidence for gene duplication in the evolution of the acid protease. *Nature* 271, 618-622.

[82] Wintjens, R.T., Rooman, M.J. and Wodak, S.J. (1996) Automatic classification and analysis of alpha alpha-turn motifs in proteins. *J. Mol. Biol.* 255, 235-253.

[83] Wintjens, R.T., Rooman, M.J. and Wodak, SJ (1998) Typical interaction patterns in alphabeta and betaalpha turn motifs. *J Mol Biol* 11, 505-522.

[84] Boutonnet, N.S., Kajava, A.V. and Rooman, M.J. (1998) Structural classification of alphabetabeta and betabetaalpha supersecondary structure. *Proteins* 30, 193-212.

[85] Kwasigroch, J.-M., Chomilier, J. and Mornon, J.-P. (1996) A global taxonomy of loops in globular proteins. *J Mol Biol.* 259, 855-872.

[86] Geetha, V. and Munson, P.J. (1997) Linkers of secondary structures in proteins. *Protein Sci.* 6, 2538-2547.

[87] Tramontano, A., Chothia, C. and Lesk, A.M. (1989) Structural determinants of the conformations of medium-sized loops in proteins. Proteins. 6, 382-394.

[88] Donate, L.E., Rufino, S.D., Canard, L.H.J. and Blundell T.L. (1996) Conformational analysis and clustering of short and medium size loops connecting secondary structures: a database for modeling and prediction. *Protein Sci.* 5, 2600-2616.

[89] Li, W., Liu, Z. and Lai, L. (1999). Protein loops on structurally similar scaffolds: database and conformational analysis. *Biopolymers.* 49, 481-495.

[90] Ring, C.S., Kneller, D.G., Langridge, R. and Cohen, F.E. (1992). Taxonomy and conformational analysis of loops in proteins. *J Mol Biol.* 224, 685-699.

[91] Fechteler, T., Dengler, U. and Schomburg, D. (1995), Prediction of protein three-dimensional structures in insertion and deletion regions: a procedure for searching data bases of representative protein fragments using geometric scoring criteria. *J Mol Biol* 267, 114-131.

[92] Rufino, S.D., Donate, L.E., Canard, L.H.J. and Blundell, T.L. (1997) Predicting the conformational class of short and medium size loops connecting regular secondary structures: application to comparative modelling. *J Mol Biol.* 267, 352-367.

[93] Vlijmen, H.W.T and Karplus, M. (1997) PDB-based protein loop prediction: parameters for selection and methods of optimization. *J Mol Biol.* 267, 975-1001.

[94] Wojick, J., Mornon, J.-P. and Chomilier, J. (1999). New efficient statistical sequence-dependent structure prediction of short to medium-sized protein loops based on an exhaustive loop classification. *J Mol Biol.* 289,1469-1490.

[95] Fiser, A., Do, R.K.G. and Sali, A (2000) Modeling of loops in protein structures. *Prot Sci.* 9, 1753-1773.

[96] Fidelis, K., Stern, P.S., Bacon, D. and Moult, J. (1994) Comparison of systematic search and database methods for constructing segments of protein structure. *Prot Eng.* 7, 953-960.

[97] Oliva, B., Bates, P.A., Querol, E., Aviles, F.X. and Sternberg, M.J.E. (1997) An automated classification of the structure of protein loops. *J Mol Biol.* 266, 814-830.

[98] Michalsky, E., Goede, A. and Preissner, R. (2003) Loops In Proteins (LIP)--a comprehensive loop database for homology modeling. *Protein Eng.* 16, 979-985.

[99] Bansal, M., Kumar, S. and Velavan, R. (2000). HELANAL - A program to characterize helix geometry in proteins. *J. Biomol. Struct. Dyn* 17, 811-819.

[100] Levitt, M. and Greer, G. (1977) Automatic identification of secondary structure in globular proteins. *J Mol Biol.* 114, 181-293.

[101] Kabsch, W. and Sander, C. (1983). Dictionary of protein secondary structure: pattern recognition of hydrogen-bonded and geometrical features. *Biopolymers* 22, 2577-2637.

[102] Bernstein, F.C., Koetzle, T.F., Williams, G.J., Meyer Jr., E.F., Brice, M.D., Rodgers, J.R., Kennard, O., Shimanouchi, T. and Tasumi, M. (1977). The Protein Data Bank: a computer-based archival file for macromolecular structures. *J Mol Biol.* 112, 535-540.

[103] Berman, H.M., Westbrook, J., Feng, Z., Gilliland, G., Bhat, T.N., Weissig, H., Shindyalov, I.N. and Bourne P.E. (2000). The Protein Data Bank. *Nucleic Acids Res.* 28, 235-242.

[104] Frishman, D. and Argos, P. (1995) Knowledge-based protein secondary structure assignment. *Proteins.* 23:566-579.

[105] Andersen, C.A.F, Palmer, A.G.H., Brunak, S. and Rost, B. (2002) Continuum secondary structure captures protein flexibility. Structure 10, 175-154.

[106] Andersen, C.A.F. and Rost, B. (2002) Secondary structure assignement in Structural Bioinformatics, Bourne (ed), pp. 341-364.

[107] Carter, P., Andersen, C.A.F. and Rost, B. (2003) DSSPcont: continuous secondary structure assignments for proteins. *Nucleic Acids Res.* 31, 3293-3295.

[108] Ridchards, F.M. and Kundrot, C.E. (1988) Identification of structural motifs from protein coordinate data: secondary structure and first-level supersecondary structure, *Proteins.* 3, 71-84.

[109] Sklenar, H., Etchebest, C. and Lavery, R. (1989) Describing protein structure: a general algorithm yielding complete helicoidal parameters and a unique overall axis. *Proteins* 6, 46-60.
[110] Labesse, G., Colloc'h, N., Pothier, J. and Mornon, J.-P. (1997) PSEA: a new efficient assignment of secondary structure from C□ trace of proteins. *Comput Appl Biosci.* 13, 291-295.
[111] King, S.M. and Johnson, WC. (1999). Assigning secondary structure from protein coordinate data. *Proteins*. 35, 313-320.
[112] Barlow, D.J. and Thornton, J.M. (1988) Helix geometry in proteins. *J Mol Biol.* 201, 601-619.
[113] Bansal, M., Kumar, S. and Velavan, R. (2000) HELANAL: a program to characterize helix geometry in proteins. *J Bio Struct Dyn*. 17, 811-820.
[114] Woodcock, S., Mornon, J-.P. and Henrissat, B. (1992) Detection of secondary structure elements in proteins by hydrophobic cluster analysis. *Prot Eng*. 5, 629-635.
[115] Colloc'h, N., Etchebest, C., Thoreau, E., Henrissat, B. and Mornon, J.-P. (1993) Comparison of three algorithms for the assignment of secondary structure in proteins: the advantages of a consensus assignment. *Protein Eng*. 6, 377-382.
[116] de Brevern, A.G., Camproux, A.C., Hazout, S., Etchebest, C. and Tuffery, P. (2001) Beyond the secondary structures : the structural alphabets, in Recent Adv In Prot Eng., Sangadai SG (ed). Research signpost, Trivandrum,India, pp. 319-331.
[117] Karchin R. (2003). Evaluating local structure alphabets for protein structure prediction. Ph.D. Computer Science.
[118] Unger, R., Harel, D., Wherland, S. and Sussman, J.L. (1989). A 3D building blocks approach to analyzing and predicting structure of proteins. *Proteins*. 5, 355-373.
[119] Prestelski, S.J., Williams Jr., A.L. and Liebman, M.N. (1992) Generation of a substructure library for the description and classification of protein secondary structure. I. Overview of the methods and results. *Proteins* 14, 430-439.
[120] Unger, R. and Sussman J.L. (1993). The importance of short structural motifs in protein structure analysis. *J Comput Aid Mol Des* 7, 457-472.
[121] Schuchhardt, J., Schneider, G., Reichelt, J., Schomburg, D. and Wrede, P. (1996). Local structural motifs of protein backbones are classified by self-organizing neural networks. *Protein Eng*. 9, 833-842.
[122] Park B.H. and Levitt, M. (1995) The complexity and accuracy of discrete state models of protein structure. *J Mol Biol.* 249, 493-507.
[123] Kolodny R., Koehl, P., Guibas, L., Levitt, M. (2002) Small libraries of protein fragments model native protein structures accurately. *J Mol Biol.* 323, 297-307.
[124] Micheletti, C., Seno, F. and Maritan, A. (2000), Recurrent oligomers in proteins: an optimal scheme reconciling accurate and concise backbone representations in automated folding and design studies. *Proteins* 40, 662-674.
[125] Rooman, M.J., Rodriguez, J., and Wodak, S.J. (1990) Automatic definition of recurrent local structure motifs in proteins. *J Mol Biol.* 213, 327-336.
[126] Fetrow, J.S., Palumbo, M.J., and Berg, G. (1997) Patterns, structures, and amino acid frequencies in structural building blocks, a protein secondary structure classification scheme. *Proteins*. 27, 249-271.
[127] Bystroff, C. and Baker, D. (1998) Prediction of local structure in proteins using a library of sequence-structure motif. *J Mol Biol.* 281, 565-577.

[128] de Brevern, A.G., Etchebest, C. and Hazout, S. (2000) Bayesian probabilistic approach for predicting backbone structures in terms of protein blocks. *Proteins*. 41, 271-287.

[129] Camproux, A.C., Tuffery, P., Buffat, L., Andre, C., Boisvieux, J.F. and Hazout, S. (1999) Using short structural building blocks defined by a Hidden Markov Model for analysing patterns between regular secondary structures. *Theor. Chem. Acc.* 101, 33-40.

[130] Camproux, A.C., de Brevern, A.G., Hazout, S. and Tuffery, P. (2001). Exploring the use of a structural alphabet for a structural prediction of protein loops. *Theor Chem Acc*. 106(1/2), 28-35.

[131] de Brevern, A.G. and Hazout, S (2001). Compacting local protein folds by a "Hybrid Protein Model". *Theor Chem Acc*. 106(1/2): 36-47.

[132] de Brevern A.G. and Hazout S. (2000), Hybrid Protein Model (HPM) : une nouvelle approche pour caractériser les relations séquence-structure dans les protéines. *Premières Journées Ouvertes de Biologie, Informatique et Mathématiques. Recueil des Actes,* pp.105-112.

[133] de Brevern, A.G., Valadié, H., Hazout, S. & Etchebest, C. (2002). Extension of a local backbone description using a structural alphabet: A new approach to the sequence-structure relationship. *Protein Sci.* 11, 2871-2886.

[134] de Brevern A.G. and Hazout S. (2001) Compactage d'une base de données protéiques recodées dans un alphabet structural. *Secondes Journées Ouvertes de Biologie, Informatique et Mathématiques. Recueil des Actes,* pp.85-92.

[135] de Brevern, A.G. and Hazout, S. (2003). Improvement of "Hybrid Protein Model" to define an optimal repertory of contiguous 3D protein structure fragments. *Bioinformatics*. 19, 345-353.

[136] Benros, C., Hazout S. and de Brevern, A.G. (2002) "Hybrid Protein Model": a new clustering approach for 3D local structures. *Proceedings of Workshop on Bioinformatics ISMIS*. Chapter 5, pp. 1-6.

[137] Benros, C., de Brevern A.G. and Hazout S. (2003) Hybrid Protein Model (HPM): A method for building a library of overlapping local structural prototypes. sensitivity study and improvements of the training. *IEEE Int Work. NNSP 2003*, 53-70.

[138] Bonneau, R., Tsai, J., Ruczinski, I., Chivian, D., Rohl, C., Strauss, C.E.M., and Baker, D. (2001) Rosetta in CASP4: Progress in ab initio protein structure prediction. *Proteins* 37(S5):119-126.

[139] Bonneau, R., and Baker, D. (2001) Ab initio protein structure prediction: progress and prospects. *Annu Rev Biophys Biomol Struct*. 30, 173-189.

[140] Karchin, R., Cline, M., Mandel-Gutfreund, Y. and Karplus, K. (2003) Hidden Markov models that use predicted local structure for fold recognition: alphabets of backbone geometry. *Proteins*. 51, 504-514.

[141] Thornton, J.M., Sibanda, B.L., Edwards, M.S. and Barlow, D.J. (1988) Analysis, design and modification of loop regions in proteins. *Bioessays* 8, 63-69.

[142] Westhead, D.R., Slidel, T.W.F., Flores, T. P. J. and Thornton J. M. (1999) Protein structural topology: automated analysis, diagrammatic representation and database searching. *Protein Sci* 8, 897-904.

[143] Murzin A. G., Brenner S. E., Hubbard T. and Chothia C. (1995) SCOP: a structural classification of proteins database for the investigation of sequences and structures. *J Mol Biol*. 247, 536-540.

[144] Orengo, C.A., Michie, A.D., Jones, S., Jones, D.T., Swindells, M.B. and Thornton, J.M. (1997) CATH--a hierarchic classification of protein domain structures *Structure* 5, 1093-1108.

[145] Day, R., Beck, D.A., Armen, R.S. and Daggett, V. (2004) A consensus view of fold space: combining SCOP, CATH, and the Dali Domain Dictionary. *Protein Sci* 12, 2150-2160.

[146] Bray, J.E., Todd, A.E., Pearl, F.M.G., Thornton, J.M. and Orengo, C.A. (2000) The CATH Dictionary of Homologous Superfamilies (DHS): a consensus approach for identifying distant structural homologues *Prot Eng*. 13, 153-165.

[147] Pearl, F.M.G, Lee, D., Bray, J.E, Sillitoe, I., Todd, A.E., Harrison, A.P., Thornton, J.M. and Orengo, C.A. (2000) Assigning genomic sequences to CATH. *Nucleic Acids Res*. 28, 277-282.

[148] Michie, A.D., Orengo, C.A. and Thornton, JM. (1996) Analysis of domain structural class using an automated class assignment protocol. *J Mol Biol*. 262, 168-185.

[149] Noguchi, T., Matsuda, H. and Akiyama, Y. (2001) PDB-REPRDB: a database of representative protein chains from the Protein Data Bank (PDB). *Nucleic Acids Res*. 29, 219-220.

[150] Hobohm, U., Scharf, F., Schneider R. and Sander, C. (1992) Selection of a representative set of structures from the Brookhaven Protein Databank. *Prot Sci.* 1, 409-417.

[151] Hobohm, U. and Sander, C. (1994) Enlarged representative set of protein structures. *Prot Sci*. 3, 522-524.

[152] Wang, G. and Dunbrack, R.L., Jr. (2003) PISCES: a protein sequence culling server. *Bioinformatics* 19, 1589-1591.

[153] Brenner, S.E., Koehl, P. and Levitt, M. (2000) The ASTRAL compendium for protein structure and sequence analysis. *Nucl Acids Res*. 28, 254-256.

[154] Kohonen, T. (1982) Self-organized formation of topologically correct feature maps. *Biol. Cybern*. 43, 59-69.

[155] Kohonen, T. (2001) Self-Organizing Maps, 3rd edition. Springer-Verlag, Berlin, Germany.

[156] Rabiner, L.R. (1989) A tutorial on Hidden Markov Models and selected applications in speech recognition. *Proc. of the IEEE*. 77, 257-285.

[157] Mardia, K.V., Kent, T. and Bibby, J.M. (1979) Multivariate Analysis, Academic Press.

[158] Sammon Jr. (1969) A non-linear mapping for data structure analysis. *IEEE Transactions on Computers C* 18, 401-409.

[159] Agrafiotis, D.K. (1997) A new method for analyzing protein sequence relationships based on Sammon maps. *Prot Sci*. 6, 287-293.

[160] Andrade, M.A., Casari, G., Sander, C. and Valencia, A. (1997) Classification of protein families and detection of the determinant residues with an improved self-organizing map. *Biol Cyber*. 74, 441-450.

[161] Bystroff, C., Thorsson, V. & Baker, D. (2000) HMMSTR: a hidden Markov model for local sequence-structure correlations in proteins. *J Mol Biol*. 301:173-190.

[162] Koradi, R., Billeter, M. and Wuthrich, K. (1996) MOLMOL: a program for display and analysis of macromolecular structures. *J Mol Graph*. 14, 29-32.

Acknowledgments

We would like to thank Estelle Calvez and Maxime Huvet for previous works on TopKAPi methods, Laurent Fourrier and Aurélie Urbain for different local fold analyses, Joelle Hochez for the informatic support, Romain Gautier for a previous databank, Catherine Etchebest, Patrick Fuchs and Anne-Claude Camproux for fruitful discussions and Rachel Karchin for the Extended Beta alphabet script.

This work was supported by grants from the Ministère de la Recherche and from "Action Bioinformatique inter EPST" number 4B005F 2001-2002 and 2003-2004. AdB was supported by a grant from the Fondation de la Recherche Médicale. CB has a grant from the Ministère de la Recherche. SH is Professor at the University Paris 7 - Denis-Diderot, Paris. AdB is a researcher at the french Institute for Health and Medical Research (INSERM).

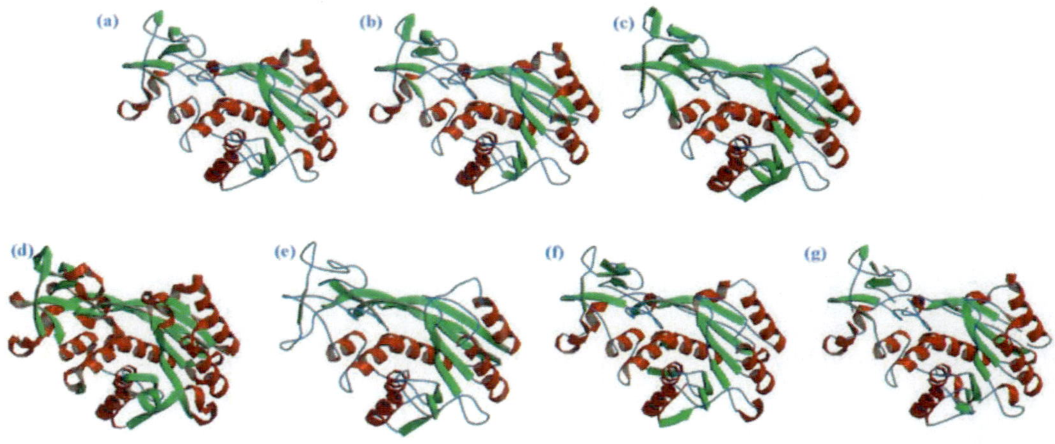

Figure 5. Example of secondary structure assignments for the protein 1OMH with (a) DSSP, (b) STRIDE, (c) PSEA, (d) DEFINE, (e) PCURVE, (f) XTLSSTR and (g) SECSTR. All the methods have been reduced to three states with the helicoidal states in red ribbons, the extended state in green arrows and the coil in blue line.

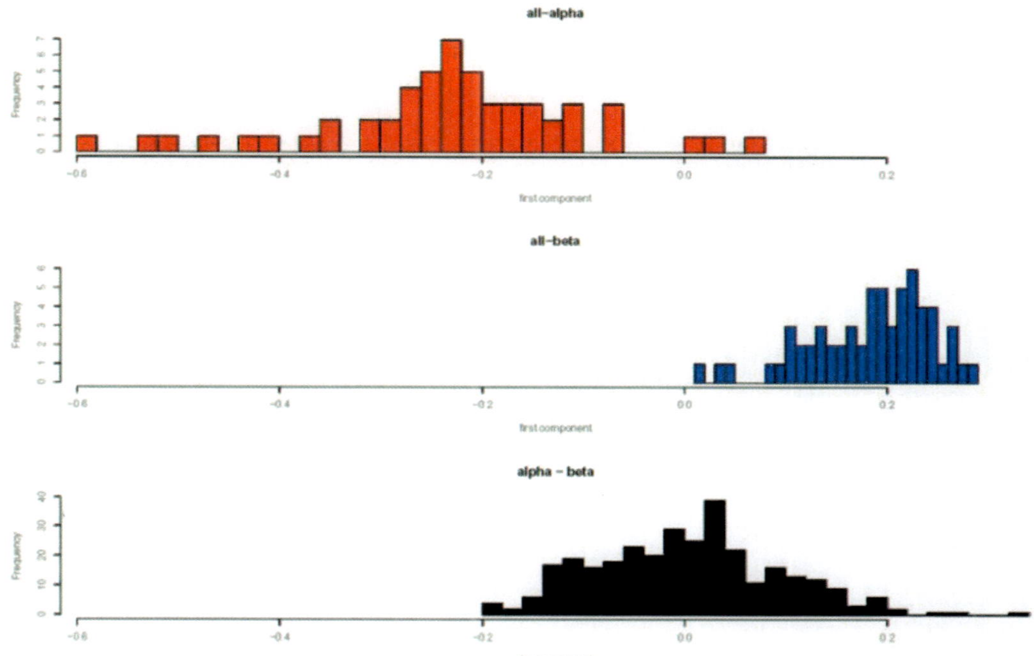

Figure 6. Values of the first component of the Principal Component Analysis carried out on the predicted frequencies of Protein Blocks, for the three studied protein classes all-α (blue), all-β (red) and mixed (black).

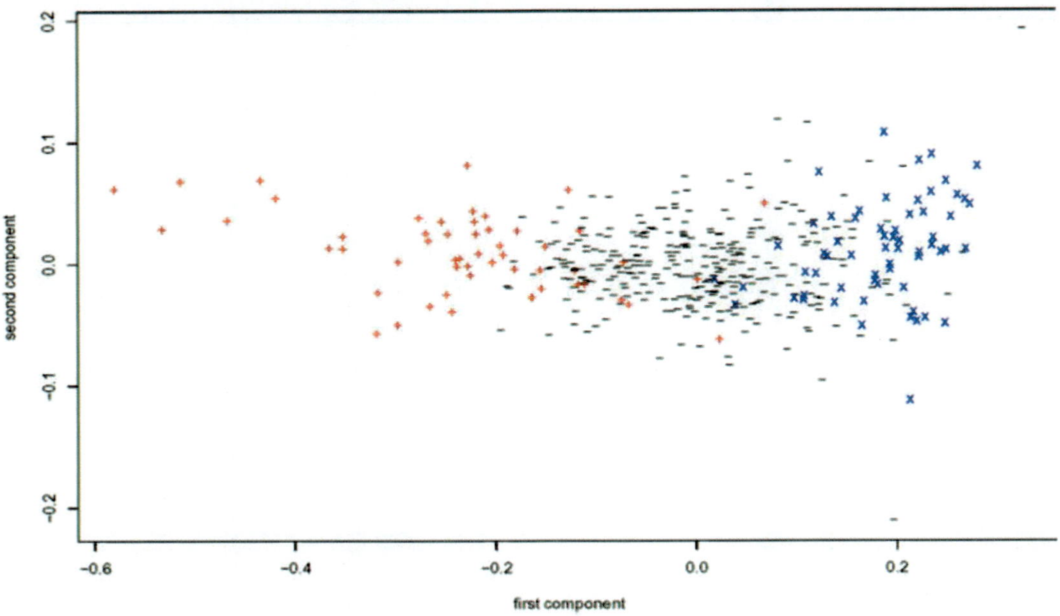

Figure 7. Description of the two first components (see Figure 6) for the three studied protein classes, all-α (blue '+'), all-β (red 'x') and mixed (black '–').

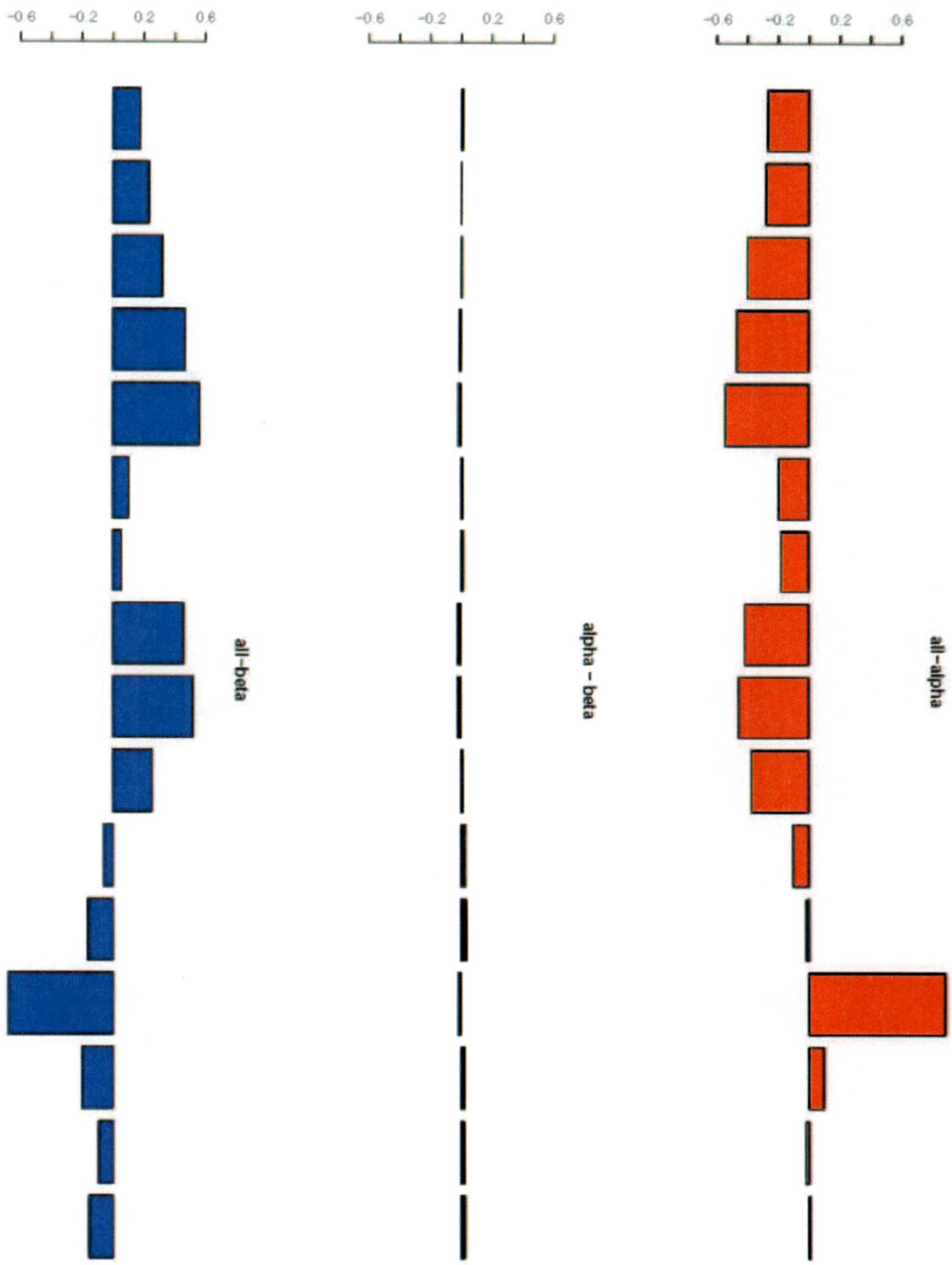

Figure 8. The three average prototypes of the relative predicted frequencies (RF) of the 16 Protein Blocks for the three studied protein classes all-α (blue), α-β (black) and all-β (red). In abscise are the Protein Blocks from PB *a* to PB *p*, in ordinate are given (RF – 1.0) to highlight the frequency differences in regards to the random distribution.

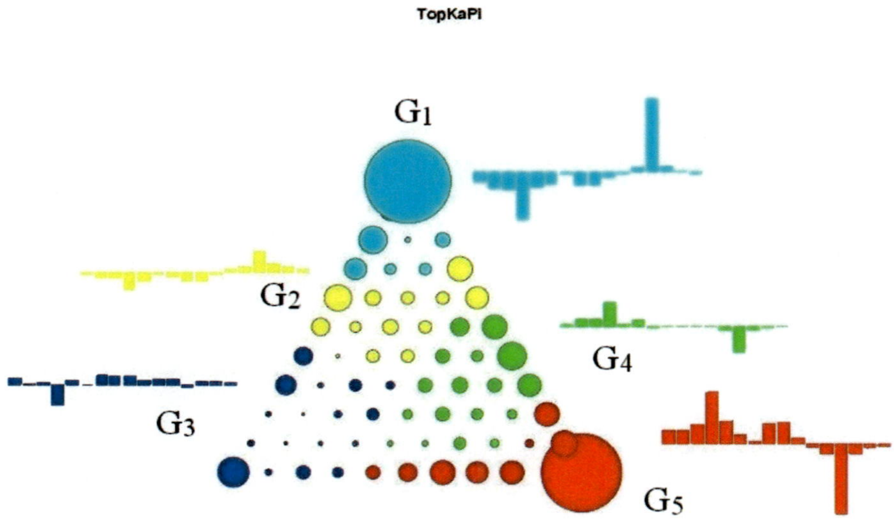

Figure 9. Final Triangular Kohonen map for Analyzing Proteins (TopKAPi) with the number of associated data for each neuron. From a hierarchical clustering, 5 clusters have been identified (*blue*, *red*, *green*, *yellow* and *cyan*) and the mean distribution of Protein Block Z-scores are indicated.

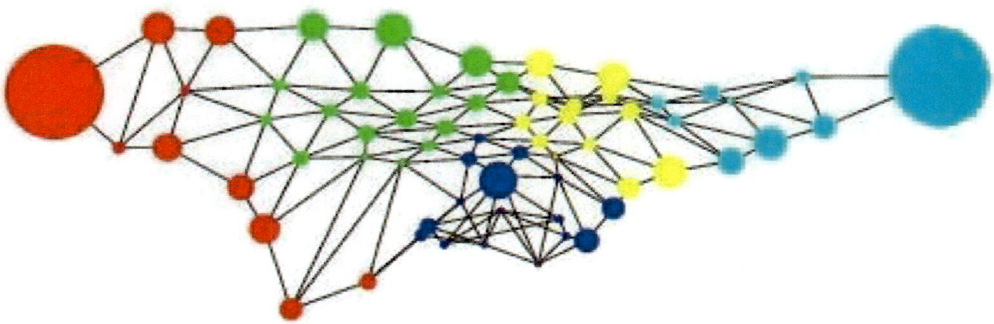

Figure 10. Sammon map of the TopKAPi neurons (cf. Figure 9).

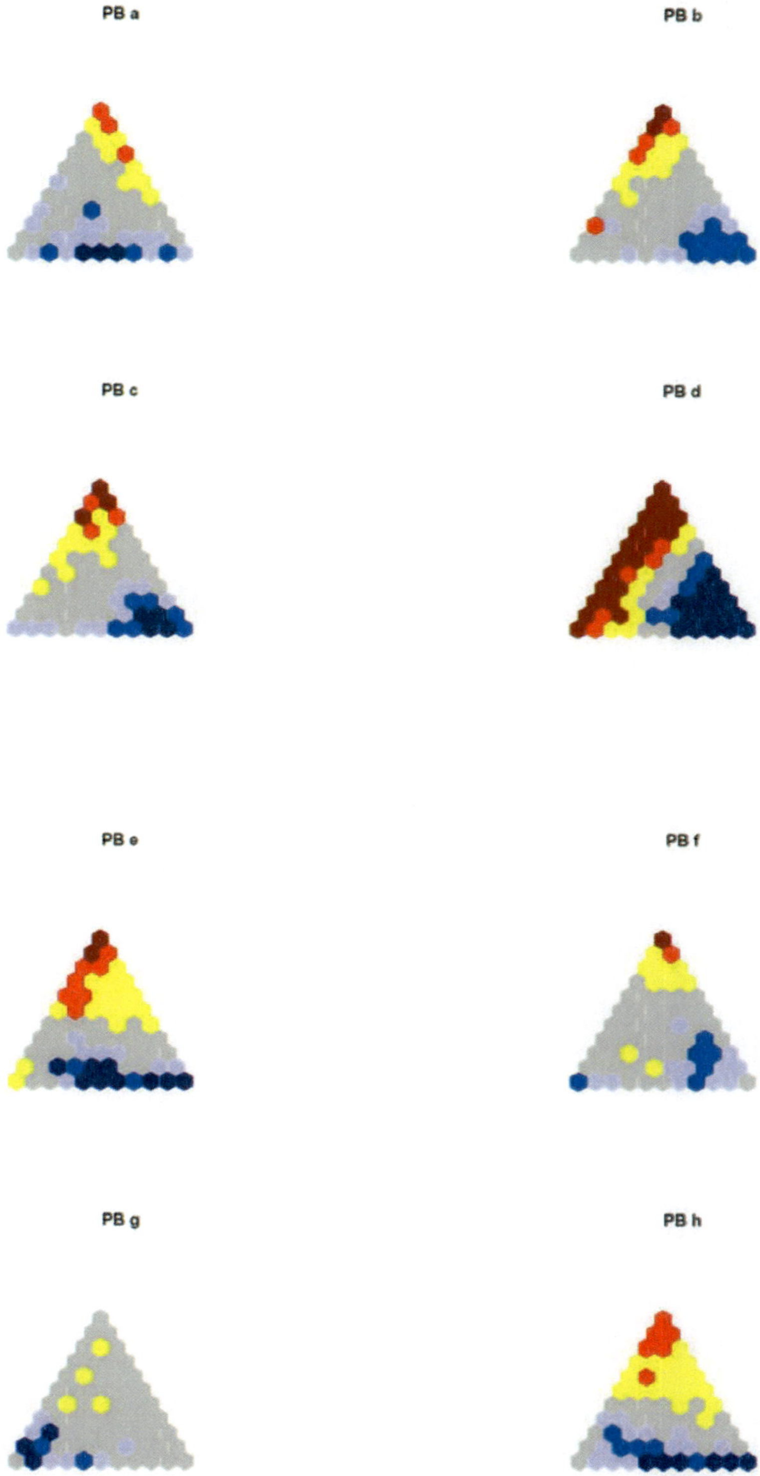
PB a
PB b
PB c
PB d
PB e
PB f
PB g
PB h

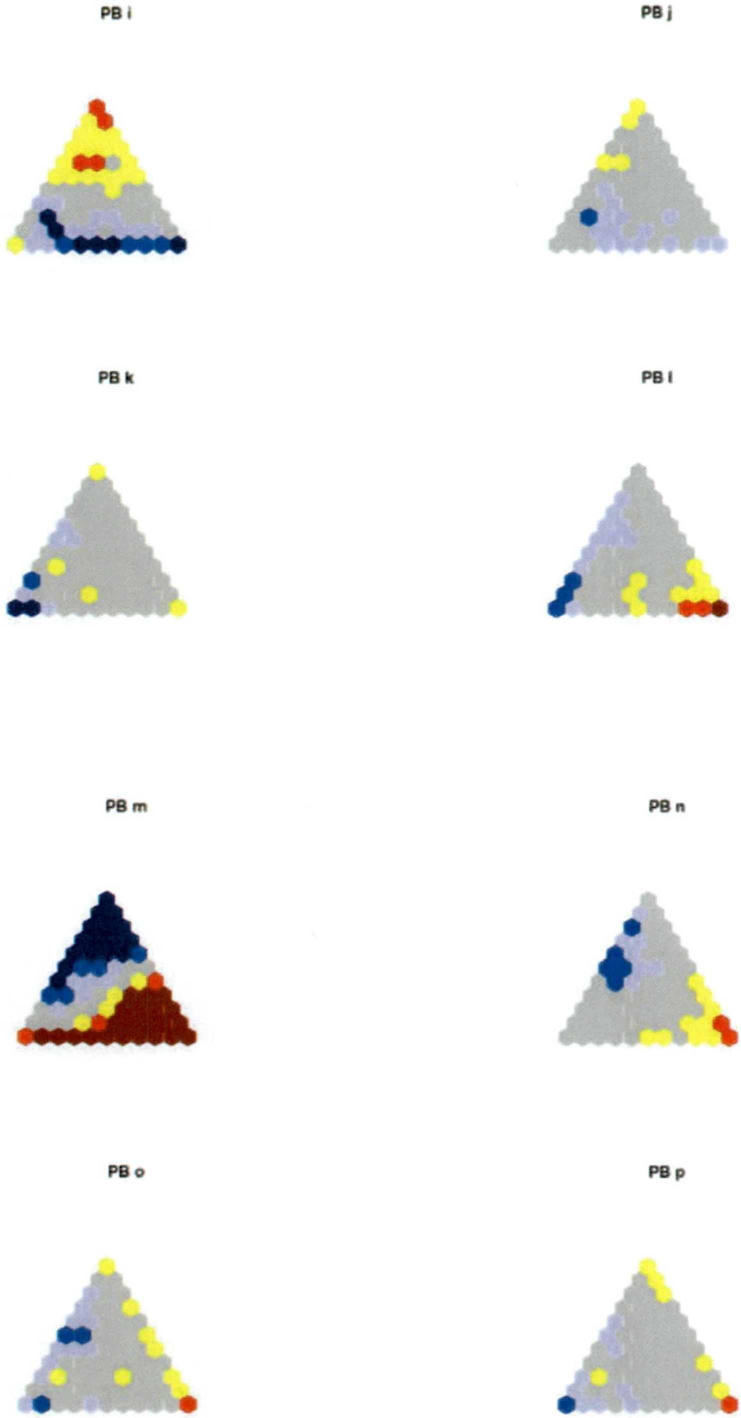

Figure 11. Distribution of the 16 Protein Blocks (PB *a* to PB *p*) in every neuron of TopKAPi (brown : Z-score < 4.4, red : Z-score within the range [-4.4; -1.96], grey : Z-score within the range [-1.96; +1.96], cyan : Z-score within the range [1.96; 4.4], red : Z-score > 4.4).

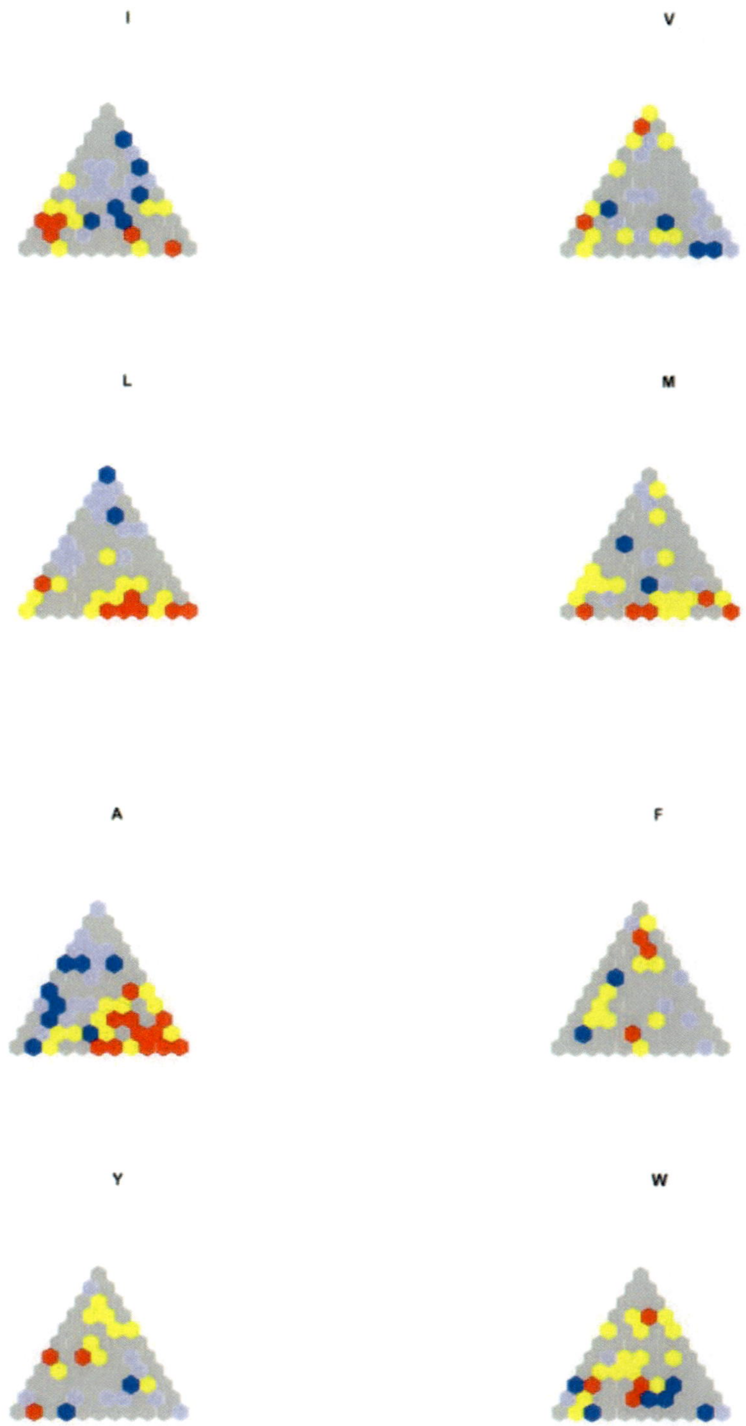
I
V
L
M
A
F
Y
W

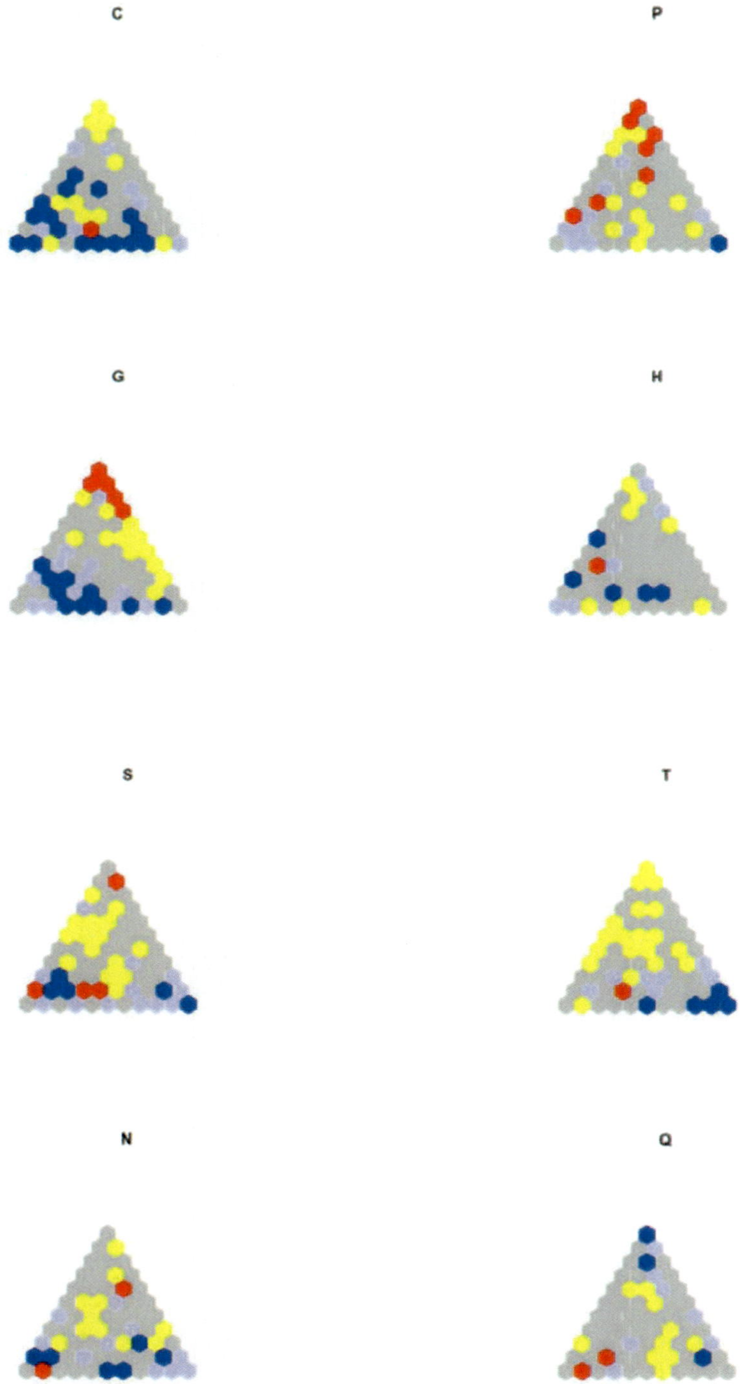
C
P
G
H
S
T
N
Q

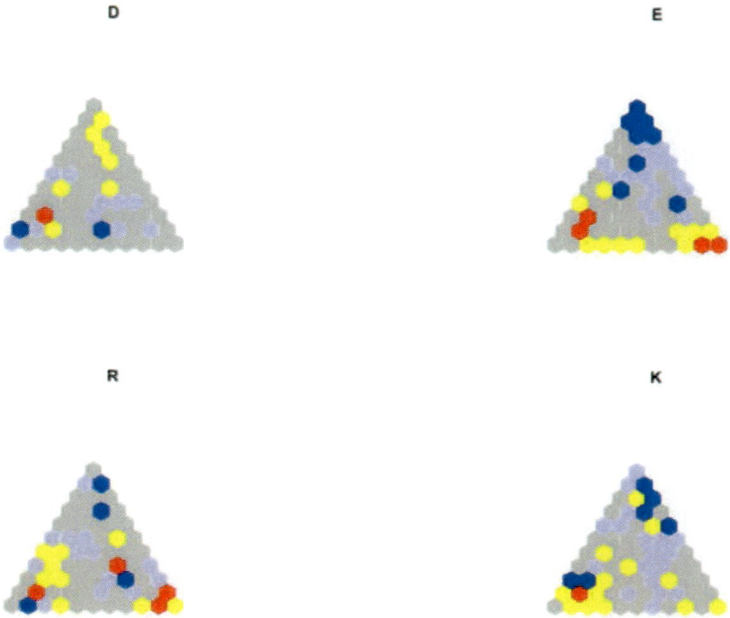

Figure 13. Distributions of the 20 types of amino acids (I, V, L, M, A, F, Y, W, C, P, G, H, S, T, N, Q, D,E R, K) in every neuron of TopKAPi (brown : Z-score < 4.4, red : Z-score within the range [-4.4; -1.96], grey : Z-score within the range [-1.96; +1.96], cyan : Z-score within the range [1.96; 4.4], red : Z-score > 4.4).

Index

A

B

C

D

E

F

G

H

I

L

M

N

O

P

R

S

T

U

V

W

X

Y